THE NEUROHYPOPHYSIS

COLSTON SYMPOSIUM ON THE NEUROHYPOPHYSIS 1956

Back Row (*left to right*) : H. I. Chinn, L. Rossi, B. A. Cross, G. W. Bisset, R. J. Fitzpatrick, J. C. Sloper, W. J. O'Connor, A. T. Cowie, L. Martini, F. Morel, T. M. Chalmers, R. J. Brocklehurst, J. M. Walker, F. P. Brooks, V. D. Eisen, W. G. McGregor.

2nd Row : H. Rodeck, E. J. Field, A. Carlyle, F. Stutinsky, Mary F. Lockett, A. Ursula Pardoe, C. W. Lloyd, F. Gross, G. K. Benson, J. M. Dodd, P. A. Jewell, B. Andersson, H. E. de Wardener, H. Wirz, A. Slessor, O. Garrod, D. F. Cole, M. Ginsburg.

3rd Row : W. Bargmann, B. Hanström, R. Gaunt, Mary Pickford, H. Croxatto, C. Fromageot, Lucie Arvy, H. Heller, H. H. Dale, S. Zuckerman, H. B. van Dyke, S. J. Folley, G. W. Harris, G. E. W. Wolstenholme, I. Chester Jones.

Front Row : W. H. Sawyer, R. L. Noble, S. M. A. Zaidi, Khurshid Chaudhri.

THE NEUROHYPOPHYSIS

Edited by

H. HELLER

Proceedings of the
Eighth Symposium of the Colston Research Society
held in the University of Bristol
April 9th — April 12th, 1956

LONDON
BUTTERWORTHS SCIENTIFIC PUBLICATIONS
1957

BUTTERWORTHS PUBLICATIONS LTD.
88 Kingsway, London, W.C.2

AFRICA: BUTTERWORTH & CO. (AFRICA) LTD.
     DURBAN: 33/35 Beach Grove

AUSTRALIA: BUTTERWORTH & CO. (AUSTRALIA) LTD.
     SYDNEY: 8 O'Connell Street
     MELBOURNE: 430 Bourke Street
     BRISBANE: 240 Queen Street

CANADA: BUTTERWORTH & CO. (CANADA) LTD.
     TORONTO: 1367 Danforth Avenue

NEW ZEALAND: BUTTERWORTH & CO. (AUSTRALIA) LTD.
     WELLINGTON: 49/51 Ballance Street
     AUCKLAND: 35 High Street

U.S.A. Edition published by
ACADEMIC PRESS INC., PUBLISHERS
111 Fifth Avenue
New York 3, New York

January 1957

This book is Volume VIII of the Colston Papers. Permission must be obtained from the Colston Research Society, 71 Winterstoke Road, Bristol 3, England, and from the Publishers, before any part of the contents can be reproduced.

Previous volumes in the Colston Papers are:

Vol. I. 1948 *Cosmic Radiation*—Editor, Professor F. C. Frank

Vol. II. 1949 *Engineering Structures*—Editor, Professor A. G. Pugsley.

Vol. III. 1950 *Colonial Administration*—Editor, Professor C. M. MacInnes.

Vol. IV. 1951 *The Universities and the Theatre*—Editor, Professor D. G. James.

Vol. V. 1952 *The Suprarenal Cortex*—Editor, Professor J. M. Yoffey.

Vol. VI. 1953 *Insecticides and Colonial Agricultural Development*—Editors, Professor T. Wallace and Dr. J. T. Martin.

Vol. VII. 1954 *Recent Developments in Cell Physiology*—Editor, Dr. J. A. Kitching.

Made and printed in Great Britain by
J. W. Arrowsmith Ltd., Bristol

Foreword

THE name of Edward Colston, the great seventeenth-century philanthropist and educationalist, is associated in Bristol with a number of scholastic and charitable institutions. It was adopted by a group of public-spirited citizens when, in 1899, they established the 'University College Colston Society', with the aim of fostering the young and struggling University College. For a decade it played a part in the movement which culminated in the institution of the University of Bristol in 1909.

The Society then changed its name and made its object more precise: it became the 'Colston Research Society' and devoted itself to the encouragement of original work in the University. It made grants for the purchase of apparatus and for the other expenses of research. As resources increased activities expanded and, notably, in the later thirties the Society financed a full-scale Social Survey of Bristol.

After the war a new reconsideration of policy led to the decision to devote the major part of the Society's efforts to the promotion of an annual symposium, the first being held in 1948. The rapid growth of the symposium as a means for the advancement of knowledge is one of the remarkable features of the intellectual life of recent years. Usually such meetings are fostered by bodies interested in one particular field of learning. As the list of titles (on the page opposite) shows, no such limitation applies to the symposia of the Colston Research Society. That the subject should be one at an interesting and active stage of development is the main factor in making a choice. The fact that the symposium is held in one of the younger seats of learning, with its home in an historic city, is a stimulus not only to the University but also, we believe, to the visiting guests who have come from many countries. The publication of the proceedings ensures the communication of the papers and discussions to wider circles.

As President of the Society for the year 1955-56 it was my privilege to preside over the eighth symposium, on 'The Neurohypophysis', the proceedings of which are printed in this, the eighth volume of the Colston Papers.

M. SKENE

Preface

THIS Symposium on the Neurohypophysis was the first international meeting devoted solely to the subject. It mirrors not only the diversity of aspects of the theme but also the rapid progress in recent years in the study of this involved endocrine system. This progress has been essentially twofold. Firstly, there is now strong suggestive evidence that the neurohypophysial hormones are elaborated not in the posterior pituitary lobe but in the hypothalamus and several of the papers read were concerned with the implications of this concept. Secondly, the chemical nature of the active principles— in some mammalian species at least—has been established. However, as Sir Henry Dale reminded us in his opening address, the physiological significance of the neurohypophysial hormones is known only incompletely. Admittedly, the regulatory role of the antidiuretic principle in the water metabolism of mammals (and most likely in that of 'lower' vertebrates) can no longer be doubted but the importance of the other pharmacologically demonstrable effects of posterior pituitary extracts is as yet based less securely. While, for example, there is strong evidence that oxytocin is normally implicated in the complex mechanism of lactation, its role in parturition is far from clear. Moreover, as is apparent from experimental results reported in this symposium, the neurohypophysis may have some further 'physiological' functions with which we are even less perfectly acquainted: vasopressin may in certain circumstances be concerned with the regulation of blood pressure; oxytocin may play a role in renal electrolyte excretion and may also be involved in the uterine mechanism for the ascent of spermatozoa.

There is another unsolved (or only partially solved) problem which was frequently mentioned, namely that of the estimation of the neurohypophysial hormones in body fluids. This has been achieved reliably when the concentration of exogenous or endogenous hormone is relatively high but the normal blood levels of the posterior pituitary hormones in animals or man have not been established. Until this has been done, clinical research on neurohypophysial function will obviously be severely handicapped. For this reason, and not only because of the limited time, papers on clinical aspects were deliberately excluded from the symposium. But as this volume shows, the subject was otherwise treated on a broad basis which included the comparative physiological approach.

There remains the pleasant duty to thank the individuals and organizations that made this symposium possible: First and foremost the Colston Research Society, and in particular its President, Professor M. Skene, and its Secretary, Mr. R. H. Brown, whose help has been invaluable. Secondly Sir Henry Dale and the Wellcome Trust for their generous grant which enabled us to invite speakers from the United States and Canada. I am also much indebted to Dr. S. J. Folley, Chairman of the Society for Endocrinology, and Dr. G. E. W. Wolstenholme, Director of the Ciba Foundation, for giving me their advice in the early stages of organizing the symposium, and to Sir Lionel Whitby, Regius Professor of Physic and Master of Downing College, Cambridge, who accepted the onerous task of acting as Guest Speaker at the Reception of the Colston Research Society. Finally, I should like to express my sincere thanks to Dr. R. J. Fitzpatrick who acted as secretary to the symposium and who carried the main administrative burden, to Miss A. T. Walker and her staff who looked after the members of the symposium at Manor Hall, to Dr. M. Ginsburg who acted as Recorder, to Miss G. H. Pope whose secretarial services have helped so much in the preparation of the manuscripts, to Messrs. J. G. Lane and K. Lederis for technical help during and after the symposium and last but not least to the printers, Messrs. J. W. Arrowsmith Ltd.

H. HELLER.

Bristol, 1956.

List of Members

Dr. B. Andersson, Department of Physiology, Veterinärhögskolan, Stockholm 51, Sweden.

Dr. Lucie Arvy, Laboratoire d'Anatomie et Histologie comparées, Sorbonne, Paris, France.

Dr. C. A. Ashford, Department of Physiology, University of Bristol.

Professor W. Bargmann, Anatomisches Institut der Universität Kiel, Germany.

Dr. G. K. Benson, National Institute for Research in Dairying, Shinfield, Berkshire.

Dr. R. E. Bernstein, Department of Physiology, University of Witwatersrand. Johannesburg, South Africa.

Dr. G. W. Bisset, Charing Cross Hospital Medical School, London, W.C.2.

Professor R. J. Brocklehurst, Department of Physiology, University of Bristol.

Dr. F. P. Brooks, Department of Physiology, School of Medicine, University of Pennsylvania, Philadelphia, U.S.A.

Mr. A. Carlyle, Department of Physiology, University of Bristol.

Dr. J. E. Cates, Department of Medicine, University of Bristol.

Dr. T. M. Chalmers, Department of Medicine, Middlesex Hospital, London, W.1.

Dr. Khurshid Chaudhri, Department of Pharmacology, Fatima Jinnah Medical College, Lahore, West Pakistan.

Dr. H. I. Chinn, Office of Naval Research, Embassy of the United States of America, 429 Oxford Street, London, W.1.

Dr. D. F. Cole, Department of Medicine, University of Durham Medical School, King's College, Newcastle upon Tyne.

Dr. A. T. Cowie, National Institute for Research in Dairying, Shinfield, Berkshire.

Dr. B. A. Cross, Zoological Laboratory, University of Cambridge.

Professor H. Croxatto, Laboratorio de Fisiologia, Universidad Catolica, Santiago, Chile.

Sir Henry Dale, The Wellcome Trust, 24 Harley Street, London, W.1.

Dr. J. M. Dodd, Gatty Marine Laboratory, University of St. Andrews, Fife.

Mrs. Margaret H. I. Dodd (Miss Macaulay), Gatty Marine Laboratory, University of St. Andrews, Fife.

Professor H. B. van Dyke, Department of Pharmacology, College of Physicians and Surgeons, Columbia University, New York, U.S.A.

Dr. V. D. Eisen, Department of Pharmacology, Middlesex Hospital Medical School, London, W.1.

Dr. E. J. Field, Department of Anatomy, University of Bristol.

Dr. R. J. Fitzpatrick, Department of Pharmacology, University of Bristol.

Dr. S. J. Folley, National Institute for Research in Dairying, Shinfield, Berkshire.

Professor C. Fromageot, Laboratoire de Chimie biologique de la Faculté de Sciences, Paris, France.

Dr. O. Garrod, Department of Medicine, Middlesex Hospital, London, W.1.

Professor R. Gaunt, Ciba Pharmaceutical Products Inc., Summit, N.J., U.S.A.

Dr. M. Ginsburg, Department of Pharmacology, University of Bristol.

Dr. F. Gross, Biological Laboratories of Ciba Ltd., Basle, Switzerland.

Professor B. Hanström, Zoological Institute, University of Lund, Sweden.

Professor G. W. Harris, Department of Neuroendocrinology, Institute of Psychiatry, Maudsley Hospital, London, S.E.5.

Professor J. E. Harris, Department of Zoology, University of Bristol.

Professor H. Heller, Department of Pharmacology, University of Bristol.

Dr. G. Herdan, Department of Preventive Medicine, University of Bristol.

Professor T. F. Hewer, Department of Pathology, University of Bristol.

Dr. Penelope M. Jenkin, Department of Zoology, University of Bristol.

Dr. P. A. Jewell, Department of Physiology, Royal Veterinary College, London.

Dr. I. Chester Jones, Department of Zoology, University of Liverpool.

Professor F. W. Landgrebe, Department of Pharmacology, Welsh National School of Medicine, Cardiff.

*Dr. A. A. G. Lewis, Department of Medicine, Middlesex Hospital, London, W.1.

Dr. C. W. Lloyd, State University of New York, Upstate Medical Centre, Syracuse, N.Y., U.S.A.

Dr. Mary F. Lockett, Department of Physiology and Pharmacology, Chelsea Polytechnic, London, S.W.3.

Mr. W. G. MacGregor, Department of Obstetrics, University of Bristol.

Dr. L. Martini, Istituto di Farmacologia e di Terapia, University of Milan, Italy.

Dr. F. Morel, Laboratoire d'Endocrinologie, Collège de France, Paris, France.

Professor R. L. Noble, Department of Medical Research, The Collip Medical Research Laboratory, University of Western Ontario, London, Canada.

Dr. W. J. O'Connor, Department of Physiology, Medical School, University of Leeds.

Dr. A. Ursula Pardoe, Department of Pharmacology, London Hospital Medical College, London, E.1.

Professor C. B. Perry, Department of Medicine, University of Bristol.

Dr. Mary Pickford, Department of Physiology, University of Edinburgh.

Dr. M. Reiss, Biochemical and Endocrinological Research Unit, Barrow Hospital, Barrow Gurney, Nr. Bristol.

Dr. H. Rodeck, Kinderklinik der Medizinischen Akademie, Düsseldorf, Germany.

Dr. L. Rossi, Department of Pathological Anatomy, University of Milan, Italy.

Dr. W. H. Sawyer, Department of Physiology, New York University College of Medicine, 550 First Av., New York, U.S.A.

Dr. A. Slessor, Department of Materia Medica, University of Glasgow.

Dr. J. C. Sloper, Institute of Pathology, London Hospital, London, E.1.

Dr. F. Stutinsky, Faculté des Sciences P.C.B., Paris Ve, France.

Dr. H. Summers, Department of Physiology, University of Bristol.

*Dr. Christine M. Tyler, Department of Pharmacology, Royal Free Hospital, London, W.C.1.

Dr. J. M. Walker, Department of Pharmacology, University of Oxford.

Dr. H. E. de Wardener, Department of Medicine, St. Thomas's Hospital, London, S.E.1.

* Prevented from attending.

Professor H. Wirz, Physiologisches Institut der Universität, Basle, Switzerland.

Dr. G. E. W. Wolstenholme, The Ciba Foundation, 41 Portland Place, London, W.1.

Professor J. M. Yoffey, Department of Anatomy, University of Bristol.

Dr. S. M. A. Zaidi, Department of Pharmacology, University of Bristol.

Professor Sir Solly Zuckerman, Department of Anatomy, University Medical School, Birmingham.

Contents

Contents

Contents

Evidence concerning the endocrine function of the neurohypophysis and its nervous control

by

Sir HENRY H. DALE

THE 1891 edition of Michael Foster's then justly famous *Text-Book of Physiology*, which provided the basis for my own undergraduate studies of the subject when these began, in 1894, was curtly explicit in its account of the knowledge then available concerning the functions of the pituitary body. 'With regard to the purposes of the organ as a whole', it stated, 'we know absolutely nothing'—a statement which, you may imagine, was not without an aspect of reassurance, for a student with an examination in prospect. And, when the first evidence, to suggest a function for this previously mysterious organ, appeared a year later, in 1895, this was concerned, as was still later to be made clear, with only one of the parts of its composite structure, namely with its posterior lobe, the neurohypophysis, which is the subject to which our discussions in this symposium are to be limited—except, of course, in so far as some contributor may need to mention data which are more directly concerned with the anterior lobe—the adenohypophysis—or with the so-called 'pars intermedia', on account of light which they may throw indirectly upon the functions of the neurohypophysis and the mechanisms of their control, which are on this occasion to be our sole concern.

The first evidence, then, suggesting any function for the pituitary body, and for the neurohypophysis in particular, was presented in a short paper by George Oliver and E. A. Schäfer (1895). This was, in effect, a supplement to their main paper on the remarkable effect on the circulation of an extract of the suprarenal gland—a potent action which they had seen and reported briefly in the previous year, 1894, when Dr. Oliver, the enterprising physician from Harrogate, had first persuaded Professor Schäfer, inclined to be impatient and incredulous, to try the effect of injecting such an extract into a vein of an anaesthetized dog, at the end of an experiment which Schäfer had been making with a different object. And having, in their full paper in the following year, given an extended account of this astonishing activity of a suprarenal extract, and having shown that the substance responsible for it was obtainable only from the medulla, Oliver and Schäfer were naturally curious to discover whether other ductless glands contained any comparable, immediately active substances. They reported the results of this survey in the paper which directly followed that on the suprarenal extract, in the same number of volume 18 of the *Journal of Physiology*, published in 1895. And there you can find this first account of the activity, with intravenous injection, of an extract prepared from the whole pituitary body, this being the only one of the other glandular extracts which they tested, which showed a pressor, or, indeed, any other specific action on the circulation, comparable in intensity with that which they had observed with the suprarenal extract; the effect of the pituitary extract, though it was much the more persistent, being the less impressive of the two, because it was wholly due to an intense vasoconstriction, and showed none of the cardio-acceleration which contributed so much to the suprarenal effect.

It was W. H. Howell (1898) who, some three years later, showed that the substance responsible for this pressor action of a pituitary extract was obtainable only from one part of the organ, and, rather surprisingly, only from its posterior, neural lobe. Howell also showed that, when the prolonged pressor effect of a substantial first injection had subsided, the animal was almost completely insensitive to the action of a further, similar, or even larger injection, and remained thus refractory for a period up to several hours, according to the size of the dose responsible for this 'tachyphylaxis'. In the following year, Schäfer & Vincent (1899) confirmed both these observations. They were puzzled, as were others later, by the finding, which they were nevertheless obliged to confirm, that such a powerful, immediate, pharmacodynamic activity should be due to something present only in the posterior lobe of the pituitary body. It would have been much easier, of course, to credit the anterior lobe, so obviously glandular in structure, with the production of something so highly and specifically active; whereas the posterior, neural lobe, from which alone the activity could be extracted, appeared to consist almost entirely of nerve-fibres and neuroglia, and to be, in fact, a kind of extension, through the infundibular stalk, from the grey matter of the floor of the third ventricle, though almost devoid of nerve-cells. Schäfer & Vincent ascertained, by experiment, that otherwise similar extracts, made from grey matter from other parts of the brain, did not, in fact, exhibit any activity of this kind. And this apparent anomaly, of the production from what looked like the almost purely nervous tissue of the posterior lobe, of an intensely active substance which no other nervous tissue yielded, with the suggestion that, nevertheless, this part of the pituitary body, like the suprarenal medulla, ought to have an important endocrine function, continued for a number of years to puzzle and to disconcert the minds of physiologists who became interested in the problem. It seemed to be difficult for them to reconcile such a finding with their sense of physiological propriety, so that they became too eagerly alert, perhaps, for any evidence which might appear to offer a plausible way of escape from so embarrassing a paradox. A key to its meaning seems now, at length, to be offered by the novel and highly suggestive lines of evidence which have been followed in recent years, concerning the relation of the structures of the posterior lobe to the nerve-cells of the hypothalamic nuclei, and the dependence upon this connexion of the hormonal content of the lobe. And this appears likely to be one of the most important subjects for our consideration at this symposium. Since my own part in our discussion can be little more than reminiscence and gossip concerning a phase in the evolution of its subject now long past, I can contribute little to the consideration of this recent development, except to emphasize the genuine difficulty which earlier investigators found in this idea, that a tissue, while it appeared to consist almost entirely of nerve-fibres and neuroglia, could also function as an endocrine gland—a difficulty which was certainly not diminished when it was found that the posterior lobe extract had other immediate physiological actions, comparable in interest and intensity to the pressor activity which had first been noticed.

Magnus & Schäfer (1901) observed that an intravenous injection of the pituitary posterior lobe extract into an anaesthetized animal produced also, after a latency, a conspicuous increase in the rate of the secretion of urine; and, a few years later, this observation was confirmed and extended by Schäfer & Herring (1906). It is, of course, now generally recognized that this effect, definite and striking though it is, and regularly as it can be reproduced under the given conditions, is, in fact, an anomalous and artificial result, due to the depressed kidney function produced by the anaesthesia, and to the use of the intravenous route for administering the pituitary extract in relatively large doses. It was later recognized that the truly physiological, *anti*diuretic effect, now accepted as the genuine, hormonal action on the kidney, could only be reproduced artificially if the extract was injected hypodermically, or in very small doses intravenously, and into unanaesthetized animals.

Before we discuss further this natural, antidiuretic effect, however, I ought to make brief mention of another action of the posterior lobe extract, on the plain muscle of the wall of the uterus, which I first described incidentally (Dale, 1906), having come across it almost by accident, when I recorded the already known pressor action for another purpose. I was studying a now familiar, but then newly discovered, action of certain alkaloids of ergot—what has since been termed a 'sympatholytic' action—in which augmentor actions of adrenaline, and corresponding effects of sympathetic nerves, transmitted as we now know by the release at their endings of adrenaline and its primary homologue, are suppressed, or replaced by inhibitor effects. In a female cat, at an early stage of pregnancy, I happened to be recording the arterial blood-pressure and the activity of the muscular wall of the uterus; and, by a previous dose of an ergot preparation, the actions of adrenaline on both of these had been so reversed, that each injection of it now produced a fall of the arterial pressure, in place of the normal rise, and a relaxation of the uterus, in place of the previous contraction. I thought that it would be of interest to know whether the pressor effect of the pituitary posterior lobe extract would also be reversed, like that of adrenaline, or, as I expected, unchanged. When, accordingly, I injected an appropriate dose of the pituitary extract, I observed that it had not only retained its normal pressor action, in contrast to the reversed, depressor action of adrenaline, but that it also produced a powerful, contractile response of the uterus, not hitherto described. Other experiments, made then to study this action deliberately (Dale, 1909), showed that it was produced on the uterus in all species and in various physiological conditions, even in those in which the natural effects of adrenaline were to produce simple inhibition of the organ's tone and rhythm. It was clear, then, that these peripheral actions of the pituitary posterior lobe extract, unlike those of adrenaline, had no relation to the effects of impulses in the sympathetic or any other autonomic nerves. And I took the opportunity to see also for myself the diuretic action on the anaesthetized animal, of which a full description had then recently been given by Schäfer & Herring (1906); also to make some observations on the nature of the substance, assumed then to be only one, which was responsible for all these actions, showing it to be excreted in the urine, stable to peptic digestion and to boiling at a mildly acid reaction, but readily destroyed by tryptic digestion or by hot alkalis, and to have, accordingly, the characters of a relatively simple polypeptide. For the time being, it seemed to me natural to suppose, in default of good evidence to the contrary, that one and the same substance was responsible for all these different actions, in accordance with the well-known logical maxim attributed to William of Occam—*entia non sint multiplicanda praeter necessitatem.*

We may leave that point for the present, noting only that in its further discussion we should also include the substance in the extract responsible for the milk-ejecting, galactogogic effect on the mammary gland, later recognized by Ott & Scott (1910). Meanwhile we must give some further consideration to the really physiological action of the extract on the function of the kidneys. This first came to light through a sequence of clinical observations on human patients. I think that we may suppose that the demonstration by Schäfer and his co-workers of the anomalous diuretic effect on anaesthetized animals, to which I have referred, had some influence in directing the attention of J. E. Frank (1912), to a possible connexion between diabetes insipidus and disease, or injury, of the hypothalamus, of the infundibulum, or of the neurohypophysis. Frank, having discovered strong pathological evidence of such an association, appeared to find it natural to attribute the effect to an excessive outpouring of the supposed diuretic hormone, evoked by irritation of the neuro-hypophysis. His observation, however, seems to have stimulated two independent investigators, von den Velden (1913) and Farmi (1913), to try the therapeutic effect of hypodermic injections of the posterior lobe pituitary extract on cases of diabetes insipidus; and both of these observers reported a result which appeared to be the direct opposite of what might have been expected, if Schäfer's conception of diuresis as the normal effect of the extract, and Frank's application of this idea to his pathological findings, had represented the true, physiological function of the neuro-hypophysis. And it may, perhaps, have some slight interest to recall, in passing, that the successful treatment of diabetes insipidus by such injections, repeated at suitable intervals, had become an item of accepted, almost of conventional, therapeutic routine, some eight or nine years before the discovery of insulin made possible a much more famous therapeutic advance, in the successful treatment of the much commoner and much more tragically serious condition, diabetes mellitus. The preparation of an active extract from the pituitary posterior lobe had, of course, no such long history, of frustration and ultimate success, as had been involved in that of the extraction and stabilization of insulin. No more complicated method had been needed to obtain the antidiuretic hormone, than the simple boiling of the posterior lobe substance with weakly acidulated water; and preparations so made had, in fact, been already available for several years for use in obstetrics, so that they were ready to hand when their remarkable value in diabetes insipidus was discovered.

Meanwhile the mode of origin and the precise physiological source of the active substance, or substances, seemed to be still in doubt. The results of operative removal of the neural lobe, by a number of different observers over a period of years, using different operative methods and different species, seemed to be difficult to interpret. The finding, for example, that removal of the neural lobe alone, or section of the infundibular stalk, caused in certain species only an evanescent diabetes, and that, when this had thus subsided, extracts from what had been regarded as hypothalamic brain substance were hormonally active, seemed for a time to make the issue only more complicated. I must not attempt to anticipate what those with direct experience of this aspect of the problem may be going to contribute to the symposium. Perhaps I may venture, however, to suggest that it seems now to be recognized, that we ought not to restrict our conception of the hormone-producing neurohypophysis to the rounded lobe which hangs, as it were, at the end of the stalk; apparently we should include also, in the neurohypophysis, tissue in the stalk and in the median eminence, which had earlier been assumed to be nervous and therefore not, or at least not normally, endocrine in function; although, as we have seen, the almost entirely nervous nature of the tissue of the lobe itself, together with its normal yield of a highly active extract, had long made it difficult to regard nervous structure and endocrine function as entirely incompatible.

There appeared meanwhile to be a paucity of more direct evidence, in favour of a supposition which is obviously of central importance to the whole direction and form of our discussion, namely, that the highly active substance (or substances) which the neurohypophysis yields to artificial extraction, are also naturally secreted from it as hormones. There are others present with far better and more direct qualifications than mine for dealing with the evidence by which this important conclusion can now be justified. Perhaps, however, I may allow myself to make special mention of a line of evidence which has developed during a period extending now over rather more than thirty years, and which began with experiments in which the late E. H. Starling and E. B. Verney employed an acute form of physiological technique. Starling & Verney (1925), perfusing the isolated kidney of a dog with blood from a simple heart-lung preparation, showed that it soon began to secrete a voluminous and highly dilute urine, entirely similar to that of diabetes insipidus; but that the addition to the artificially circulated blood of a small dose of the pituitary posterior lobe extract was sufficient to restore to the kidney its normal, reconcentrating function. And then, in the following year, after Starling's death, Verney (1926) included also, in the heart-lung circulation, the isolated head of the dog, and showed that this sufficed to enable the perfused kidney to continue the production of a urine which was normal in volume and concentration, until the pituitary body was removed from the perfused head, when the voluminous and dilute urine of diabetes insipidus soon appeared. To me this seemed to be the most direct and convincing evidence till then available, not only of the perfused kidney's requirement, for the production of a normally concentrated urine, of a substance present in an artificial extract of the neurohypophysis, but also, and most convincingly, of the active secretion of that substance from the neurohypophysis, into blood which was circulated through it. In other words, it seemed to be at least as complete a proof of a normal endocrine function for the neurohypophysis as any which had been given, or, indeed, has since been given, for any other organ. And you will, I am sure, be familiar with the series of elegant experiments on normal, conscious animals, which have since enabled Verney and his co-workers, including Dr. Pickford whom we shall hear later, to study in detail the conditions by which this endocrine activity of the neurohypophysis is naturally excited and controlled; and of the part played, in that excitation and control, by emotional factors, acting upon the neurohypophysis through the nuclei of the hypothalamus.

I must also say something more directly about the question, already mentioned by implication, whether these different effects of the neurohypophysis, or of artificial extracts from it, are due to only one, or to more than one hormone, or active principle.

5

I am not going to revive the details of a controversy, in which my late colleague Harold Dudley and I found ourselves most unwillingly involved with a very greatly revered old friend of mine, the late Professor Abel. I only wish to emphasize the fact that our own experiments were concerned throughout with one limited question, namely, whether the different activities of the ordinary, boiled extract of the posterior lobe substance were due to one common active principle, as several of us had earlier supposed, or to at least two different principles, responsible for different features of the complex activity. Dudley (1919) made what seemed to me an unquestionable, though incomplete, separation of the oxytocic from the vasopressor constituent, using a method of continuous extraction, from the weakly acid watery extract, with a partially miscible, neutral solvent, normal butyl alcohol. The method, indeed, was similar in principle to that with which du Vigneaud and his team, during years still quite recent, have eventually achieved so complete and astonishing a success. It will be remembered also that, in the intervening period, Kamm and Aldrich and their co-workers (1928), in the laboratories of Parke, Davis and Company, had worked out a method for separating these two principles on a manufacturing scale, so that they could be offered for general use in separate solutions, with activities sufficiently pure for practical, therapeutic purposes. And now, of course, the brilliant success of du Vigneaud and his team has settled this question of one or two active principles in the extract, beyond all further discussion. Using the modern resources of counter-current distribution and chromatography, they have succeeded beyond all expectation, not only in isolating both the oxytocic and the vasopressor principle, each in a state of sufficient purity to enable them to determine completely its complex cyclo-polypeptide constitution, but even in confirming that of the oxytocic principle by artificial synthesis. It is a disappointment to us all that Professor du Vigneaud has not been able to come over and join us in this symposium. We should all have welcomed the opportunity of expressing to him directly our very great admiration for a truly astonishing achievement. The work of Professor van Dyke, and others who have given their co-operation in physiological experiments, allows us, I think, further to accept, as now also beyond the need for discussion, the fact that the main oxytocic action and the galactogogic action of the extract are both due to one of the two substances, and that the pressor and antidiuretic actions are both due to the other, which also has intrinsically, not from imperfect separation, a minor oxytocic activity of its own. There are probably other points of interest about these two active substances, about which we may hope to hear in our discussions. Some years ago Professor Heller (1939) produced evidence, which seemed to show that the pressor activity of an extract from the neurohypophysis was less stable to heating at any reaction than the antidiuretic activity, and that a preparation could even be obtained which had no pressor, but retained some antidiuretic activity. A difference of sensitiveness between the two types of reaction may be involved; but I have wondered if, possibly, the amino-acid structure of the natural pressor-antidiuretic principle might undergo a minor change, involving an unequal loss of the two types of activity, and whether the constitution of this hormone might even undergo some change in the gland during growth from infancy to maturity. Du Vigneaud and his team have already discovered an important difference between the constitution of the vasopressin from the bovine and of that from the porcine posterior lobe; and perhaps somebody may be able to tell us, whether any comparison has yet been made of the ratios between pressor and antidiuretic activity in these two different vasopressins, containing arginine and lysine respectively; and, if so, with what result.

With the investigation of the related, but essentially different question, whether these different active polypeptides exist separately in the living gland, or as components of a single, multivalent macromolecule, I have had no direct concern. Professor van Dyke, as we all know, obtained, in a press-juice from the fresh substance, evidence of a protein moving as a unit under electrophoresis, separable by differential centrifugation, and yielding both types of activity to extraction, apparently in the natural proportions. I should have been more impressed by this evidence, if I had not myself had bitter experience, over a wide interval of years, of the tenacity with which the two active principles from the boiled extract, in which we now know that they exist separately, adhere even to well-crystallized precipitates, and apparently in proportions not obviously different from those in which they were present in the original extract. Two distinguished chemical colleagues of mine, the late George Barger and the late Harold Dudley, suffered separate and harrowing disappointments, at an interval of many years. Each of them in turn obtained from the extract, after months of careful work, a well-crystallized salt, showing the different activities with a high intensity, and in apparently unchanged proportion; and each in turn, not unnaturally, thought for a time that he had prepared a pure salt of a single, multivalent principle. A more careful scrutiny of details, however, especially of the *degree* of such activity per unit of weight, induced each of them in turn to apply further methods of purification; with the result that the crystalline salt proved, in the one case, to be a picrolonate of lysine, and, in the other, a double picrate of potassium and creatinine. To each of these salts both the active principles had adhered with an astonishing tenacity, evidently only in traces; but these had been sufficient to endow the crystals with such misleading activity. I am, accordingly, a little disposed to doubt, whether we can safely assume that even what seems to be an electrophoretically uniform protein, from the fresh gland substance, might not retain sufficient of these obstinately clinging polypeptides by mere physical adhesion, to create the impression of a single, multivalent, macromolecular hormone. I am very much hoping that Professor Fromageot is going to throw some further light on this question for us. The really important question for the physiologist, however, is whether these active substances can be separately released from the living lobe, in response to the appropriate stimuli, or must always be shed into the circulation together, as components of the suggested macromolecule. Teleology, of course, would strongly favour the probability of separate release, in response to specific needs; but teleology is a dangerous guide, and, as Starling once said to me, one must always suspect Nature of setting booby-traps.

And then we shall certainly have discussion—and I look forward to the opportunity of learning much from it—concerning the relation between the neurohypophysis, with its specific hormone, or hormones, and the nuclei, in particular the supraoptic and paraventricular nuclei, of the hypothalamus. This aspect of our subject seems to me to have a very special interest, on account of the suggestion which seems to emerge from the evidence, of a relation which, so far as I know, is the first of its kind to be recognized in any endocrine system of the higher vertebrates. I know that the organizers of the symposium had been hoping that we should have with us some of the American colleagues, such as Professor Scharrer and Dr. Bodian, who have made such important contributions to this chapter of our subject, but who, to our regret, have not been able to come. Fortunately we have with us, in Professor Bargmann of Kiel and Professor Hanström of Lund, investigators who have been among the pioneers in the exploration, in different directions, of this rapidly opening field of knowledge. So far as I am aware, there is no other instance yet known in the endocrine systems of higher vertebrates, in which not only the output of a hormone from an endocrine gland, but also its production and maintenance there, are under such complete and immediate nervous control, as seems undoubtedly to exist in this case. The severance of the nervous connexion, between the neural lobe and the hypothalamic nuclei, leads to the disappearance of the hormones from the lobe within a few days. There have, further, been most suggestive descriptions of a specifically staining material, sheathing the endings in the lobe of the axons from the cells of the hypothalamic nuclei, which form, indeed, so large a constituent of its fabric; and we shall hear, I think, that material with the same staining properties has been traced along the whole course of these axonal fibres, right back to the nerve-cells of the hypothalamic nuclei in which they originate. I hope that it is not too fantastic to find, in the relation thus suggested, an analogy, not too remote, to the case of the ordinary efferent nerve-fibres, as found in the peripheral nervous system. I think that we can now take it to be accepted, that the effects of impulses in these fibres are transmitted to the effector cells, in close contiguity with which they have their endings, by the release from those endings of one or another specific transmitter substance, accumulated there, indeed, in readiness for such release, but traceable also, in minor amounts, along the whole course of such fibres, back to the nerve-cells in which they originate. And, here again, the transmitter disappears in a few days, and completely, from any part of such a fibre, including the depot at its ending, when it is separated by section from its nerve-cell of origin. And, if we can accept the suggested method of the formation, maintenance and release of the neurohypophysial hormones, as also dependent on a maintained continuity with the cells of the hypo-thalamic nuclei, we seem to have at least a suggestive analogy with these peripheral nerve-fibres and their specific transmitters; with the very important difference, of course, that the specifically stimulating substances, released from the endings of the nerve-fibres in the neurohypophysis, do not act as immediate transmitters of the effects of nerve impulses to contiguous effector cells or secondary neurones, but as hormones, carried in the blood-stream to the plain muscle and epithelial cells of distant organs, on which they then produce, at this long range, their specific stimulat-ing effects.

I have already stated that, so far as I am aware, this is the only case which has yet been discovered in the higher vertebrates, and especially in the Mammalia, from which so large a part of the evidence has been obtained, in which substances with a truly hormonal function have been found to be thus produced by essentially nervous structures. Apart, however, from certain mechanisms for controlling the activities of chromatophores in some cold-blooded vertebrates, I expect that Professor Hanström will be giving us an account of some, at least, of the now numerous examples avail-able, of suggestively analogous neuro-hormonal mechanisms in insects, crustaceans

8

and, possibly, other classes of invertebrates. And I think that I need not further emphasize the relief which these recent developments offer, from the embarrassments experienced by earlier workers, and from the unprofitable diversions of experiment and speculation, which were caused by their efforts to evade what they regarded as an incompatibility—an assumed incompatibility between an essentially nervous structure and a content of substances with activities so intense and so specific, that it was difficult not to credit them with important functions as hormones.

REFERENCES

DALE, H. H. (1906). On some physiological actions of ergot. *J. Physiol. (Lond.)* **34**, 163–206.

DALE, H. H. (1909). The action of extracts of the pituitary body. *Biochem. J.* **4**, 427–47.

DUDLEY, H. W. (1919). Some observations on the active principles of the pituitary gland. *J. Pharmacol.* **14**, 295–312.

FARMI, F. (1913). Über Diabetes insipidus und Hypophysistherapie. *Wien. klin. Wschr.* **26**, 1867.

FRANK, J. E. (1912). Über Beziehungen der Hypophyse zum Diabetes insipidus. *Klin. Wschr.* **49**, 393–7.

HELLER, H. (1939). The effect of the hydrogen-ion concentration on the stability of the antidiuretic and vasopressor activities of posterior pituitary extracts. *J. Physiol. (Lond.)* **96**, 337–47.

HOWELL, W. H. (1898). The physiological effects of extracts of the hypophysis cerebri and infundibular body. *J. exp. Med.* **3**, 245–258.

KAMM, O., ALDRICH, T. B., GROTE, I. W., ROWE, L. W. & BUGBEE, E. P. (1928). The active principles of the posterior lobe of the pituitary gland. I. The demonstration of the presence of two active principles. II. The separation of the two principles and their concentration in the form of potent solid preparations. *J. Amer. Chem. Soc.*, **50**, 533–601.

MAGNUS, R. & SCHÄFER, E. A. (1901). The action of pituitary extracts upon the kidney. *J. Physiol. (Lond.)* **27**, ix–x.

OLIVER, G. & SCHÄFER, E. A. (1895). On the physiological action of extracts of pituitary body and certain other glandular organs. *J. Physiol. (Lond.)* **18**, 277–9.

OTT, I. & SCOTT, J. C. (1910). The action of infundibulin upon the mammary secretion. *Proc. Soc. exp. Biol. (N.Y.)* **8**, 48–49.

SCHÄFER, E. A. & HERRING, P. T. (1906). The action of pituitary extracts upon the kidney. *Proc. roy. Soc. B* **77**, 271.

SCHÄFER, E. A. & VINCENT, S. (1899). The physiological effect of extracts of the pituitary body. *J. Physiol (Lond.)* **25**, 87–97.

STARLING, E. H. & VERNEY, E. B. (1925). The secretion of urine as studied on the isolated kidney. *Proc. roy. Soc. B* **97**, 321–63.

VON DEN VELDEN, R. (1913). Die Nierenwirkung von Hypophysenextrakten beim Menschen. *Klin. Wschr.* **50**, 2083–6.

VERNEY, E. B. (1926). The secretion of pituitrin in mammals, as shown by perfusion of the isolated kidney of the dog. *Proc. roy. Soc. B* **99**, 487–517.

Relationship between neurohypophysial structure and function

by

W. BARGMANN

Department of Anatomy, University of Kiel

AT the turn of the century, the application of a variety of histological techniques revealed the most important structural elements in the posterior lobe of the hypophysis. Thus, in 1894, Cajal (1911) noted that fine nerve-fibres were remarkably abundant in the posterior pituitary; he claimed that these fibres had their origin in a group of cells situated behind the optic chiasma.

He reported the presence of other cells which he did not identify, embedded in the plexus formed by these nerve-fibres, cells which later workers have interpreted as glial cells. The capillaries of the neurohypophysis, with their associated argyrophil connective tissue, form a third and essential component of the gland. These were not described until some twenty years after Cajal's original paper.

At that time it was impossible to make any reasonable functional interpretation of the so-called pars nervosa. Neither clinical nor experimental observations pointed unequivocally towards any specific role for the neurohypophysis, that is, towards any role which could account for the abundance of nerve-fibres and glial tissue it contained. This is not to say, of course, that there were not claims that substances extracted from the posterior pituitary of certain animals had specific humoral properties, capable of causing, for example, an elevation of the blood pressure. At this stage Biedl (1913) made an important point, namely, that it is extremely difficult to make a complete separation of the pars nervosa from the pars intermedia, in such a way as to be quite certain that the posterior pituitary tissue is completely free of epithelial cells. Workers in this new field of endocrine research were inclined to focus their attention on epithelial rather than on nervous tissues, since at that time, at the beginning of the century, all the organs of known endocrine activity were epithelial in structure and we can thus readily understand why Biedl (1913) in his standard work on the endocrine system, left open the question of the function of the posterior lobe, although he was ready to include the anterior lobe and pars intermedia of the pituitary among the endocrine organs.

However, the morphological investigation of the neurohypophysis received a new stimulus when it was shown that Biedl's classification was untenable and that the posterior pituitary had indeed a specific endocrine function.

This was first established by Geiling and his co-workers (1937) who studied animals in which the pituitary lacks a pars intermedia and in which a connective tissue septum separates the adenohypophysis from the neurohypophysis. From the posterior pituitaries of these animals these workers were able to extract oxytocin and vaso-pressin. It cannot for a moment be supposed that these extracts were derived from adenohypophysial tissue. Oldham's (1938) observations are equally unequivocal. She studied *Dasypus*, an animal in which the posterior pituitary is sharply divided from the adenohypophysis, and she found that the posterior pituitary contained antidiuretic as well as pressor and oxytocic activity.

These observations indicated that the neurohypophysis had a specific hormonal function. The question arose as to which structural elements were responsible for the production of the hormones. In answer to this question we can say that neither the glial cells of the posterior pituitary nor its nerve-fibres, nor both together, represent the site of formation of the three posterior pituitary activities.

The problem has been investigated in a number of ways, in particular with the aid of tissue culture. There have at the same time been further morphological studies which have amplified the original findings of Cajal.

Now, first, with regard to the glial cells of the neurohypophysis, Bucy (1932), who named these cells pituicytes, put forward the theory that they were responsible for the formation of the posterior pituitary hormones. Their secretory activity was corroborated, according to Griffiths (1940), by the observations of Geiling & Lewis (1935), who found vasopressin in tissue cultures of the posterior pituitary of the mouse. These observations were confirmed by Andersson & Haymaker (1935). Griffiths held that in such explants of posterior pituitary tissue the nerve-fibres had degenerated and therefore, by exclusion, only the pituicytes could be regarded as the source of the posterior pituitary hormones. Romeis (1940) endorsed this view. He stressed the presence of foamy vacuolation, of karyorrhexis and of karyolysis, which histological changes he regarded as evidence of holocrine secretion. Independently Gersh (1939) had also described what he termed glandular cells, in the neuro-hypophysis of the rat, which were filled with granules and which he held to be the site of formation of antidiuretic hormone. Indeed, I myself believed in the secretory nature of these glial cells for their nuclei contain large spherical inclusions which I interpreted as evidence of a secretory function.

The nerve-fibres which run between the diencephalon and the neural lobe were held by Gersh (1940) to regulate the release of the antidiuretic hormone. In this respect Gersh's views are in accord with those put forward by Ranson (1938, 1939) and his school. These workers studied the development of experimental diabetes insipidus following the interruption of the supraoptico-hypophysial tract. They attributed this condition to the destruction of the secretomotor innervation of the pituicytes.

However, as Hild (1954) has recently noted, there is one difficulty inherent in any attempt to combine Ranson's hypothesis with the views put forward by Griffiths, Gersh and other workers. According to Ranson, interference with the secretomotor innervation of the pituicytes leads to the cessation of hormone production. Griffiths on the other hand held that the pituicytes in tissue culture had an intrinsic secretory activity, and stressed the fact that the supposed secretomotor fibres in such explants were no longer viable. In view of these difficulties it seemed important to repeat the older tissue-culture experiments so as to make a critical appraisal of this problem of hormone production *in vitro*.

We must bear in mind at this point that the recognition of hormone in a tissue culture is no proof in itself of the formation of hormone by that tissue: it could merely indicate the persistence in that tissue of a store of hormone.

Now, Geiling & Lewis (1935) made their investigation on cultures at their most six days old. Hild (1954) has been able to show that hormone contained in tissue cultures from the mammalian posterior pituitary disappears within ten days and that following this no hormone is elaborated by pituicytes in spite of the fact that they remain viable. Further, no active substance can be extracted from explanted posterior pituitary if taken from an animal in which the posterior pituitary has been depleted of hormone by physiological means. Hild claims also that the morphological behaviour of pituicytes *in vitro* suggests that these cells are not secretory cells, but rather are protoplasmic astrocytes modified by their situation.

In short, we must regard the nerves of the posterior pituitary as the source of the posterior pituitary hormones, as Gaupp (1941) among many others has insisted on. These nerves form a thick network composed of fine unmyelinated fibres, which in silver-preparations are remarkable for their numerous nodular thickenings. In the vicinity of blood vessels these fibres form a particularly fine meshed plexus. Their endings clearly do not form synapses with pituicytes, as they should do, if the innervation of pituicytes were necessary for their secretory activity. To understand the function of these fibres, we must consider their origin. We have to take into account axons, the cell-bodies of which are, in part, ganglion cells in the nuclei of the tuber cinereum, but, the majority of nerve-fibres in the posterior pituitary are derived from the cells of the supraoptic and paraventricular nuclei. By and large therefore we can look upon these fibres as the terminations of the supraoptico-hypophysial tract.

These cells have in their cytoplasm granules or droplets of a colloidal substance, which can be regarded as neurosecretory material. The secretory function of the nerve-cells was first recognized by E. Scharrer and his co-workers (1954*a*, *b*), but only in the proximal part of the neurosecretory pathway. Now, however, it is possible to demonstrate this neurosecretory material in the entire distribution of the supraoptico-hypophysial tract, from the nuclear region (Plates I, II and III) to where the fibres fan out in the posterior pituitary (Plate IV). This has been achieved by a variety of staining and histochemical techniques which selectively demonstrate neurosecretory substance within the neuroplasm, namely, the chrome-alum-haematoxylin technique (Bargmann, 1949), the paraldehyde-fuchsin technique (Gabe 1953; Dawson, 1952), the thioglycollate-ferric-ferricyanide reaction for cystine (Sloper, 1955) and the performic acid-Alcian blue reaction for cystine (Sloper & Adams 1955) (Plate V). With these methods one can see that the colloid droplets, called Herring bodies, which were once thought to lie free in the posterior pituitary, are in fact swellings on neurosecretory fibres (Plate VI). Apart from them we find everywhere fibres characterized by smaller thickenings, that is, beaded fibres resembling strings of pearls. We also find granules and droplets of secretion which are free in the interstitial space of the neurohypophysis and which are not apparently related to nerve-fibres.

As for the manner in which neurosecretory products are released into the blood-stream, it is not yet clear whether they normally pass into the capillaries of the posterior pituitary (Plate VII) in the manner suggested by Hanström (1952) and others.

13

In a preparation stained to demonstrate neurosecretory material it can be shown that the neural lobe contains much more of this substance than any other part of the neurosecretory pathway. This suggests that the posterior pituitary stores the material. A point much in favour of this view is that one can virtually empty the pituitary of neurosecretory substance in a wide variety of ways, for example by dehydration, (Ortmann, 1951), adrenalectomy (Eichner, 1953) or stress. With return to a normal allowance of drinking-water after dehydration the posterior pituitary fills once more with neurosecretory substance. In Hild & Zetler's (1953) experiments this was shown to take some days.

Such observations raise a number of interesting problems: First, how does neurosecretory material accumulate in the neurohypophysis? Secondly, where does this material come from? and thirdly, what is its functional significance?

There is a good deal of evidence to suggest that neurosecretory substance is formed in the supraoptic and paraventricular nuclei and is transported down the neurosecretory pathway, the supraoptico-hypophysial tract, to its depot organ, the posterior pituitary. The same appears to be the case in invertebrates, for example in the intercerebral-corpus allatum system of insects and in the X-organ-sinus gland system in the eyestalk of Crustacea (Berta Scharrer, 1951, 1952a, 1952b, 1952c, 1952d; B. & E. Scharrer, 1944, 1954; Hanström, 1953). Further, in a large number of vertebrates, from mammals down to Amphibia, operative interference with the neurosecretory pathway leads to the proximal accumulation of neurosecretory substance and to a diminution in the amount of this material in the posterior pituitary. A similar accumulation has been observed in the human pituitary stalk, by Müller (1955), following compression of the infundibulum by a meningioma, and by Sloper (1955), following hypophysectomy for the relief of malignant disease. Finally it is of interest that Hild (1954) has observed and filmed in tissue culture the transport of granules in a distal direction down the axons of living supraoptic cells in the dog. A point which presents some difficulty is that in the developing foetus stainable neurosecretory material is first demonstrable, not in the supraoptic and paraventricular nuclei, but in the neurohypophysis. This observation does not in my opinion weaken the theory of the transport of neurosecretory substance. For it seems to me that the granules of neurosecretion probably require an initial period of maturation, only after which they become visible in the light-microscope.

It is difficult to be dogmatic about the chemical nature of neurosecretory material. Schiebler (1951, 1952) supposed it on histochemical grounds to be a glycolipoprotein complex, Barnett & Seligman (1954) with their dihydroxyl-dinaphthyl-disulphide reaction observed that it was rich in cystine, a point made independently by Sloper (1955) with the thioglycollate-ferricyanide reaction. For this and other reasons, these workers claim that the neurosecretory substance is essentially a protein. The supposedly high content of cystine in this substance is of some interest, in view of the fact that posterior pituitary extracts are also very rich in cystine.

This brings me to the question of the functional significance of neurosecretory material. Whether we regard this material as representing the posterior pituitary hormones themselves, or as the carrier substance for these hormones, it is clearly necessary to prove that there is a close relationship between the two, that is, between what we can *stain* and what we can *extract*. This of course requires that oxytocin,

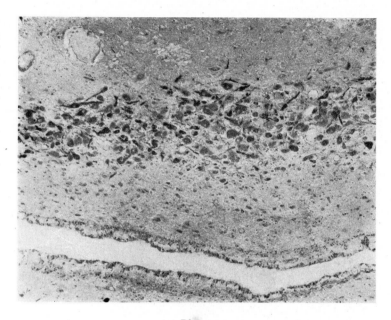

Plate I

Paraventricular nucleus, dog. Nerve-cells stained selectively with chrom-alum-haematoxylin (Gomori). 90 ×

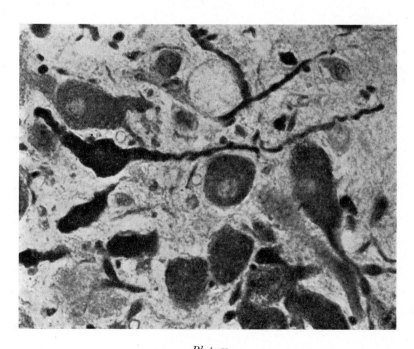

Plate II

Group of neurosecretory cells (nucleus supraopticus, dog). Note the nerve-fibres. (Chrom-alum-haematoxylin, Gomori.) 650 ×.

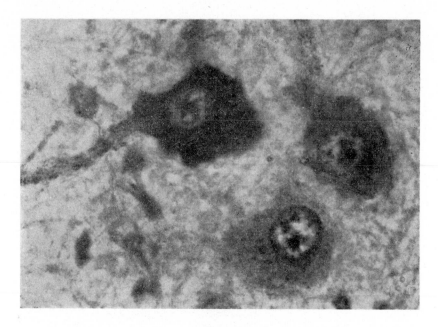

Plate III

Neurosecretory cells (nucleus supraopticus, dog), showing different amounts of neurosecretory substance. (Chrom-alum-haematoxylin, Gomori.) 1,200 ✕.

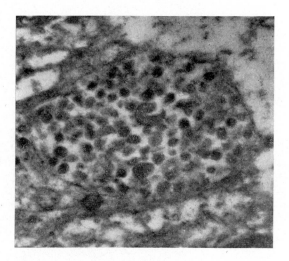

Plate IV

Electron-microphotograph of a single nerve-fibre in the
neural lobe of the cat, containing many granules. (Fix-
ation: osmic acid.) 23,000 ✕.

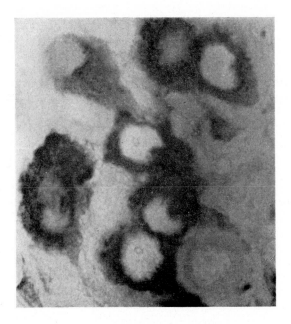

Plate v

Nucleus praeopticus of the tench (*Tinca vulgaris*), stained
with Alcian blue (Sloper's method). Nuclei of the nerve
cells unstained. 615×.

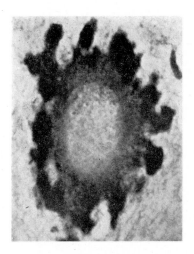

Plate vi

Herring-body with protuberances,
dog. (Chrom-alum-haematoxylin,
Gomori.) 1,400×.

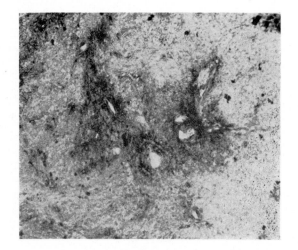

Plate vii

Neurosecretory material, surrounding capillaries of the
neural lobe (dog, chrom-alum-haematoxylin). 150×.

vasopressin and antidiuretic hormone can be found not only in the posterior pituitary, but also throughout the whole neurosecretory pathway from the nuclear region to the neural lobe.

In this connexion we must recall the investigations made long ago by Trendelenburg (1928), and Sato (1928) and Melville & Hare (1945) concerning the presence of posterior pituitary hormones in the hypothalamus. These investigations were based on material the exact source of which in the brain is rather obscure. However, Hild & Zetler (1951) made extracts from pieces of brain which contained little tissue save the ganglion cells of the supraoptic and paraventricular nuclei and fibres of the supraoptico-hypophysial tract. These extracts contained material with oxytocic, antidiuretic and vasopressor activity, as shown by the customary methods of biological assay. On the other hand extracts made from neighbouring brain tissue, which contained no neurosecretory material, were inactive. Further, there was a direct relationship between the amount of neurosecretory substance and the biological activity of the tissue. This was found to apply also to the accumulations of neurosecretory material which, as I have already noted, are to be found above the cut end of the pituitary stalk, for the hormone content in such regions is higher than would normally be in extracts made from these regions. It is of interest too, that comparative studies have established a relationship between the amounts of neurosecretory material and the amounts of the hormones in the diencephalon of the dog, pig and man (Hild & Zetler, 1952). Thus, the dog is rich in neurosecretory substance, and a large amount of hormone can be extracted compared with man in whom both the amounts of neurosecretory substance and hormones are low.

Again, Heller's, (Heller, 1947, Heller & Zaimis, 1949) observation, that the posterior pituitary of the newborn contains only a small amount of antidiuretic hormone, has its histological equivalent in the scantiness of the amount of neurosecretory material which can be demonstrated in this organ shortly after birth. We must not forget, too, the many and repeated experiments in which it has been shown that dehydration is accompanied by the disappearance of neurosecretory material from the posterior pituitary. It is reasonable to correlate this with the observation that there is a fall in the amount of vasopressin, which can be extracted from the posterior pituitary after dehydration (Ortmann, 1951; Leveque & Scharrer, 1953). Finally I must refer to the diminution in the amount of neurosecretory material which accompanies lactation. This observation may be connected with the release of the milk let-down factor, that is, perhaps with the secretion of oxytocin (Stutinsky, 1953; Malandra, 1955–56). Recently, Vogt (1953) has raised the interesting question as to whether the hormone content of the material secreted in the hypothalamus alters in its composition during its transport to the neurohypophysis. This is of course primarily a pharmacological rather than morphological problem. Her own idea is that oxytocin, which is only present in scanty amounts in the hypothalamus, is either formed during the passage of this material down the supraoptico-hypophysial tract, or else that it is first formed in the posterior pituitary, where it is added to the material formed in the hypothalamus.

To sum up, it seems reasonable to regard the neurosecretory neurons in the hypothalamus as responsible for the formation of adiuretin, oxytocin and vasopressin, while the terminations of these neurons in the posterior pituitary may be regarded as the site of hormone release. The distribution of these nerve-endings in the pituitary of the opossum conforms extremely well with this conception; in this animal, as Bodian (1951) noted, the posterior pituitary shows a remarkable accumulation of neurosecretory material within the rod-like nerve-endings (palisade zone) at the periphery of the neurohypophysial lobules.

Hormone can be rapidly released, from the posterior lobe that is, in a matter of minutes. This was well demonstrated by Verney's (1947, 1948) elegant experiments in the dog. He showed that variations in the osmotic pressure of blood reaching the head were followed by the rapid release of adiuretin from the posterior pituitary.

Verney's experiments imply the immediate stimulation of the neurosecretory cells in the hypothalamus by these variations in osmotic pressure, and in this respect the remarkably close contact between these cells and their capillaries may be significant; his experiments also imply the transference of an impulse down the supraoptico-hypophysial tract to its endings in the posterior pituitary. We do not know whether the pituicytes participate in the release of hormone from these endings. From studies made with the electron-microscope by Palay (1955) the capillaries of the posterior pituitary seem to be well adapted for the transfer of material through their walls, for their endothelium contains submicroscopic pores, which until now have only been described in the capillaries of the renal glomerulus.

Finally, I feel that, for the sake of completeness, I must briefly mention the part played by the supraoptico-hypophysial tract in the innervation of the pars intermedia and the pars tuberalis. Neurosecretory fibres do undoubtedly enter the pars intermedia, an organ, indeed, which is rich in glial tissue. This applies particularly to fishes, but also to some mammals. As a result it is impossible to make a sharp distinction between the pars intermedia and the neurohypophysis. Neurosecretory fibres also come into contact with the special vessels of the pituitary stalk, from which the blood passes into the pars tuberalis. Occasionally such fibres can be seen to cross over into the pars tuberalis.

These observations lead one to suppose that the hormones formed in the supraoptic and paraventricular nuclei may have some influence on the pars intermedia and also perhaps on the pars distalis. This seems to me to be an interesting and profitable subject for future research. Such problems certainly make it only too clear that the structure and the function of the neurohypophysis are considerably more complicated than we used to suppose.

REFERENCES

ANDERSSON, E. & HAYMAKER, W. (1935). Elaboration of hormones by pituitary cells growing in vitro. *Proc. Soc. exper. Biol. Med. N.Y.* **33**, 313–6.

BARGMANN, W. (1949). Über die neurosekretorische Verknüpfung von Hypothalamus und Neurohypophyse. *Z. Zellforsch.* **34**, 610–34.

BARGMANN, W. (1954). *Das Zwischenhirn-Hypophysensystem.* Berlin-Göttingen-Heidelberg: Springer.

BARNETT, R. J. & SELIGMAN, A. M. (1954). Histochemical demonstration of sulfhydryl and disulfide groups of protein. *J. nat. Cancer Inst.* **14**, 769–803.

BIEDL, A. (1913). *Innere Sekretion.* 2nd ed. Berlin: Urban-Schwarzenberg.

BODIAN, D. (1951). Nerve endings, neurosecretory substance and lobular organization of the neurohypophysis. *Bull. Johns Hopk. Hosp.* **89**, 354–76.

BUCY, P. C. (1932). The hypophysis cerebri. In: *Cytology and cellular pathology of the nervous system*. Ed. Penfield, W. New York: Hoeber.

CAJAL, S. RAMON Y (1911). *Histologie du systeme nerveux*. Vol. 2. Paris: Maloine.

DAWSON, A. B. (1953). Hypothalamo-hypophysial relationships in *Rana pipiens* demonstrated by Gomori's chrom-alumhematoxylin method. *Anat. Rec.* **112**, 443–4.

EICHNER, D. (1953). Über den morphologischen Ausdruck funktioneller Beziehungen zwischen Nebennierenrinde und neurosekretorischem Zwischenhirnsystem der Ratte. *Z. Zellforsch.* **38**, 488–508.

GABE, M. (1953). Sur quelques applications de la coloration par la fuchsine-paraldehyde. *Bull. Micr. appl.* **3**, 153–62.

GAUPP, R. (1941). Die Beziehungen von Zwischenhirn und Hypophyse in der morphologischen und experimentellen Forschung. *Fortschr. Neurol.* **13**, 257–80.

GEILING, E. M. K. & LEWIS, M. R. (1935). Further information regarding the melanophore hormone of the hypophysis cerebri. *Amer. J. Physiol.* **113**, 534–7.

GEILING, E. M. K. & OLDHAM, F. K. (1937). The site of formation of the posterior lobe hormones. *Trans. Ass. Amer. Phys.* **52**, 132–6.

GERSH, J. (1939). The structure and function of the parenchymatous glandular cells in the neurohypophysis of the rat. *Amer. J. Anat.* **64**, 407–43.

GERSH, J. (1940). Water metabolism: Endocrine factors. In: *Res. Publ. Ass. nerv. ment. Dis.* **20**, 436–48.

GRIFFITHS, M. (1940). The relationship between the secretory cells of the pars nervosa of the hypophysis and classical neuroglia. *Endocrinology* **26**, 1032–41.

HANSTRÖM, B. (1952). Transportation of colloid from the neurosecretory hypothalamic centres of the brain into the blood-vessels of the neural lobe of the hypophysis. *Kgl. Fysiogr. Sällsk. Förhandl. (Lund).* **22**, 1–5.

HANSTRÖM, B. (1953). Neurosecretory pathways in the head of crustaceans, insects and vertebrates. *Nature (Lond.)* **171**, 72–3.

HARRIS, G. W. (1955). *Neural control of the pituitary gland*. London: Edward Arnold.

HELLER, H. (1947). Antidiuretic hormone in pituitary glands of newborn rats. *J. Physiol. (Lond.)* **106**, 28–32.

HELLER, H. & ZAIMIS, E. J. (1949). The antidiuretic and oxytocic hormones in the posterior pituitary glands of newborn infants and adults. *J. Physiol. (Lond.)* **109**, 162–9.

HILD, W. (1954). Das morphologische, kinetische und endokrinologische Verhalten von hypothalamischem und neurohypophysärem Gewebe in vitro. *Z. Zellforsch.* **40**. 257–312.

HILD, W. & ZETLER, G. (1951). Über das Vorkommen der Hypophysenhinterlappenhormone im Zwischenhirn. *Arch. exp. Path. Pharmak.* **213**, 139–53.

HILD, W. & ZETLER, G. (1952). Vergleichende Untersuchungen über das Vorkommen des Hypophysenhinterlappenhormons im Zwischenhirn einiger Säugetiere. *Dtsch. Z. Nervenheilk.* **167**, 105–214.

HILD, W. & ZETLER, G. (1953) Experimenteller Beweis für die Entstehung der sog. Hypophysenhinterlappenwirkstoffe im Hypothalamus. *Pflügers Arch. ges. Phsyiol.* **257**, 169–201.

LEVEQUE, T. F. & SCHARRER, E. (1953). Pituicytes and the origin of the antidiuretic hormones. *Endocrinology*, **52**, 436–47.

MALANDRA, B. (1955–56). Beobachtungen am neurosekretorischen Zwischenhirnsystem der normalen, trächtigen und laktierenden Ratte. *Z. Zellforsch.* **43**, 594–610.

MELVILLE, E. V. & HARE, K. (1945). Antidiuretic material in the supraoptic nucleus. *Endocrinology* **36**, 323–9.

MÜLLER, W. (1955). Neurosekretstauung im Tractus supraoptico-hypophyseus des Menschen durch einen raumbeengenden Prozess. *Z. Zellforsch.* **42**, 439–42.

OLDHAM, F. K. (1938). The pharmacology and anatomy of the hypophysis of the armadillo. *Anat. Rec.* **72**, 265–92.

ORTMANN, R. (1951). Über experimentelle Veränderungen der Morphologie des Hypophysenzwischenhirnsystems und die Beziehung der sog. 'Gomori substanz' zum Adiuretin. *Z. Zellforsch.* **36**, 92–140.

PALAY, S. L. (1955). An electron-microscope study of the neurohypophysis in normal hydrated and dehydrated rats. *Anat. Rec.* **121**, 384.

RANSON, S. W., FISHER, C. & INGRAM, W. R. (1938). The hypothalamico-hypophyseal mechanism in diabetes insipidus. *Res. Publ. Ass. nerv. ment. Dis.* **17**, 410–32.

RANSON, S. W. & MAGOUN, H. W. (1939). The hypothalamus. *Ergebn. Physiol.* **41**, 56–163.

ROMEIS, B. (1940). Hypophyse. In: *Handbuch der mikroskopischen Anatomie des Menschen.* Band 6, Teil 3. Berlin: Springer.

SATO, G. (1928). Über die Beziehungen des Diabetes insipidus zum Hypophysenhinterlappen und zum Tuber cinereum. *Arch. exp. Path. Pharmak.* **131**, 45–69.

SCHARRER, B. (1951). The storage of neurosecretory material in the corpus cardiacum. *Anat. Rec.* **111**, 554–5.

SCHARRER, B. (1952a). The effect of the interruption of the neurosecretory pathway in the insect *Leukophaea maderae.* *Anat. Rec.* **112**, 386–7.

SCHARRER, B. (1952b). Hormones in insects. In: *The Action of Hormones in Plants and Invertebrates.* Ed. Thimann, K.V. New York: Academic Press.

SCHARRER, B. (1952c). Über neuroendokrine Vorgänge bei Insekten. *Pflügers Arch. ges. Physiol.* **255**, 154–63.

SCHARRER, B. (1952d). Neurosecretion. XI. The effects of nerve section on the intercerebralis-cardiacum-allatum system of the insect *Leukophaea maderae.* *Biol. Bull.* **102**, 261–72.

SCHARRER, B. & SCHARRER, E. (1944). Neurosecretion VI. A comparison between the intercerebralis-cardiacum-allatum system of the insects and the hypothalamo-hypophyseal system of the vertebrate. *Biol. Bull.* **87**, 242–51.

SCHARRER, B. & SCHARRER, E. (1954a). Neurosekretion. In: *Handbuch der mikroskopischen Anatomie des Menschen.* Ed. Bargmann, W. Band 6, Teil 5, Berlin: Springer.

SCHARRER, B. & SCHARRER, E. (1954b). Hormones produced by neurosecretory cells. *Recent Progr. Hormone Res.* **10**, 182–240.

SCHIEBLER, T. H. (1951). Zur Histochemie des neurosekretorischen hypothalamisch-neurohypophysären Systems. *Acta anat. (Basel)* **13**, 233–55.

SCHIEBLER, T. H. (1952). Zur Histochemie des neurosekretorischen hypothalamisch-neurohypophysären Systems. II. *Acta anat. (Basel)*, **15**, 393–416.

SLOPER, J. C. (1955). Hypothalamic neurosecretion in the dog and cat, with particular reference to the identification of neurosecretory material with posterior lobe hormone. *J. Anat. (Lond.)* **89**, 301–16.

SLOPER, J. C. & ADAMS, C. W. M. (1955). Effect of hypophysectomy on hypothalamic neurosecretion in the human hypothalamus. *Excerpta med. (Amst.)* Sect. VIII, **8**, 878–9.

STUTINSKY, F. (1953). La neurosecretion au cours de la gestation et le post-partum chez la rate. *Ann. Endocr. (Paris)* **14**, 722–5.

TRENDELENBURG, P. (1928). Anteil der Hypophyse und des Hypothalamus am experimentellen Diabetes insipidus. *Klin. Wschr.* **7**, 1679–80.

VERNEY, E. B. (1947). The antidiuretic hormone and the factors which determine its release. *Proc. Roy. Soc. B* **135**, 27–106.

VERNEY, E. B. (1948). Agents determining and influencing the function of the pars nervosa of the pituitary. *Brit. Med. J.* i, 119–23.

VOGT, M. (1953). Vasopressor, antidiuretic and oxytocic activities of extracts of the dog's hypothalamus. *Brit. J. Pharmacol.* **8**. 193–196.

Discussion

Chairman: Sir Henry Dale

Dale. Might I put one question to Professor Bargmann? Have any experiments been done to show whether water deprivation, which robs the neural lobe of its specifically stainable material deprived it only of the antidiuretic-vasopressor principle, or whether the oxytocic principle goes with it too?

Bargmann. I remember only Hild & Zetler's (*Pflügers Arch. ges. Physiol.* **257**, 169, 1953) experiments in the dog.

Dale. Do you know whether this stainable material represents one hormone alone, or whether it is a substance with all the activities?

Bargmann. I want to be very careful about this. I think that the substance we can see is a carrier.

van Dyke. I think that one such investigation has been done by Simon (*Amer. J. Physiol.* **107**, 220, 1934) or by Simon & Kardos (*Arch. exp. Path. Pharmak.* **176**, 238, 1934). They found that after prolonged deprivation of water there was decrease in both hormones. These observations were made in rats.

Jewell. Professor Bargmann did mention that during lactation it has been shown that there was a depletion of stainable neurosecretory material. Has there been any differentiation between the paraventricular and supraoptic nucleus in this regard? Does it disappear from both?

Bargmann. The results were very variable. Sometimes it appeared that the supraoptic nucleus contained more of the material than the paraventricular and vice versa. There are comments by Malandra (*Z. Zellforsch.* **43**, 594, 1956) on this point.

Heller. You mentioned the interesting experiments of Marthe Vogt. I don't know whether you remember that on her suggestion the ratio of oxytocic to vasopressor activity has also been investigated in other species by Schlichtegroll (*Naturwissenschaften* **41**, 188, 1954). He found that in the cat hypothalamus the ratio was one to one, showing that the ratio does vary significantly from species to species.

Bargmann. The situation is very difficult; we used only the dog and we need more investigations on other species.

Field. In some species the globules which are stainable by the Gomori stain are so very large that it is very difficult to see how they would pass down the axons. Also in the dog one finds some nerve cells in the supraoptic nucleus that are so distended that they are virtually signet ring cells.

Bargmann. They seem to me to be cells in a state of degeneration. Occasionally I have seen very small and karyolytic nuclei which are like the vesicles which Verney described as osmoreceptors. They are swollen ganglionic cells. Concerning the huge droplets mentioned: I have not seen such inclusions in the dog but they have been seen in birds. I cannot see how these huge particles could move down to the stalk but we must consider the possibility that in some species hormones may be released from the stainable material into the capillaries of the nuclei or that they may be transported to the third ventricle. I do not believe we should draw general conclusions from the findings in the dog, the cat and the human being. The situation in birds seems to be quite different.

Fromageot. With reference to the material which takes the Gomori stain: we have observed that the 'van Dyke protein' both in its active form and free of the oxytocic and vasopressor peptides gives this reaction. But we do not know what this fact has to do with the chemical constitution of this molecule.

van Dyke. I was interested in what Professor Bargmann had to say about the nature of the neurosecretory substance. I think that Hild (*Z̧. Anat. EntwGesch.* **115**, 459, 1951) maintained that this substance is a carrier and that he could extract this carrier and leave the hormones intact. In respect of the protein to which Professor Fromageot referred, the only view I hold today is that it may be a storage form of the hormones in the ox gland, which I believe is the only one in which it has been investigated. I think that it is hazardous to draw conclusions as to whether it is released and in what form the hormones are released. A protein like the one isolated by us seems to explain the first experiments of Rosenfeld (*Bull. Johns Hopk. Hosp.* **66**, 398, 1940) who made simple extracts and found that the hormones sedimented as though parts of a protein and that the active materials could be liberated by mild treatment with heat in a weakly acid medium.

These findings do support the view that it may be the storage form of the hormone in the ox gland. One always has to take into account the possibility of adsorption as pointed out by Sir Henry Dale.

Dale. This storage form of the hormone gives the vasopressor and the oxytocic actions. Does it also give the melanophore expanding action?

van Dyke. No, I think that was one of the great pleasures of investigation that the protein containing the activities was virtually free of the hormone affecting melanophores.

Croxatto. What is the basis for the belief that there are three different substances in the hypothalamus, namely vasopressin, adiuretin and oxytocin?

Bargmann. When I spoke of three I meant the three different activities tested in the experimental animals. The problem whether they should be attributed to three substances is a pharmacological one.

Dale. Professor van Dyke, and other people who have worked with the du Vigneaud pure peptides, tells us that vasopressin and antidiuretin are the same substance, and that oxytocin and the milk-ejecting principle are another.

Pickford. I would like to ask Professor Bargmann's opinion of things that one does see in animals which have had diabetes insipidus for a long time. When we stain the hypothalamus afterwards in the areas where the nerve-fibres are, we see bunches of black granules rather like bunches of grapes. Are these nerve-fibres which have produced so much material that they cannot pass it on to the posterior lobe and have burst and distributed this material? That is what it looks like.

Bargmann. To answer this question it would be necessary to see your slides.

Noble. I believe you said that other forms of stress produce a picture similar to that in which you showed depletion of the gland. This brings to mind the finding of the Californian group of workers (Castor, Baker, Ingle & Li, *Proc. Soc. exp. Biol.,* (*N.Y.*) **76**, 353, 1951) who showed that cortisone apparently produces changes in the hypothalamic nuclei and I wonder if it is possible that dehydration as well as stress act by stimulation of the adrenal cortex. Have you studied the effects of cortisone?

Bargmann. We have no experience with cortisone. We can see depletion of the neural lobe after total adrenalectomy and you will also see it if you give a rat painful stimuli.

Hanström. There are some points in which my investigations on the mammalian pituitary disagree with those of Professor Bargmann. I have found like Professor Bargmann that Gomori-stained fibres may end within the pars intermedia, but in my experience these fibres are very rare and can probably be regarded as fibres which have gone astray. There is another point which must be taken into consideration: it is that several mammals have no pars intermedia. In whales and elephants there is instead of the pars intermedia a thick membrane of connective tissue between the neural and the distal lobe which must prevent hormones from the posterior lobe from reaching the anterior one. The only connexion between these lobes is through the eminentia mediana (infundibulum) and the pars tuberalis by means of the portal vessels.

Bargmann. I agree entirely with Professor Hanström but I said in *some* mammals. In the opossum for instance there is a very thin intermediate lobe and you cannot see any connexion with the neural lobe. As you know this is a lobulated posterior pituitary and there is no connexion between the two parts but in some species it is very remarkable how the two parts are connected. In the golden hamster you can very often see neurosecretory fibres within the intermediary lobe.

Rodeck. Last year I had the good fortune to spend six months in Professor Bargmann's Institute in Kiel, where I was able to study neurosecretion in human foetuses, in newborn babies and in young infants. Very young infants need a remarkably high quantity of fluid, which in a single day may amount to about one-sixth or one-fifth of their body-weight. If a grown-up person drank the equivalent volume of liquid, he would undoubtedly suffer from 'diabetes insipidus'. Hitherto the so-called physiological diabetes insipidus of the newborn child or young infant has usually been attributed to immaturity of the kidney. The question is, whether the regulatory system in the hypothalamus and the neurohypophysis, which is responsible for the facultative reabsorption in the distal tubules, is fully developed or whether this mechanism matures only gradually during the first year of life as does the kidney. We have investigated the whole neurosecretory system (nucleus supraopticus, nucleus paraventricularis, tractus supraoptico-hypophyseus, and the neural lobe) in 121 rats, 21 guinea-pigs, 28 dogs and 18 human foetuses, newborn infants, and children in all stages of life. It could be shown that the neurosecretory and hormone-producing system is not fully differentiated at the time of birth. The majority of the ganglion cells do not show a noticeable development of cytoplasm. The neurohypophysis also does not contain neurosecretory material at the time of birth. A normal production of neurosecretory material is seen only after several months of post-natal life. These findings are in accordance with the observations of Heller & Zaimis (*J. Physiol. (Lond.)* **109**, 162, 1949) who found that the neurohypophysis of newborn children and young infants contained only a fraction of antidiuretic-vasopressor and oxytocic activity of the adult. Thus, during the time of neonatal development the regulatory system (the neurohypophysis) and the effector organ (kidney) are in wonderfully complete harmony. The maturity of the regulatory system corresponds always to that of the effector organ.

Heller. I am of course very interested in Dr. Rodeck's results which agree very well with our findings. However, I should like to stress that the small amounts of anti-diuretic activity that we found in newborn rats and in human infants may not be insignificant functionally. Significance can only be judged in terms of ease of liberation and the minimum effective dose on the kidney. Even comparatively small amounts stored in the gland of newborns may thus be important.

Dale. Did Dr. Rodeck represent you correctly in saying that the oxytocin content was also very small?

Heller. Yes, per mg. neurohypophysial tissue, the glands of infants contained much less oxytocic activity than those of adults.

Sloper. With reference to Dr. Rodeck's observations it is of interest that the newborn seal is far advanced in the matter of hypothalamic neurosecretion. The amount of neurosecretory material present in the hypothalamus matches with that of a two-month-old dog in Dr. Rodeck's series.

Dale. Perhaps the seal has not the common need to concentrate his urine?

Sloper. I don't know much about that, Sir. Can the seal drink sea-water?

The comparative aspect of neurosecretion with special reference to the hypothalamo–hypophysial system

by

BERTIL HANSTRÖM

Zoological Institute, University of Lund

THE hypothesis that nerve-cells produce a secretion with functions which are not associated with the transmission of nervous impulses, was for several years regarded as suspect by many biologists. However, investigations in the first place by E. Scharrer in 1928 and later by an ever-growing number of scientists, has proved without doubt that such neurosecretory material exists and that it differs in several ways from the humoral substances (acetylcholine, noradrenaline) which serve the transmission of peripheral nervous impulses: It is produced in considerable amounts, it can be stained by several histological methods and it is related to hormonal reactions in organs which may be situated far from the site where the neurosecretory material is released into the circulation.

WORMS AND MOLLUSCS

Neurosecretory cells have been detected in all groups of animals except the lowest class of invertebrates which possess a nervous system, viz. the coelenterates. But there are some reasons to believe that neurosecretion occurs in as primitive forms as in planarians. In segmented worms (polychaetes, earthworms) conspicuous signs of neurosecretory activity within numerous cell-groups in the brain and the ventral nerve-chord have been detected in the shape of vacuoles and brightly staining droplets. Some of these cells appear to produce a growth factor, which is active in the regeneration of the anterior segments of the body, others seem to be concerned with reproduction. Extracts from the brain of earthworms increase the frequency of intestinal movements, while a decrease of the frequency is caused by extracts from the ventral ganglia. The brain of some polychaetes produces an inhibitory hormone which regulates reproduction and prevents a precocious transformation of *Nereis* into the sexually mature form.

In molluscs, two neuroglandular organs occur in cephalopods, the subpeduncular gland and the epistellar body, and clusters of neurosecretory cells have been detected in several species of other molluscs (prosobranchs, opistobranchs, bivalves). However, their function is in most cases unknown. In some species a relation to the reproductory cycle is suggested and in others a chromatophorotropic action, which was shown in species different from that of the donors. Moreover, the nervous system

23

of *Buccinum* and the hearts of *Buccinum*, *Pecten* and *Mytilus* contain a cardio-inhibitory substance, resembling acetylcholine in its action on the heart of *Buccinum*, and also a cardio-excitatory substance whose action on the heart resembles 5-hydroxytryptamine (Welsh, 1956).

In most of these instances of neurosecretory activity in lower invertebrates, the cells which perform this activity, appear to possess the shape of ordinary nerve-cells. They have dendrites and an axon, and form a link in a chain of neurons or innervate effector organs (a muscle or a gland). The neurosecretory product has been observed not only in the cell-plasm but also in the axons, and migration of the secretory material along the axons has been occasionally demonstrated in polychaetes. In addition, in some polychaetes (nereids and nephtyids) according to Clark (1956) 'an axon tract in the brain runs to a connective tissue sheath at its base where it and the pericapsular membrane come to have an intimate connexion with a blood plexus' and where the neurosecretory material can be found accumulated on either side of the sheath and around the blood vessels. This suggests that in this case the neuro-secretory nerve-fibres end blindly, i.e. that they do not form a link in a neuron chain but deliver the neurosecretory substance from the axon endings directly into the blood.

In a single case in molluscs too, Lemche's (1955) observations suggest the presence of the first differentiation of the neurosecretory apparatus into two morphological subdivisions: (1) the central neurosecretory cell group, and (2) a separate storage organ. This differentiation has been found in all the more closely investigated complex neurohormonal systems in higher invertebrates.

CRUSTACEANS

The simplest type of a storage organ in arthropods (if it actually deserves this designation) is the so-called neurohaemal organ in crustaceans (Carlisle & Knowles, 1953) which consists of lamellae of neuropile-like neurosecretory nerve-endings in the pericardium (Alexandrowicz & Carlisle, 1953). Some of these nerve-endings rise above the inner surface of the pericardium and are supposed to release a cardio-accelerating principle (5-hydroxytryptamine) into the blood, while a cardio-depressant substance is produced by nerve-cells of the trito-cerebral commissure. Although the nerve-cells from which the neurohaemal organs originate are still unidentified, their structure ought to be of the same type as those in nereids and nephtyids in which they run to the connective tissue sheath at the base of the brain. In crustaceans also, these axons terminate blindly. Thus they neither innervate any effector organs nor transmit impulses nor form normal links in a neuronal chain.

On a still higher level of differentiation is the X-organ-sinus gland system in crustaceans. Here a group of neurosecretory cells, constituting the X-organ (in a part of the brain which has migrated into the eyestalks) send their axons to a clearly differentiated storage organ, the sinus gland, the walls of which consist mainly of the swollen endings of the neurosecretory axons (Plates I and II). Like the X-organ, the sinus gland in higher crustaceans is situated in the eyestalks where it forms part of the wall of a large blood sinus. Recent investigations have shown that, in addition to the X-organ, numerous neurosecretory cell-groups within the brain proper send their axons into the sinus gland which thus serves mainly as a multiple storage and release

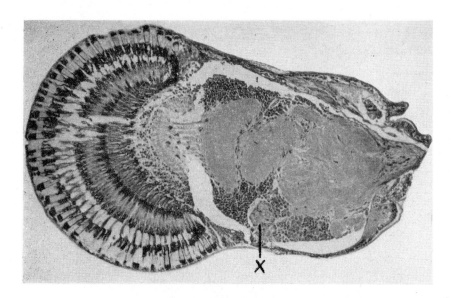

Plate I

Longitudinal section of the eyestalk of a shrimp with the eye to the left, the nervous mass in the centre, and the X-organ (X) ventrally.

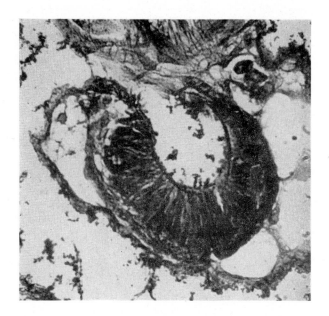

Plate II

Sac-like sinus gland of a shrimp. Its wall consists chiefly of the swollen nerve-endings of the X-cells and other neurosecretory cells (see also Fig. 1.).

Plate III

To the left an originally dark-adapted shrimp (*Crangon*), which 30 minutes previously had been injected with 0·1 ml. of a sea-water extract of the head of an insect (*Ectobius*); to the right a specimen, which 30 minutes previously had been injected with the same amount of pure filtered sea-water. The latter caused no change of the colour while the extract of the insect head concentrated the pigments of the left specimen so that it became almost pure white. Both animals were on a dark background.

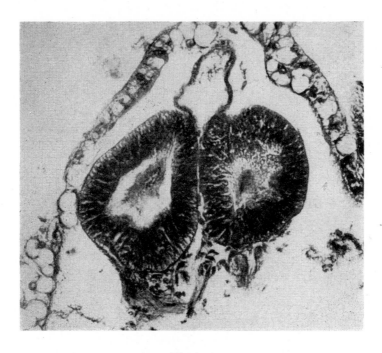

Plate IV

Corpora allata in a walking stick insect (*Dixippus*). In this instance the original
sac-like form of the gland is retained.

organ for neurosecretory material (Fig. 1). The transport of the neurosecretory substance from its place of origin to its place of storage seems to be by the axoplasmatic current; the speed has been determined in supravital preparations as about 3 mm. per day.

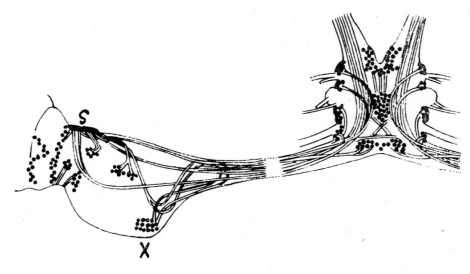

Figure 1

Neurosecretory cell-groups and pathways in a crab. The axons of the X-cells (*X*) and several other clusters are connected with the sinus gland (*S*). (After Bliss & Welsh, 1952.)

The existence of two subdivisions of the neurosecretory apparatus in crustaceans explains several facts of physiological importance: Thus the effects of the substance which is stored in the sinus gland are in part the same as those which can be obtained by extracts from the X-organ. Implants of sinus glands into other specimens may be effective at least for a short period, although complete removal of the gland may have a very slight or no effect. In addition, removal of the X-organ does not cause an immediate deficiency if the sinus gland with its supply of stored hormones is left intact. Experiments done along these lines have proved that an impressive array of hormonal actions are associated with principles which are stored in the sinus glands of crustaceans and produced by neurosecretory cells within different regions of the nervous mass in the eyestalks and the brain proper. It is probable that different groups and cytological types of neurosecretory cells produce different hormones.

The study of hormonal mechanisms in crustaceans started with investigations on colour change, which, according to recent results appears to be governed by no less than three (perhaps five) principles, one of which probably represents a simple aromatic amine (Östlund-Fänge, 1956). Two other principles regulate the adaptation of the eyes to light and darkness by means of pigment migrations. All these substances are derived from the sinus gland and the central nervous system. The chromatophorotropic hormones are produced in different regions of the central nervous system and accumulate in the sinus gland, extracts and implants of which thus act very strongly on the chromatophores of the skin. In the most beautiful way, and sometimes instantly, the colour is changed to suit the background, according to the intensity of light or to the diurnal period (Plate III).

While only some species of crustaceans show a pronounced physiological colour change, all of them have to shed their hard exoskeleton to be able to grow. Thus a still more important hormonal function in these animals is the regulation of moulting, and it has been proved that the regulatory substances are neurohormones. Most crustaceans from temperate regions exhibit seasonal moultings, the intervals of which are governed by a moult-inhibiting hormone produced by the X-cells and similar cells in the brain. The moult-inhibitory hormone is also stored in the sinus gland. Lack of this hormone (after extirpation of the X-organ or amputation of the eye-stalks) is followed by absorption of calcium from the cuticle, increase of body water, increased oxygen consumption and repeated moulting. The hormone appears to be absent in crustaceans which moult throughout the year. In a species of shrimp (*Lysmata*) which belongs to this group, there occurs on the contrary a moult-promoting hormone which is also produced by cells in the brain and the thoracic ganglion, but which is not stored in the sinus gland. The primary function of this hormone seems to be the stimulation of a moulting gland proper (the gland of Gabe) which directly starts the preparations for moulting.

Like the moult-inhibiting hormone, another growth-inhibiting principle which acts on the ovaries and the testes, is produced by cells of the X-organ and the brain. In spite of this the hormones do not appear to be identical. Hormones from the eye-stalks also control the secondary sex characters.

In spite of the small size of the X-organ and the seemingly simple structure of its cells, it produces still another hormone (or more than one hormone) which controls the calcium, phosphorus and water metabolism. In the absence of this metabolic hormone, the blood sugar concentration decreases. The factor which is responsible for the regulation of the water balance appears (at least in *Carcinus*) to be distinct from the principles which control moulting and the development of the sexual glands.

INSECTS

In insects also neurosecretory cells are numerous and have important functions. They consist of a medial and a lateral group in the brain and of other clusters in the frontal, the suboesophageal and the ventral ganglia. The nerves from the brain-cells end in the corpora cardiaca which lie in the head, in close vicinity to the aorta and beneath the brain. From the corpora cardiaca in most insects, another nerve runs to two ectodermal glands, the corpora allata (Fig. 2). Physiologically the neuro-secretory cell groups of the insect brain correspond to the X-organ in crustaceans and the corpus cardiacum to the sinus gland. Like in these organs the neurosecretory material is transported from the brain along the axons into the corpora cardiaca, where it may be stored or released into the circulation. In some insects, however, a further transport of neurosecretory material along the corpus cardiacum-allatum nerve has been observed, and thus the corpus allatum may be directly stimulated by the active principles contained in the neurosecretory material. Finally, there is in the thorax of insects another endocrine organ, the prothoracic gland, which in some respects resembles the moulting gland in crustaceans and which is activated by the neurohormones of the brain.

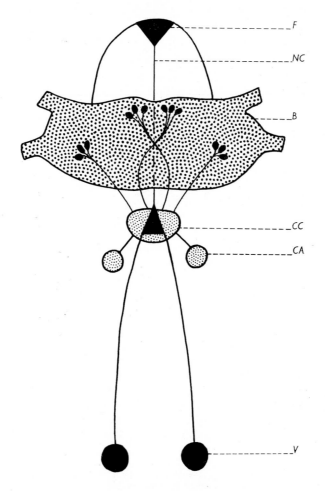

Figure 2

Outline of the brain and the incretory system of the head in insects. *F*, frontal ganglion; *NC*, nervus recurrens; *B*, brain, from above, with a medial and a lateral group of neurosecretory cells; *CC*, corpora cardiaca, surrounding the hypocerebral ganglion (black); *CA*, corpora allata; *V*, ventricular ganglion.

Only a few insects show a physiological colour change which, however, appears to be controlled by hormones produced by neurosecretory cells in the brain. Because of the connexion between these cells and the corpus cardiacum, this organ also contains the pigment-activating hormone, which, by the way, has a very strong effect on crustacean chromatophores. The slow morphological colour adaptation in locusts however, is regulated by a hormone derived from the corpus allatum.

The neurosecretory brain cells, the corpora cardiaca, corpora allata and the prothoracic gland all partake in the regulation of the complicated morphological and histological changes and the still more complicated co-ordination of chemical reactions by means of enzymes which are involved in the metamorphosis of insects

(Fig. 3). During these changes the prothoracotropic hormone from the brain, which is stored in and released from the corpora cardiaca, causes the prothoracic gland to release the so-called growth and differentiation hormone. This hormone (which was isolated and crystallized by Butenandt & Karlsson in 1954 and found to contain only carbon, hydrogen and oxygen in the proportion 4·4 : 7·3 : 1·0), is directly responsible for the growth and differentiation which transforms the wingless immature larva (the nymph) into a winged imago with sexual organs. In order to prevent a precocious imaginal development the corpora allata during the early life of insects produce a juvenile hormone which counterbalances the hormone of the prothoracic gland. The interaction of these two hormones results in the larval moultings during

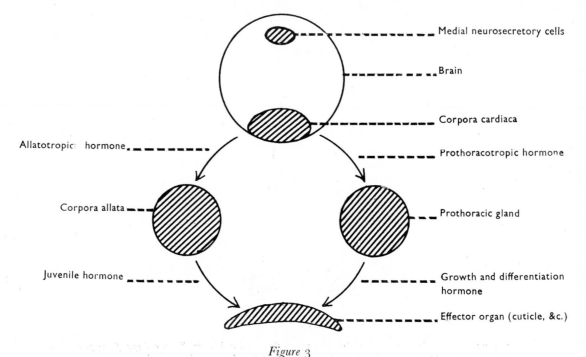

Medial neurosecretory cells

Brain

Corpora cardiaca

Allatotropic hormone

Prothoracotropic hormone

Corpora allata

Prothoracic gland

Juvenile hormone

Growth and differentiation hormone

Effector organ (cuticle, &c.)

Figure 3

Outline of the nervous and secretory mechanisms which controls the moultings in insects.

which the animal develops chiefly by growing with very slight signs, if any, of adult differentiation. Finally, at the last larval or nymphal stage the production of the juvenile hormone ceases or is considerably decreased and complete metamorphosis takes place. It is characteristic of the interaction of the hormones which regulate the post-embryonic development in insects, that by removal or transplantations of the endocrine glands and by means of parabiosis experiments, it is possible to force adults to undergo supernumerary moultings and become 'giants', to cause larvae or nymphs to undergo a precocious differentiation and to become dwarfs and, finally by supplying an excessive amount of juvenile hormone, to cause adult tissues to reassume a juvenile shape.

In insects as in crustaceans neurosecretory hormones play an important role in reproductive processes. In flies extirpation of the medial brain region, which contains one of the neurosecretory cell-groups, prevents egg maturation, while reimplantation of the same cells promotes it. Thus the neurosecretory cells produce a gonad-stimulating substance which is stored in the corpora cardiaca. Other experiments suggest that the corpora allata also contribute to the regulation of egg maturation and that the principle involved is not identical with that derived from the brain.

In certain insects the neurosecretory cells, the corpora cardiaca and the corpora allata contribute to the control of metabolism. Thus in a species of fly, *Calliphora*, the absence of the medial neurosecretory brain cells results in a decreased fat and an increased glycogen content in the fat body; the corpora allata seem also to be involved in the fat and carbohydrate metabolism and the corpora cardiaca may play a role in the control of the protein metabolism. The water balance also appears to be regulated by neurosecretory brain cells, but only scattered observations are found in the literature on this subject and no general conclusions can as yet be drawn.

Finally, the excretory organs in insects, the Malpighian tubules, show rhythmic movements, the frequency of which is stimulated by extracts from the brain and the corpora cardiaca. The active principle from the latter organs also increases the amplitudes of the muscle contractions of the Malpighian tubules, of the intestine and of the heart. The active principle appears to be secreted by specific cells of the corpora cardiaca and to be different from the active neurosecretory substance of the brain. Chemically it resembles an orthodiphenol and is thus related to adrenaline.

COMPARISONS BETWEEN THE MORE COMPLEX NEUROSECRETORY SYSTEMS OF INVERTEBRATES AND VERTEBRATES

In both crustaceans and insects the principal neurosecretory systems consist of two parts: (1) the neurosecretory cell clusters in the brain (several groups in crustaceans, two in insects) and (2) a special organ (the sinus gland in crustaceans, the corpora cardiaca in insects) in which the neurosecretion is stored. The former subdivision corresponds to the nucleus supraopticus and nucleus paraventricularis in the vertebrate hypothalamus and the latter to the neural lobe of the hypophysis (Table 1). Thus the neural lobe represents one of several organs of neurosecretory

TABLE I

The incretory systems of the head in crustaceans, insects, and vertebrates

	CRUSTACEANS	INSECTS	VERTEBRATES
I.	X-organ and other neurosecretory cells of the brain.	Medial and lateral neurosecretory brain cells.	Nucleus preopticus, Nucleus supraopticus, Nucleus paraventricularis.
II.	Sinus gland.	Corpora cardiaca.	Posterior lobe.
III.		Corpora allata.	Anterior lobe.

storage and release in the animal kingdom. In 1941 when I published the first (but very incomplete) comparison of the neurosecretory systems of insects and vertebrates, I was deeply impressed by the occurrence of such similar complicated systems in very distantly related animal groups. This seems, now, still more striking since recent investigations have shown that similar neurosecretory systems exist in chilopodes, diplopodes and arachnoids (Gabe, 1955). The only instance in which a homology between these systems could be suspected is in the myriapodes and insects. But be this as it may, it is clear that complex neurosecretory systems have appeared independently at least four and perhaps six times in the animal kingdom.

While all the neurosecretory systems reviewed here show the two subdivisions mentioned, a third one has to be added in insects and vertebrates, viz. the corpora allata and the glandular lobe of the hypophysis respectively. This represents a further analogy: these organs are both of ectodermal origin, the corpora allata being pouch-like invaginations from the ventral side of the head (Plate IV) while the glandular lobe originally forms a similar sac-like invagination from the embryonic stomodæum, i.e. Rathke's pouch. Thus in both insects and vertebrates the principal neurosecretory systems consist of a nervous component, which forms the first two subdivisions, and an ectodermal component, forming the third subdivision.

The functional relations between the neural and the glandular lobe of the pituitary are still keenly debated but, taken together, the hormones released by the pituitary cover about the same functions as the neurosecretory system in insects, namely colour change, growth, reproduction, metabolism and water balance. The array of hormones produced by the main incretory organs of insects (and crustaceans) would therefore seem to be hardly less complex than that of vertebrates, including man. Histologically, the neurosecretory cells of the crustacean X-organ and those of the insect brain may indeed be regarded as of a more specialized type than most of the cells of the nucleus supraopticus and paraventricularis in vertebrates. I have already pointed out that the neurosecretory cells of the lower invertebrates thus far described seem to have the shape of normal nerve-cells (with dendrites and an axon) which form a link in a neuron chain or innervate an effector organ. Most cells of the nucleus supraopticus and paraventricularis have dendrites but the corresponding cells in crustaceans and insects are unipolar and have no dendrites or collaterals. Like the neurosecretory cells of the hypothalamus they end blindly and do not form links in a neuron chain in so far as they do not innervate any effectors. Morphologically, they are reduced to a simple thread-like transport apparatus for the carriage of the neurosecretory substance from the place of production to the place of storage.

This account of neurosecretion in invertebrates has of necessity been brief and many important details had to be omitted. Our knowledge of invertebrate endocrinology has very much increased since I published my monograph on the subject (Hanström, 1939). I therefore recommend the more recent reviews by Ernst & Berta Scharrer (1954a, b), Gabe (1954), Berta Scharrer, (1953, 1955) and Arvy, Gabe & B. Scharrer (1956), and, concerning the comparison between the neurosecretory systems of invertebrates and vertebrates the papers of Hanström (1941, 1954) and E. & B. Scharrer (1944).

Another conclusion resulting from this comparison is connected with the fact that in insects the neurosecretory brain cells consist of two groups and in crustaceans of several. There are some reasons to presume that the two cell groups in insects have different functions, and very strong arguments have been presented in favour of the view that in crustaceans different clusters and cytological types of neurosecretory cells produce different hormones. Although the nucleus supraopticus and nucleus paraventricularis of higher vertebrates are presumed to be derived from the nucleus preopticus in lower vertebrates, one must consider the possibility that they also may have different functions.

A third and very striking fact which derives from the study of the neurosecretory cells in polychaetes, crustaceans and insects, is the domination of neurosecretory function in these animals. Thus in *Nepthys* three-quarters of the brain consist of cells which exhibit signs of a neurosecretory activity (Clark, 1955), and all the better investigated hormonal phenomena in crustaceans and insects are governed by neurohormones. The nervous system in these animals is evidently as much concerned with the regulation of body functions by the slower hormonal processes as by the more speedy nervous mechanisms. Thus the close similarities between the architecture of the neurosecretory systems in invertebrates and vertebrates almost force one to suspect that there must be more numerous neurosecretory mechanisms in vertebrates than the production of the posterior lobe hormones.

It is now about ten years since I worked on neurosecretion in invertebrates and since I turned to similar studies in vertebrates. On this occasion therefore I should have liked to report some new results of investigations of the pituitary and the neurosecretory system in mammals. The results of current work on the neurosecretory pathways in hibernating mammals such as the hedgehog (*Erinaceus europaeus*) during the winter and in mammals from hot deserts such as the kangaroo rat (*Dipodomys merriami*) are, however, not quite complete. Although living under very different conditions both these animals have to economize body water. The kangaroo rat and related forms live in the hot dry regions of the south-western U.S.A., one of these species occurs even in the Death Valley, the deepest point of which is 84 m. below sea-level. A maximum air temperature of $+56°C$ has been recorded in this area, for a long time a world record. According to K. & B. Schmidt-Nielsen (1952) the kangaroo rat is able to live and thrive on dry plants without any access to drinking-water and has survived for years in the laboratory when fed on dry grain only. It does not store an excess of water in the body and it has no exceptional resistance to dehydration. It obtains water by oxidation of its food and expends it with the greatest economy. The extrarenal water loss of the kangaroo rat is only about half of that of the white rat and its urine may be about twice as concentrated. Kangaroo rats which are forced to drink water excrete it with great difficulty and are liable to 'water intoxication' (Hofmann, 1956). The unphysiological situation was indicated by the occurrence of haematuria in more than half of the animals in the experiment. Ames & van Dyke (1950) have investigated the amounts of antidiuretic hormone in the urine and the posterior lobe of kangaroo rats. They found up to 50 mU. of antidiuretic hormone in the urine as against about 6 mU./ml. in dogs after powerful osmotic stimulation and about the same in laboratory rats deprived of water for 48–72 hours. The posterior lobe in kangaroo rats contained 0·9 mU. of antidiuretic hormone per microgramme against only about 0·3 mU. in normal laboratory rats. Moreover the neural lobe of *Dipodomys* weighs relatively more. Thus, although laboratory rats are 5 to 6 times larger than kangaroo rats, their neural lobes are only 3 times the size of those of kangaroo rats and their pituitary contains less antidiuretic hormone.

When I examined the neurosecretory system in *Dipodomys*, I did not find any features which are essentially different from those in laboratory rats as described by Hillarp (1949), Ortmann (1951), Eichner (1953), Wagenvoort (1954) and Imai (1954). It is possible that a laborious count of the number of cells in the hypothalamic neurosecretory nuclei may give a clue to the high concentration of the antidiuretic hormone in the neural lobe of the kangaroo rat. Preliminary examination in several species of rodents of the size of the neural lobe, relative to that of the glandular lobe indicates that, in general, the neural lobe in desert and hibernating species is relatively larger than in other rodents from temperate regions (Enemar & Hanström, 1956).

Herring and Cushing among others assumed that the posterior lobe hormones derived from cells of the pars intermedia which invaded the processus infundibuli. This hypothesis was still maintained by Büchner (1950) and Romieu, Stahl & Occelli (1952) perhaps because these authors considered the human hypophysis only, in which such an invasion is a normal phenomenon. However, in other mammals which I examined during comparative studies of the pituitary (Hanström, 1952) I often found no invasion of intermedia elements into the posterior lobe, and in the desert rodents investigated it was not found at all.

Bucy, Romeis and the school of Ranson regarded the pituicytes as the source of the posterior lobe hormones. The role of these cells is as yet, not quite clear, but the best founded hypothesis is undoubtedly that formulated by E. Scharrer and W. Bargmann who assume a neurosecretory origin for the neurohypophysial hormones. It is of interest in this connexion that in crustaceans and insects also the water balance is regulated by neurosecretory hormones. The concept of the origin of the posterior lobe hormones from invading intermedia cells or from pituicytes made it necessary for the protagonists of this view to assume migration of the posterior lobe hormones from the pituitary gland towards the hypothalamus, from which considerable amounts of the hormones have been extracted. The conception of neurosecretion postulates movement of the neurosecretory substance and the hormones in the opposite direction, i.e. from the hypothalamus to the neural lobe. This process however, is only yet another instance of the truth of the proverb 'nothing new under the sun'. For, as Zuckerman (1954) has pointed out, Andreas Vesalius wrote in his work *De humani corporis fabrica libri septum* published 400 years ago (1555), that the infundibulum was a funnel through which the phlegm from the brain trickled down into the pituitary (Fig. 4). The Swede, Emanuel Swedenborg, expressed the same opinion

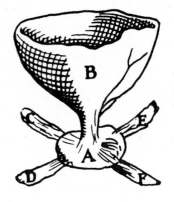

Figure 4

Vesalius's conception of the funnel (infundibulum) (*B*) through which the phlegm from the brain trickles down into the pituitary (*A*). The four imaginary ducts (*C, D, E, F*) carry the phlegm from the gland. (After Zuckerman, 1954.)

in his book of 1742: *The brain, considered anatomically, physiologically and philosophically.* In this treatise he declared that 'the soul has established in the cerebrum an illustrious chymical laboratory', the products of which, he considered, were separated and filtered in the infundibulum, finally to trickle down to the hypophysis. 'The chymical operation', he continued, 'may be called not only a secretion and purification, but also a rectification and alcoholization.' May I be permitted to add that Swedenborg was hardly thinking of alcohol in the present meaning of the word but evidently used it as a synonym for spirit and evanescent essence.

REFERENCES

ALEXANDROWICZ, J. S. & CARLISLE, D. (1953). Some experiments on the function of the pericardial organs in crustacea. *J. marine biol. Ass. U.K.* **32**, 175–92.

AMES, R. G. & VAN DYKE, H. B. (1950). Antidiuretic hormone in the urine and pituitary of the kangaroo rat. *Proc. Soc. exp. Biol. (N.Y.)* **75**, 417–20.

ARVY, L., GABE, M. & SCHARRER, B. (1956) editors. Colloq. Int. Endocr. Invertébrés. *Ann. Sci. Nat.* **18** (Fasc. 2), II Sér., 123–340.

BLISS, D. & WELSH, J. H. (1952). The neurosecretory system of brachyuran Crustacea. *Biol. Bull.* **103**, 157–69.

BÜCHNER, F. (1950). *Allgemeine Pathologie.* München und Berlin: Urban & Schwarzenberg.

BUTENANDT, A. & KARLSSON, P. (1954). Über die Isolierung eines Metamorphosen-Hormons der Insekten in kristallisierter Form. *Z. Naturforsch.* **9**, 389–91.

CARLISLE, D. & KNOWLES, F. G. W. (1953). Neurohaemal organs in crustaceans. *Nature* **172**, 404–5.

CLARK, R. B. (1955): The posterior lobes of the brain of *Nephtys* and the mucus-glands of the prostomium. *Quart. J. micr. Sci.* **96**, 545–65.

CLARK, R. B. (1956). On the transformation of neurosecretory cells into ordinary nerve-cells. *Kgl. Fysiogr. Sällsk. Förhandl., (Lund)* **26**, 1–8.

EICHNER, D. (1953). Über den morphologischen Ausdruck funktioneller Beziehungen zwischen Nebennierenrinde und neurosekretorischem Zwischenhirnsystem der Ratte. *Z. Zellforsch.* **38**, 488–508.

ENEMAR, A. & HANSTRÖM, B. (1956). The relative sizes of the neural and glandular lobes in some rodents. *Kgl. Fysiogr. Sällsk. Handl. (Lund)*, N.F. **67**. No. 17, 1–5.

GABE, M. (1954). La neuro-sécrétion chez les invertébrés. *Ann. biol.* **30**, 5–62.

GABE, M. (1955). Particularités histologiques des cellules neuro-sécrétrices chez quelques Lamellibranches. *C.R. Acad. Sci. (Paris).* **240**, 1810–2.

HANSTRÖM, B. (1939). *Hormones in invertebrates.* Oxford: University Press.

HANSTRÖM, B. (1941). Einige Parallelen im Bau und in der Herkunft der inkretorischen Organe der Arthropoden und der Vertebraten. *Kgl. Fysiogr. Sällsk. Handl. (Lund)*, N.F. **52**, No. 4, 1–19.

HANSTRÖM, B. (1952). The hypophysis in some South-African Insectivora, Carnivora, Hyracoidea, Proboscidea, Artiodactyla and Primates. *Ark. Zool.*, (ser. 2) **4**, 187–294.

HANSTRÖM, B. (1954). On the transformation of ordinary nerve-cells into neurosecretory cells. *Kgl. Fysiogr. Sällsk. Förhandl. (Lund)* **24**, No. 8, 1–8.

HANSTRÖM, B. (1956). Studies on mammalian neurosecretion. *Kgl. Fysiogr. Sällsk. Handl. (Lund)*, N.F. **67**. No. 16, 1–21.

HOFMANN, F. G. in HELLER, H. (1956). The hormonal control of water and salt-electrolyte metabolism with special reference to higher vertebrates. *Mem. Soc. Endocr.* **5**, 37–43.

HILLARP, N. Å. (1949). Cell reactions in the hypothalamus following overloading of the antidiuretic function. *Acta Endocr. (Kbh.)* **2**, 33–43.

IMAI, K. (1954). Some observations on the hypothalamo-hypophyseal neurosecretory system in the albino rat. *Gunma J. Med. Sci.* **3**, 281–9.

LEMCHE, H. (1955). Neurosecretion and incretory glands in a tectibranch mollusc. *Experientia* **11**, 320–6.

ORTMANN, R. (1951). Über experimentelle Veränderungen der Morphologie des Hypophysen-Zwischenhirnsystems und die Beziehung der sog. 'Gomorisubstanz' zum Adiuretin. *Z. Zellforsch* **36**, 92–140.

ÖUTLUND, E. & FÄNGE, R. (1956). On the nature of the eye-stalk hormone which causes concentration of red pigment in shrimps (Natantia). *Ann. Zool.* **18**. 325–34.

ROMIEU, M. & STAHL, A. & OCCELLI, R. (1952). Nature et signification des cellules basophiles qui envahissent la neurohypophyse chez l'homme. *C.R. Soc. Biol. (Paris)* **146**, 585–7.

SCHARRER, B. (1953). Comparative physiology of invertebrate endocrines. *Ann. Rev. Physiol.* **15**, 457–72.

SCHARRER, B. (1955). Hormones in invertebrates. In *The Hormones*. Ed. Pincus, G. & Thimann, K. V. Vol. 3, 57–95. New York: Academic Press.

SCHARRER, B. & SCHARRER, E. (1944). A comparison between the intercerebralis-cardiacum-allatum system of the insects and the hypothalamic-hypophyseal system of the vertebrates. *Biol. Bull.* **87**, 242–51.

SCHARRER, E. (1928). Untersuchungen über das Zwischenhirn der Fische. *Z. vergl. Physiol.* **7**, 1–38.

SCHARRER, E. & SCHARRER, B. (1954a). Hormones produced by neurosecretory cells. *Recent Progr. Hormone Res.* **10**, 183–240.

SCHARRER, E. & SCHARRER, B. (1954b). Neurosekretion. In: *Handbuch der mikroskopischeu Anatomie des Menschen*. Ed. Bargmann, W. 6, 953–1066. Berlin, Göttingen, Heidelberg: Springer.

SCHMIDT-NIELSEN, K. & SCHMIDT-NIELSEN, B. (1952). Water metabolism of desert mammals. *Physiol. Rev.* **32**, 135–66.

SWEDENBORG, E. (1882). *The brain, considered anatomically, physiologically and philosophically*. Ed. Tafel, R.L. London: James Speirs.

WAGENVOORT, C. A. (1954). Some histological aspects of neurosecretion. *Acta physiol. pharmacol. neerl.* **3**, 275–98.

WELSH, J. H. (1956). Neurohormones of invertebrates. I. Cardioregulators of *Cyprina* and *Buccinum*. *J. marine biol. Ass.*, U.K. **35**, 193–261.

ZUCKERMANN, S. (1954). The secretions of the brain. *Lancet*, i 739–43.

Discussion

Chairman : Sir H. Dale

Jewell. There is a question I would like to ask Professor Hanström about the first part of his talk. Have experiments been done to exchange the hormones from insects to crustaceans or vice versa?

Hanström. Yes, especially the colour change hormones. When one makes an extract of the corpus cardiacum of insects and injects this extract into shrimps, they change their colour as completely as they would if they had been injected with their own colour-change hormone and the hormone from the insect corpus cardiacum is some-times even more potent than the true shrimp hormone.

Dale. There was a letter recently in *Nature* (Carlisle & Butler, **177**, 276, 1956) which described an extraordinarily interesting observation, that the ovary-inhibiting hormone from the eyestalk of the prawn is effective also in bees, producing sterile workers. And it was also stated that a substance from the Queen Bee will keep a female prawn from ovulating.

Jewell. Dr. B. Andersson and I have made some observations on the neurosecretory material of dogs hydrated for a period of days. We gave a dog 200 ml. of water by stomach tube once an hour day and night for 10 days. Serial sections through the hypothalamus were stained by Gomori's method simultaneously with sections from a 'control' animal that had been maintained on a similar diet. Comparison of the sections from the two animals showed the following features: In the anterior division of the supraoptic nucleus the cells of the hydrated animal were markedly paler than the control, with an apparent deficiency of neurosecretory material. In the posterior division of the supraoptic nucleus the differences were less marked, but a higher proportion of pale cells were exhibited by the experimental animals than the controls. The cells of the paraventricular nucleus showed the greatest change. In the hydrated animal these cells were uniformly pale and almost completely devoid of neurosecretory material. Conversely the descending tracts from the paraventricular nuclei of the hydrated animal were characterized by heavy accumulations of stainable material, in the form of stained axons and clumps, which extended throughout the dorso-ventral extent of the hypothalamus. The appearances of the posterior lobes of the two animals did not differ in any marked way. Changes seen in a second hydrated animal were in the same sense but were less marked. This second animal had become somewhat lethargic during the experiment, whereas the first hydrated animal had remained perfectly happy.

Dale. What was the effect on the specifically staining substance in the posterior lobe itself?

Jewell. There was no detectable difference in the posterior lobes.

Dale. I am trying to get a picture of what this staining material is doing. It is increased in the nerve-cells and it has got into the tracts, but apparently it hasn't yet reached the lobe; or is it being poured out of the lobe as fast as it gets there?

Jewell. I would be very interested to hear Professor Bargmann's comments.

Bargmann. I wonder if these accumulations of stainable material are the same as Dr. Pickford has seen.

Pickford. Yes, very similar.

Bargmann. These are lobulated Herring bodies, and they seem to be a sign of storage in the course of the axon. Under normal conditions we can see the same thing in birds. Possibly you saw some ruptures on your slides, perhaps due to physiological or technical conditions. You can show that these Herring bodies are part of the axon.

Hanström. We have found such lobulated or star-shaped structures several times in mammals for instance in wolves, and sometimes they appear to be connected to one proximal and another distal fibre. In some instances I think that they may constitute nerve-endings and in some respects resemble the bulb-shaped endings which I have described in a number of mammals. These endings are very common and outstanding in some specimens.

Dale. What species are you speaking about?

Hanström. The tiger.

Jewell. Did you notice a lot of this material in the tiger?

Hanström. Yes.

Jewell. Has Professor Hanström any suggestion to offer to explain the remarkable development of stainable material in the carnivores? The dog and cat, and apparently the tiger, show large quantities; Dr. Sloper mentioned earlier the large amounts to be seen in the seal. I have examined the supraoptic and paraventricular nuclear cells of the grey seal, using Gomori's method, and the intensity of staining in these cells is similar to the dog. In the desert rat, on the other hand, in conformity with Professor Hanström's observations on his desert animals, I found no unusual amount of material.

Hanström. I have also found lobulated Herring bodies in a marsupial and in a tree shrew. It is not only carnivores, I think.

Lloyd. Would you estimate that there is more of this neurosecretory material in the hypothalami of these animals which you hydrated? The reason I ask is that if you hydrate a rat giving it nothing but liquid for three or four days, you will find that the content of antidiuretic material in the hypothalamus is actually less than the normal. If you hydrate it acutely there appears to be more. It looks as though the supply is keeping up with the demand.

Jewell. If you estimated the amount in the cell-bodies in the hydrated dog there would certainly be less but since there is great accumulation in the axons in the lateral hypothalamus, the total amount in the hypothalamus may still be high.

Martini. Dr. Kovacs has observed that hydration produces in rats a drop of neurosecretory material, both in the supraoptic and paraventricular nuclei and in the hypothalamo-hypophysial tract.

Lloyd. One has to dehydrate animals severely by giving them a hypertonic solution to cut down on the hypothalamic antidiuretic activity.

Sloper. Dr. Jewell's observations on the loss of neurosecretory material from the paraventricular neurones of the hydrated dog are of the greatest interest. I would like first to make a plea for great caution in the interpretation of these changes. Variations in staining intensity and section thickness can be most deceptive, although of course the changes in Dr. Jewell's sections were clear cut. I would secondly like to ask Dr. Jewell whether all the paraventricular neurones were similarly affected. I ask because I have been making photometric estimations of histochemically demonstrated neurosecretory material in the hypothalamus of the dehydrated rat. Although most neurones show depletion, a number are full of neurosecretion. Has Dr. Jewell seen such neurones in the hydrated dog and, if so, how does he account for their occurrence?

Jewell. There was uniform depletion of the neurons in the paraventricular nucleus whereas in the supraoptic nucleus there were often neurons persisting which were quite as full as in the normal animal. This was a very curious observation, I thought, for if there is a real correlation between the state of hydration of the animal and the amount of this material, it implies that the paraventricular nucleus is particularly concerned with the process. Yet there are observations of Olivecrona (*Nature*, (*Lond.*) **173**, 1001, 1954) which suggest that the paraventricular nucleus is particularly concerned with oxytocin production. So this is still very much in the air.

Harris, G. W. There is one question I would like to ask Professor Hanström, and that is whether he had done anything to alter the activity of the anterior lobe and whether he had noticed any difference in the neurosecretory material. I am thinking particularly of ovariectomy increasing the production of gonadotrophic hormone and whether there is then any difference in the neurosecretory material in the median eminence.

Hanström. No, I am sorry, we haven't done that.

Martini. I wanted to ask Professor Bargmann what he thinks about Barnett's method which stains disulphide groups and thus seems to reveal directly the oxytocic and antidiuretic hormones in hypothalamic neurons. Are the results obtained by Gomori's and by Barnett's methods comparable?

Bargmann. I am very careful concerning histological and histochemical questions. I said only yesterday to Professor Heller that while we are able to stain the tracts electively we are not able to make any conclusions about the chemical nature of the substances stained. I know Dr. Sloper has another opinion—perhaps he would say something because he is an expert on these matters.

Sloper. Professor Bargmann has asked me to discuss the applicability of Barnett's thioglycollate-DDD reaction for cystine to the study of neurosecretion. This reaction is difficult to perform. I learnt it from Professor Montagna and like him find it useful when applied to skin. Perhaps because of its sensitivity it is far less useful in the hypothalamus, because it has not the selectivity for neurosecretion of the Gomori techniques. On the other hand the thioglycollate-ferric-ferricyanide and performic acid-Alcian blue reactions introduced by Adams and myself demonstrate structures rich in cystine, and are if anything more selective than the Gomori techniques. With these techniques we demonstrate a protein rich in cystine in the hypothalamus and neurohypophysis. It diminishes after dehydration and accumulates above the cut pituitary stalk. I do not think it is for me as a pathologist to say more concerning its relationship to posterior pituitary principles.

The relationship of oxytocin and vasopressin to active proteins of posterior pituitary origin

Studies concerning the existence or non-existence of a single neurohypophysial hormone

by

ROGER ACHER *and* CLAUDE FROMAGEOT*

Laboratoire de Chimie biologique de la Faculté des Sciences, Paris.

FOUR activities of extracts of the bovine posterior hypophysis have been known for a long time; these are: the uterus-stimulating (oxytocic) activity, the milk-ejecting (galactogogic) activity, the blood pressure-raising action (vasopressor activity), and the antidiuretic activity. *A priori* one might think that these four activities correspond to four different substances. Since 1920 there have been two opposing views, one held by Abel and his co-workers (Abel, Rouiller & Geiling, 1923; Abel, 1930) according to which the oxytocic, vasopressor and antidiuretic properties belong to a single substance, and that of Dudley (1919) who considered that the oxytocic and vasopressor activities were due to different substances. The first conception led MacArthur (1931), and later van Dyke and his co-workers (van Dyke, Chow, Greep & Rothen, 1942) to isolate a pure protein which possessed the four activities mentioned. The second concept led Kamm (Kamm, Aldrich, Grote, Rowe & Bugbee, 1928) and later du Vigneaud (1952) and his team to purify the different active principles. In the course of this work two peptides were obtained in pure form, the one—oxytocin—possessing oxytocic and galactogogic properties, the other—vasopressin—possessing the vasopressor and antidiuretic activities. The problem therefore was whether one or two substances are normally responsible for the activities in posterior pituitary extracts, i.e. whether the hormone is a protein of which the two peptides, oxytocin and vasopressin, are degradation products which retain the activities; or whether these peptides normally exist in the gland, and are used independently by the organism in accordance with its needs. The concept of the existence of a single hormone rests on a physiological as well as on a chemical basis: the ratio of vasopressin to oxytocin activity (V/O) in the neurohypophysis of several mammals is unity when the activities are determined by reference to the International Standard (Waring & Landgrebe, 1950). Moreover, there is simultaneous liberation of the oxytocic and antidiuretic (or vasopressor) activities on electrical (Harris, 1947), osmotic (Abrahams & Pickford, 1954) or chemical stimulation (Chamorro & Minz, 1955).

It appeared desirable to us to study the question of the existence of a single hormone using both the chemical and the physiological approach. In the chemical

* Read by C. Fromageot.

investigation we have subjected the protein of van Dyke (ox gland extract) to different purifying procedures to determine whether the oxytocic and vasopressor activities always remain with the protein. In the physiological investigation we have studied the changes in the V/O ratio of the neurohypophysis of the rat during growth and reproduction.

RELATIONSHIP BETWEEN OXYTOCIN, VASOPRESSIN AND THE PROTEIN OF VAN DYKE

The active protein was prepared according to van Dyke *et al.* (1942). A powder having oxytocic or vasopressor activity of 18–20 I.U. per mg. was obtained. The nitrogen content and the sedimentation and diffusion constants corresponded to the values given by the American authors. We have subjected the active protein to various procedures of purification which did not involve the possibility of hydrolytic cleavage.

Dialysis and ultrafiltration

On dialysis against water all the activity and nitrogen remained inside the sac. After ultrafiltration of most of the solution through a cellophane membrane (oscillating ultrafiltration technique of Ambard), neither nitrogen nor biological activity was found in the ultrafiltrate. Therefore neither dialysis against water nor ultrafiltration permit the separation of active substances of low molecular weight from the protein of van Dyke. On the other hand when a solution of 50 mg. of the protein in 0·2 N acetic acid was dialysed against 80 volumes of acetic acid (0·2 N, pH 2·75) at room temperature, all the oxytocic and vasopressor activity was found outside the bag, although 88 per cent. of the initial nitrogen was recovered from inside showing that mere dialysis against dilute acetic acid produces dissociation.

Electrolysis and electrodialysis

The active protein dissolved in acetate buffer at pH 4·4 was subjected to electrophoresis in the Tiselius apparatus. After 4·5 hours, the solutions in the anode, cathode and central compartments were analysed for nitrogen and vasopressor activity. The activity of the initial solution per mg. of nitrogen was equivalent to that of 125 I.U. of vasopressin. After electrophoresis the solutions in the anode, central and cathode compartments had vasopressor activities equivalent to 44, 150 and 190 I.U. per mg. N respectively. As no inactivation occurred, the heterogeneity of the material was obvious: the principle responsible for the vasopressor activity was more rapidly displaced towards the cathode than the other constituents.

Fifty mg. of the active protein were dissolved in water with the assistance of a trace of acetic acid and placed into the central compartment of an electrodialysis cell consisting of three compartments. The anode and cathode compartments contained water. Cellophane membranes were used. A potential of 900–1,000 volts was applied and precautions were taken to assure that the temperature of the solution did not rise above 25° C. After 9–11 hours, 90–100 per cent. of the initial oxytocic and vasopressor activities (about 1,000 I.U.) were recovered in the cathode compartment but only 7–8 per cent. of the initial nitrogen. The 'cathode solution' was concentrated and studied by electrophoresis on paper. It was possible to demonstrate two substances only: these migrated like pure oxytocin and pure vasopressin, and had the activities and amino-acid composition of the two peptides. Thus, electrodialysis permits separation of oxytocin and vasopressin from inert protein material without hydrolysis.

Precipitation with trichloracetic acid

A 1 per cent. solution of active protein was precipitated by 5 per cent. trichloracetic acid: 50 per cent. of the oxytocic activity, 70 per cent. of the vasopressin activity, and 8 per cent. of the initial nitrogen were found in the supernatant solution. After removal of the acid by electrodialysis, the active substances in the cathode solution were studied. Here again, electrophoresis on paper revealed only the two substances which behaved like pure oxytocin and vasopressin. A preparative electrophoresis was carried out and the paper was cut into sections of 2 cm. These were eluted with water and the activities of the eluates were determined. No oxytocic activity was found except at the point corresponding to oxytocin, and no vasopressor activity was found anywhere except at the point corresponding to vasopressin (Fig. 1). Moreover,

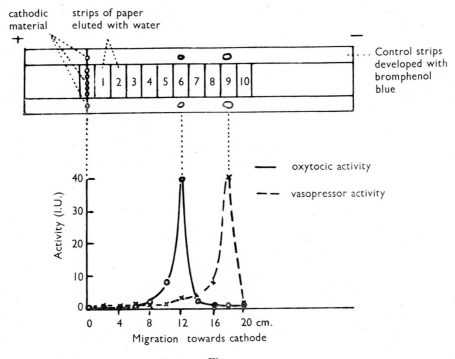

Figure 1

Paper electrophoresis of the cathodic material obtained after electrodialysis of the supernatant resulting from the precipitation of 'active protein' with 5 per cent. trichloractic acid.

hydrolysis of the substances yielded the amino-acids corresponding to the composition of oxytocin and vasopressin. Thus trichloracetic acid precipitates the protein while leaving the major part of the oxytocic and vasopressin activities in solution.

Counter-current distribution

Twenty mg. of the active protein were subjected to counter-current distribution in the system secondary butanol – 0·5 per cent. trichloracetic acid. After 24 transfers, the contents of each tube were homogenized by the addition of water and the biological activities and the nitrogen content were determined. It was found that the oxytocic and vasopressor activities were separated from one another, and from the principal nitrogen-containing substance (Fig. 2). The active substances were isolated.

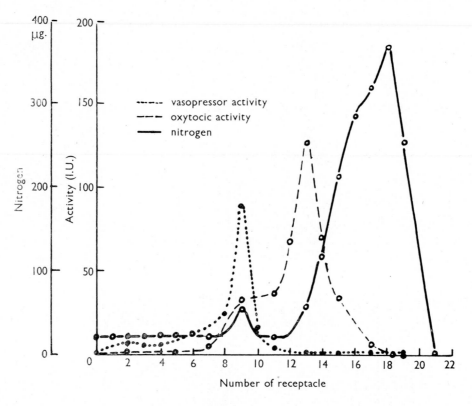

Figure 2

Counter-current distribution of the 'active protein' in the system secondary butanol—0·5 per cent. trichloracetic acid.

Subjected to paper chromatography they behaved like oxytocin and vasopressin. Moreover, vasopressin and oxytocin, subjected to counter-current distribution in the system described, had the same partition coefficient as the principles obtained from the active protein.

Action of chemical agents and enzymes

Sealock & du Vigneaud (1935) reported that oxytocin and vasopressin were not inactivated by reductions with cysteine. We have reduced the active protein with cysteine (30 mg. of cysteine hydrochloride per 0·15 mg. of nitrogen at pH 7·8) and have detected no inactivation after 5 hours' treatment at room temperature. Further, Lawler & du Vigneaud (1935) have shown that trypsin inactivates vasopressin but not oxytocin. We have hydrolysed the active protein with trypsin (enzyme substrate ratio 1 : 50; pH 7·8; 38° C.). After 6 hours the vasopressor activity of the protein had completely disappeared but the oxytocic activity was quite unaffected.

Taken as a whole, it is evident from these experiments that the vasopressor and oxytocic activities of the active protein behave towards chemical and enzymatic agents exactly like the vasopressor and oxytocic activities of vasopressin and oxytocin. On the other hand, processes which do not involve hydrolysis, such as dialysis against dilute acetic acid, electrodialysis, precipitation by trichloracetic acid and counter-current distribution, dissociate the active protein into substances responsible for the oxytocic and vasopressor activities and at least one inert protein. The complex, which is broken neither by dialysis against water, nor ultrafiltration, nor ultra-centrifugation (Rosenfeld, 1940; van Dyke *et al.*, 1942) may be an artefact of the extraction process or may possess biological significance. In the latter case, it appeared of interest to determine whether the complex behaved in the same manner during the course of the synthesis of the active principles and their utilization by the organism.

VARIATIONS IN OXYTOCIC AND VASOPRESSOR ACTIVITIES DURING GROWTH AND LACTATION

Several authors (Simon, 1934; Waring & Landgrebe, 1950; Dicker & Tyler, 1953*b*) have found that the V/O ratio is approximately unity in the neurohypophysis of the adult rat. Although Dicker & Tyler (1953*b*) found a ratio of 1, the absolute values of the two activities were 50 per cent. less than those of Simon (1934). On the other hand, Kuschinsky & Liebert (1939) found a ratio of about 2 (these authors determined the antidiuretic activity which corresponds to the vasopressor activity. New determinations seemed therefore necessary. Adult albino rats of 220 ± 30 g. were used which were obtained from four different colonies. The animals were killed by decapitation. The hypophysis was immediately removed and allowed to stand in pure cold acetone several hours. The posterior lobe was then separated, homogenized with 0·5 ml. of 0·25 per cent. acetic acid and heated at 100° C. for 1·5 minutes. The volume was adjusted to 1 ml. with water and the material assayed for vasopressor activity by the method of Landgrebe, Macaulay & Waring (1946), and for oxytocic activity by the method of Holton (1948). The determinations were made at different times of the year. The results obtained are shown in Table 1.

The following conclusions may be drawn:
(1) the activities are very constant (0·8 unit per gland); (2) the ratio of vasopressor activity to oxytocic activity is about 1; (3) there is no difference between the two sexes.

These results are in excellent agreement with those of Simon (1934). Several authors have determined the antidiuretic activity, which is a property of vasopressin and have found values around 0·8–1·0 unit per gland (Heller, 1947; Cavallero, Dova & Rossi, 1954; Morel, 1954). The agreement is therefore very good.

A ratio of vasopressor (or antidiuretic) to oxytocic activity, of approximately 1 has also been found in man, cat, dog, sheep, pig and horse (Heller & Zaimis, 1949; Waring & Landgrebe, 1950; Dicker & Tyler, 1953*a, b*). This ratio holds generally for mammals, though not in the whale, guinea-pig and rabbit (Waring & Landgrebe, 1950; Dicker & Tyler, 1953b; Schlichtegroll, 1954).

We have studied the change in the V/O ratio in the neurohypophysis of the rat during growth and lactation.

TABLE I

Content of oxytocic and vasopressor activity in the neurohypophysis of the adult rat

V = Vasopressor activity in milliunits per gland.
O = Oxytocic activity in millunits per gland.

Female			Male		
V	O	V/O	V	O	V/O
800	850	0·94	825	825	1·00
800	850	0·94	800	840	0·95
825	825	1·00	800	820	0·97
800	840	0·97	825	840	0·98
820	810	1·01	810	850	0·95
800	850	0·94	800	820	0·97
Mean 804	837	0·97	810	832	0·97

Variation in the ratio of vasopressor to oxytocic activity during growth

In the case of 5 day old animals, 10–15 glands were pooled for extraction; 5–10 glands were used of 10–20 day old rats and in the case of older animals a single gland. The hypophyses of 5 day-old rats were extracted without removal of the anterior lobe. Figure 3 shows the variation in the V/O ratio as a function of age.

Our results indicate that the V/O ratio reaches unity during growth. An identical shift has been found by Dicker & Tyler (1953a, b) in the dog and in man during embryonic development. Moreover, these authors have observed that the V/O ratio was higher in young than in adult rats, cats and guinea-pigs. It appears therefore that the synthesis of the substance with vasopressor activity is not synchronized with that of the oxytocic substance. It is possible that the second principle is only of importance in reproduction and for this reason is synthesized somewhat later.

Variation in the ratio of vasopressor to oxytocic activity during lactation

Five groups of rats were used: animals which were killed 2–3 hours, 12–24 hours, 5 days, 10 days and 20 days after parturition. Rats of the first group, unlike those of the others, had not yet commenced to lactate. Figure 4 shows the variation in the V/O ratio as a function of the stage of lactation.

The ratio, which is unity in normal animals, is approximately 1 at the time of parturition and during the subsequent 24 hours, but it increases during lactation due to a decrease in the amounts of the oxytocic principle.

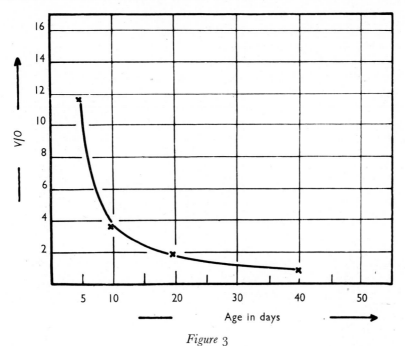

Figure 3

Ratio of vasopressor to oxytocic activity (*V/O*) in the pituitary glands of infant rats.

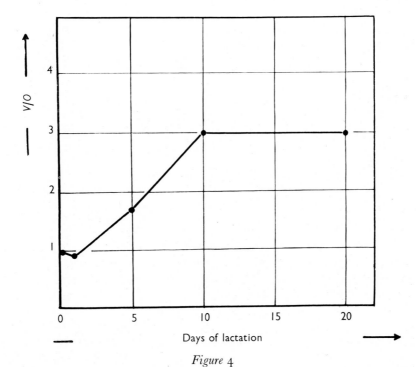

Figure 4

Ratio of vasopressor to oxytocic activity (*V/O*) in the neurohypophysis of lactating rats.

Figure 5 shows the levels of vasopressor and oxytocic activity in the neuro-hypophyses of the animals in the five groups.

We found that the levels of the vasopressor and oxytocic activities were about 50 per cent. below normal at the time of parturition but that they returned to normal 12–24 hours later; then, the oxytocic activity alone diminishes. The last observation is in agreement with the results of Dicker & Tyler (1953b).

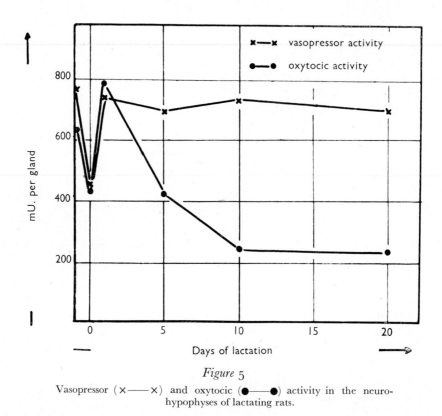

Figure 5

Vasopressor (×——×) and oxytocic (●——●) activity in the neuro-hypophyses of lactating rats.

The first effect of suckling is the re-establishment of the levels of the neuro-hypophysial hormones to their normal value during the first 24 hours. This was shown as follows: The rats were separated from their offsprings 2–3 hours after parturition and killed 12–24 hours or 10 days afterwards. After 12–24 hours the levels of the two activities in the glands were only slightly higher than those observed at the time of parturition: they had not become normal as in lactating animals. After 10 days the levels had slightly increased but had only reached 70–80 per cent. of the normal. Suckling which produces an increase in vasopressor and oxytocic activity during the first day following parturition, acts inversely on the level of the substance in the neurohypophysis which is stained by the Gomori reaction, as modified by Bargmann (1950). Stutinsky (1953) observed in rats that this material which is present in approximately normal quantity at parturition, diminishes considerably during the following 24 hours. This decrease does not occur if one prevents the young from suckling. It appears therefore that the neurosecretory material, if it actually corresponds to a chemical substance and not to a non-specific physical configuration (Scharrer & Scharrer, 1954), decreases at the beginning of lactation while the hormone content increases. However, Hild & Zetler (1953) have reported that maceration of the glands in a mixture of alcohol and chloroform eliminated the chromogenic material of the neurohypophysis without causing loss of the activities.

Our experiments as a whole, demonstrate on the one hand that it is not possible to extract from the neurohypophysis a chemically pure substance endowed with both vasopressor and oxytocic activity, and on the other that under normal physiological conditions, the organism synthesizes and utilizes the vasopressor substance and the substance with oxytocic activity independently. Thus it appears that vasopressin and oxytocin are true hormones. Further investigations are necessary to determine whether the complex formed by vasopressin, oxytocin and inert protein is an artefact of extraction or whether it has biological significance.

REFERENCES

ABEL, J. J. (1930). On the unitary versus the multiple hormone theory of posterior principle. *J. Pharmacol.* **40,** 139–69.

ABEL, J. J., ROUILLER, C. A. & GEILING, E. M. K. (1923). Further investigations on the oxytocic-pressor-diuretic principle of the infundibular portion of the pituitary gland. *J. Pharmacol.* **22,** 289–316.

ABRAHAMS, V. V. & PICKFORD, M. (1954). Simultaneous observations on the rate of urine flow and spontaneous uterine movements in the dog and their relationship to posterior lobe activity. *J. Physiol. (Lond.)* **126,** 329–46.

BARGMANN, W. (1950). Die elektive Darstellung einer marklosen diencephalen Bahn. *Mikroskopie* **5,** 289–92.

CAVALLERO, C., DOVA, E. & ROSSI, L. (1954). Antidiuretic activity in the neurohypophysis of rats after adrenalectomy and replacement therapy. *J. Endocr.* **10,** 228–37.

CHAMORRO, A. & MINZ, B. (1955). Secrétion d'oxytocine et de vasopressine par l'hypothalamus sous l'influence de l'application d'adrénaline sur le cortex cérébral. *C. R. Acad. Sci. (Paris)* **240,** 1368–70.

DICKER, S. E. & TYLER, C. (1953a). Estimation of the antidiuretic, vasopressor and oxytocic hormones in the pituitary gland of dogs and puppies. *J. Physiol. (Lond.)* **120,** 141–5.

DICKER, S. E. & TYLER, T. (1953b). Vasopressor and oxytocic activities of the pituitary glands of rats, guinea-pigs and cats and of human foetuses. *J. Physiol. (Lond.)* **121,** 206–14.

DUDLEY, H. W. (1919). Some observations on the active principles of the pituitary gland. *J. Pharmacol.* **14,** 295–312.

VAN DYKE, H. B., CHOW, B. F., GREEP, R. O. & ROTHEN, A. (1942). The isolation of a protein from the pars neuralis of the ox pituitary with constant oxytocic, pressor and diuresis-inhibiting activities. *J. Pharmacol.* **74,** 190–209.

HARRIS, G. W. (1947). The innervation and actions of the neurohypophysis; an investigation using the method of remote-control stimulation. *Philos. Trans.* B **232,** 385–441.

HELLER, H. (1947). Antidiuretic hormone in pituitary glands of newborn rats. *J. Physiol. (Lond.)* **106,** 28–32.

HELLER, H. & ZAIMIS, E. J. (1949). The antidiuretic and oxytocic hormones in the posterior pituitary glands of newborn infants and adults. *J. Physiol. (Lond.)* **109,** 162–9.

HILD, W. & ZETLER, G. (1953). Über die Funktion des Neurosekrets im Zwischenhirn-Neurohypophysensystem als Trägersubstanz für Vasopressin, Adiuretin und Oxytocin. *Z. ges. exp. Med.* **120,** 236–43.

HOLTON, P. (1948). A modification of the method of Dale and Laidlaw for standardization of posterior pituitary extracts. *Brit. J. Pharmacol.* **3,** 328–34.

KAMM, O., ALDRICH, T. B., GROTE, I. W., ROWE, L. W. & BUGBEE, E. P. (1928). The active principles of the posterior lobe of the pituitary gland. *J. Amer. Chem. Soc.* **50,** 573–601.

KUSCHINSKY, G. & LIEBERT, P. (1939). Untersuchungen über der Hormongehalt des Hypophysenhinterlappens der Ratte unter dem Einfluss von Wasser, Kochsalz und Novasurol. *Klni. Wschr.* **18,** 823.

LANDGREBE, F. W., MACAULAY, M. H. & WARING, H. (1946). The use of rats for pressor assays of pituitary extracts, with a note on response to histamine and adrenaline. *Proc. roy. Soc. Edin.* B **62,** 202–10.

LAWLER, C. H. & DU VIGNEAUD, V. (1953). Enzymatic evidence for intrinsic oxytocic activity of the pressor-antidiuretic hormone. *Proc. Soc. exp. Biol. Med. (N.Y.)* **84,** 114–6.

MACARTHUR, C. G. (1931). A new posterior pituitary preparation. *Science* **73,** 448.

MOREL, F. (1954). Quelques aspects de la régulation endocrinienne de l'équilibre hydrominéral enregistrés chez le rat à l'aide du radio-sodium Na^{24}. *Thèse de Doctorat*, Paris.

ROSENFELD, M. (1940). The native hormones of the posterior pituitary gland: the pressor and oxytocic principles. *Bull. Johns Hopk. Hosp.* **66,** 398–403.

SCHARRER, E. & SCHARRER, B. (1954) Hormones produced by neurosecretory cells. *Recent Prog. Hormone Res.* **10,** 183–240.

SCHLICHTEGROLL, A. V. (1954). Vasopressorische und oxytocische Wirksamkeit in Hypothalamus- und Hypophysenhinterlappenextrakten. *Naturwissenschaften* **41,** 188–9.

SEALOCK, R. R. & DU VIGNEAUD, V. (1935). Studies on the reduction of Pitressin and Pitocin with cysteine. *J. Pharmacol.* **54,** 433–47.

SIMON, A. (1934). The pressor and oxytocic content of the hypophysis of rats under various conditions. *Amer. J. Physiol.* **107,** 220–6.

STUTINSKY, F. (1953). La neurosecrétion au cours de la gestation et le post-partum chez la rate. *Ann. Endocr. (Paris)* **14,** 722–5.

DU VIGNEAUD, V. (1952) *A trail of research*. Ithaca: Cornell University Press.

WARING, H. & LANDGREBE, F. W. (1950). Hormones of the posterior pituitary. In *The Hormones*. Ed. Pincus, G. and Thimann, K. V. New York: Academic Press.

Discussion

Chairman: R. Gaunt

Heller. I should like to make a plea for not relying too much on the amounts of oxytocic or vasopressor activity found in the glands of any particular strain of rat. If one looks through the literature one finds that some workers have found as much as 800 mU. per 100 g. rat and others only 250 mU. 100 g. We originally found high values, but a year later, with another strain, we obtained values that were very much lower. As to the hormone ratio, I think it is certainly, as I have shown, with many others, of the order of 1 in the adult rat, but again I do not think one should interpret that too precisely. After all there are two biological assays involved in these estimations and both of them have very considerable errors. One cannot therefore say more than that the value is somewhere near 1 but in some animals it may be 1·3 or even 1·5. Whether this is a real difference I cannot say. With the Chairman's permission, I would like to show a slide of the vasopressin-oxytocin ratios in the neural lobe of lactating rats as determined by Mr. K. Lederis in my laboratory. We have used rats from 1 to 21 days after parturition. The methods of assay were very much the same as those used by Fromageot and his co-workers, and the results at first glance appear similar to Professor Fromageot's curve. On the first and third day a ratio of something like unity was found, thereafter it rises but these values must be compared with the ratios in non-pregnant female rats of the same strain, which in our hands at least show a considerable variation. I have taken statistical advice on this and I am informed that in the small groups so far available, there is no clear difference between the *mean* values for the controls and the lactating animals. I think perhaps that to see more clearly we should follow the suggestion of Professor van Dyke and assay oxytocin by a milk ejection method as well as by uterine response; and vasopressin by antidiuretic assay as well as on the blood-pressure. We are in the process of doing so.

Fromageot. I quite agree with Professor Heller that one must be careful about methods of assay: many factors may indeed interfere with the titrations, such as the presence of substances with potentiating or inhibitory effects, the physiological state of the animals or of the organs used, &c.: but care has been taken to make the assays as correct as possible, and in the curves which I showed each point is the average of six different experiments. The variations within each of the series were significantly less than the differences observed between the groups of animals.

Croxatto. Professor Fromageot: what is the amino-acid composition of the inactive protein molecule after the separation of the active peptides. Is it different from vasopressin and oxytocin?

Fromageot. The amino-acid composition of the inactive protein obtained after separation of the active peptides is not very different from that of the active protein as a whole, because of the small weight of the peptides compared to that of the protein. Without remembering what this amino-acid composition is, I may say that apart from its richness in cystine, the protein in question contains much proline. A preliminary analysis has been made by Block & van Dyke; (*Arch. Biochem.* **36**, 1, 1952) and it differs quite clearly from the composition of each of the peptides. I might add that the molecular weight of the active protein is about 28,000. The molecular weight of each active peptide is about 1000. Therefore what remains after this removal does not differ significantly from the initial substance in respect also of its molecular weight.

Landgrebe. I was very interested in Professor Fromageot's results with lactating rats and since van Dyke's protein comes from ox glands I should like to tell you our results in the ox. We have tested glands from heifers, milking cows and bulls, at various times of the year, and found that there was amazing uniformity in the amount of activity in the glands. There is no difference between the milking cow, the heifer or the bull in the amount of activity or in the ratio.

Mrs. Dodd. We have investigated this problem in goats in relation to lactation. We tried milking them out immediately before killing and removing the gland. The glands were removed in from 90 seconds to 4 minutes and there was no difference in the vasopressin-oxytocin ratio and again not very much difference in the total amount, weight for weight of dry gland tissue, between lactating goats and non-lactating goats.

Ginsburg. I think this is very interesting because I do not think it has been appreciated how rapidly the gland can be repleted. Professor Fromageot showed that there was rapid repletion of hormones in the glands of rats suckled immediately after parturition. Perhaps in Mrs. Dodd's experiments although the gland was depleted very quickly it was also repleted very quickly and the time interval between killing the animals might have been too long. If repletion rate is rapid and variable this will render the estimation of hormone content of glands an unreliable index of secretion.

Mrs. Dodd. We took it that the total amount of hormone which would be released from the gland by the natural stimulus of the let-down of milk, would be so minute in relation to the total amount of substance there, that one would not be able to demonstrate it.

Herdan. Professor Heller's experiments, on statistical analysis, show that there is a trend in the vasopressin-oxytocin ratio but its probable error is of the same order of magnitude as the trend itself and hence it fails to be significant. The mean values for vasopressin-oxytocin ratios in lactating rats and control rats were 1·138 and 1·147 respectively with a probable error of 0·075. Taking twice the standard error as the borderline between significance and non-significance, one concludes that, firstly, the ratio is not significantly different from unity, and secondly, that there is no significant difference between the average vasopressin-oxytocin ratios for the lactating and the control group.

These results are given with the proviso that they refer to small numbers of experiments (20 in the lactating and 9 in the control group). Since the standard error is inversely dependent on the sample size, it is quite possible that greater samples may show significant differences.

Polypeptides with posterior pituitary-like activities

by

H. CROXATTO

Laboratorio de Fisiologia Instituto Pedagogico, Universidad de Chile. Laboratorio de Fisiologia, Universidad Catolica, Santiago, Chile.

HYDROLYSIS of blood serum or of some of its proteins by certain proteolytic enzymes liberates polypeptides which have many of the pharmacological actions of the neuro-hypophysial hormones.

On one hand, it has been reported that the digestion of either blood serum or hypertensinogen with trypsin (or with snake venoms) produces a substance called 'bradykinin' (Rocha e Silva, 1951) which has a pronounced vasodepressor effect and a motor action upon the plain muscles of the hollow viscera, including the uterus. On the other, hydrolysis of these substrates with pepsin sets free several peptides, including a hypertensin-like substance, viz. pepsitensin (Croxatto & Croxatto, 1942). Some of these peptides have a motor effect upon uterine muscle and at least one of them has an inhibitory effect upon urinary excretion (Croxatto, Rojas & Barnafi, 1951). This antidiuretic substance has been provisionally named 'pepsanurin'. It attracted our attention because although the uterotonic activity is shared by many peptides, e.g. hypertensin, pepsitensin, bradykinin, kallidin (Werle, 1955) pepsitocin and substance P (von Euler, 1936), no peptide resembling vasopressin has so far been found in tissues other than the hypothalamus or the hypophysis.

Since oxytocin and vasopressin are simple octapeptides (du Vigneaud, Ressler, & Trippet, 1953; du Vigneaud, Lawler & Popenoe, 1953) and a larger molecule may be endowed with the same activities (van Dyke, Chow, Greep & Rothen, 1942), it does not seem strange that polypeptides set free from other substrates show some of the same pharmacological effects. Hypertensin, according to a recent paper of Skeggs, Marsh, Kahn & Shumway (1955), contains 8 amino-acids in approximately unimolecular proportion plus two moles of histidine. Seven of these amino-acids are also contained in either oxytocin or vasopressin. The purest preparations of hypertensin so far obtained besides producing a powerful vasopressor effect have intense oxytocic activity and are also capable of modifying diuresis and natriuresis (Pickering & Prinzmetal, 1940).

I would like to take this opportunity to describe some polypeptides which are liberated from hypertensinogen, as well as from other fractions of blood serum by pepsin and which show the activities of neurohypophysial hormones. Since these substances have not yet been purified, some of the results given here must obviously be regarded as preliminary.

It was established first of all that by treating hypertensinogen with pepsin, a vaso-pressor substance (which we called 'pepsitensin') could be obtained. Besides having various chemical properties in common with hypertensin, pepsitensin acts in a similar way upon several types of plain muscle. Like hypertensin it is inactivated by all the crystalline proteolytic enzymes including pepsin. After pepsitensin has been formed by the incubation of hypertensinogen with pepsin (at pH 3·5 for 3 to 4 hours) and the protein has been discarded, the residual extract contains the vasopressor principle, mixed with large amounts of inactive peptides. If this is subjected to further digestion with pepsin (at pH 2·5) it loses all of its vasopressor effects and a great deal of its oxytocic activity, but an antidiuretic activity appears. The same result can be obtained, if instead of the two successive digestions, hydrolysis is performed in one stage for a longer period (8–14 hours).

The antidiuretic substance does not necessarily derive from pepsitensin: if hyper-tensinogen preparations are treated with renin long enough to convert the hyper-tensinogen entirely to hypertensin, which is then dialysed away, treatment with pepsin does not then cause liberation of pepsitensin. Instead, it gives rise to a potent antidiuretic substance. Sera of different mammals have been used as starting material (human, ox, cat, and rat) with similar qualitative results. Hydrolysis of human and ox serum albumin by pepsin also sets free substances with a marked antidiuretic action. After purification involving adsorption with charcoal, elution with glacial acetic acid and fractional precipitation with acetone and ether, an extract is obtained containing 30 per cent. of the initial activity. 0·2 ml. of this extract, contain-ing 1 to 3 mg. of solids produces an antidiuretic effect which lasts up to 2 to 3 hours after injection (Fig. 1).

ANTIDIURETIC ACTIVITY OF PEPSANURIN (PN). (GILMAN-GOODMAN TEST).

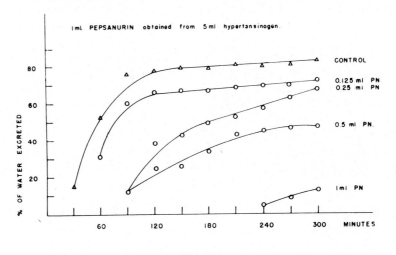

Figure 1

Antidiuretic effect of different doses of an extract from horse serum hypertensinogen.

THE PROPERTIES OF THE ANTIDIURETIC SUBSTANCE (PEPSANURIN)

Pepsanurin is soluble in formic acid, acetic acid and in 20 per cent. trichloroacetic acid, insoluble in benzene, petrol ether, ether, pyridine and acetone, and scarcely soluble in absolute alcohol, concentrated N-butanol and secondary butanol. It can be precipitated from aqueous solutions by the addition of 10 volumes of acetone. Charcoal, amberlite (IR-50) and permutite (pH 4·5) adsorb it. It can be eluted from charcoal by glacial acetic acid in which it keeps its activity indefinitely. It can be separated from glacial acetic acid by a mixture of absolute ethanol and petrol ether (1 : 1) or with purified ether. It can be eluted from permutite with a solution containing 1 per cent. acetic acid and 5 per cent. NaCl. In contrast to vasopressin, pepsanurin is partially extracted by secondary butanol equilibrated with 0·05 per cent. acetic acid. It dialyses through cellophane membranes. It is destroyed by alkali but withstands heating in organic acids. Performic acid as employed by Popenoe & du Vigneaud (1953) to oxydize vasopressin (a procedure that leads to its inactivation) also destroys the activity of pepsanurin-containing extracts.

The antidiuretic effect can be obtained in rats by injecting the extract in different ways: intraperitoneally, subcutaneously or intravenously. The effect is longer lasting and greater after intraperitoneal than after subcutaneous injection.

The inhibition of diuresis in water-loaded rats (conscious or in ethanol anaesthesia) is not the result of delayed water absorption from the intestine: at the end of an experiment the amount of water in the digestive tract is slightly higher than in non-injected controls, but it is about the same as that found in rats injected with vasopressin. Since the injection of pepsanurin-containing extracts into hypophysectomized rats with diabetes insipidus produces a profound inhibition of diuresis, the antidiuretic effect cannot be explained by stimulation of the neurohypophysis and release of vasopressin. Polyuria in such rats can be counteracted by an adequate dose of the extract administered at intervals from 6 to 12 hours. The inhibition of diuresis can also be obtained in water-loaded hypophysectomized rats which have been treated with cortisone (Fig. 2). Both pepsanurin and vasopressin can completely inhibit the polyuria produced by renin. Both substances inhibit more markedly when injected 60 to 90 minutes after renin.

In the white rat, pepsanurin as well as vasopressin can antagonize the increased diuresis and natriuresis produced by 25 to 50 mU. of purified oxytocin containing less than 3 per cent. of vasopressin (Fig. 3).

Sympatholytic drugs such as dibenamine or hydrogenated ergot alkaloids, which produce a powerful inhibition of the antidiuretic effects of enteramine (Erspamer, 1952), do not modify the antidiuresis caused by either vasopressin or pepsanurin.

The antidiuretic effect of pepsanurin seems to be due mainly to an increase of water absorption by the renal tubules. However, a vasoconstrictor action upon the glomerular vessels cannot be excluded although there is no systemic hypertensive effect. Moderate amounts of pepsanurin (providing they do not decrease the output of urine below 50 per cent. of that of the controls) do not have a significant effect upon creatinine clearance; but if there is an intense inhibition of diuresis, creatinine clearance is strongly affected. It can be assumed from this, that in addition to increased tubular reabsorption of water a decrease in glomerular filtration may be

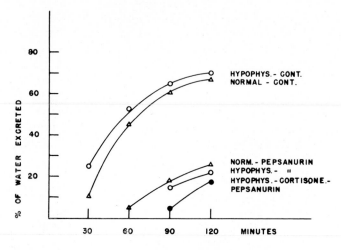

EFFECT OF PEPSANURIN ON DIURESIS OF
HYPOPHYSECTOMIZED (HYPERHYDRATED) RATS.

Figure 2

Percentage urine output of water-loaded rats (water load: 5 per cent. of body-weight)

(1) Hypophys.-Cont. = Hypophysectomized rats injected with 0·5 ml. of 0·9 per cent. NaCl solution and previously treated with cortisone.
(2) Normal-Cont. = Normal rats injected with 0·5 ml. of 0·9 per cent. NaCl solution.
(3) Norm.-Pepsanurin = Normal rats injected with 0·5 ml. pepsanurin (horse serum hypertensinogen) extract.
(4) Hypophys.-Pepsanurin = Hypophysectomized rats injected with 0·5 ml. pepsanurin extract.
(5) Hypophys.-Cortisone-Pepsanurin = Hypophysectomized rats previously treated with cortisone and injected with 0·5 ml. pepsanurin extract.

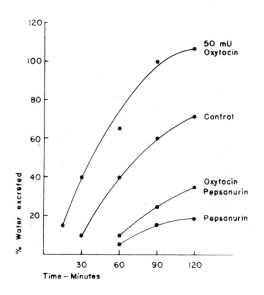

Figure 3

Effects upon diuresis obtained in water-loaded rats with injections of:

(a) 50 mU. oxytocin, subcutaneously.
(b) 0·9 per cent. NaCl solution, subcutaneously.
(c) 50 mU. oxytocin subcutaneously plus 0·1 ml. pepsanurin extract intraperitoneally.
(d) 0·1 ml. pepsanurin extract intraperitoneally.

produced. The latter effect has also been noticed when a pronounced antidiuretic effect is obtained with vasopressin (Barnafi, Croxatto & Krause, 1956).

The profound influence that neurohypophysial extracts exert upon the water balance of the amphibians can also be observed with digests of hypertensinogen or of plasma hydrolysates. In *Bufo chilensis* the latter preparations increase the water uptake through the skin, i.e. they produce a similar effect as that caused by posterior lobe extracts in frogs (Brunn, 1921).

Persanurin seems to be a peptide since chymotrypsin completely destroys its activity (Figs. 4 and 5) which neither pepsin nor carboxypeptidase are able to do; trypsin has only a slight effect. Vasopressin shows a surprisingly similar behaviour: carboxypeptidase and pepsin have no effect and chymotrypsin destroys it completely; trypsin quickly destroys the vasopressor activity but the antidiuretic activity of vasopressin is only partially affected.

EFFECT OF CHYMOTRYPSIN ON PEPSANURIN ACTIVITY.

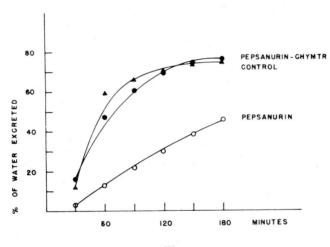

Figure 4

Antidiuretic effect (Burn's test) of 0·2 ml. of an extract containing pepsanurin and of 0·2 ml. of the same extract incubated with chymotrypsin. The
preparation was obtained from horse serum hypertensinogen.

Pepsanurin does not seem to originate from a specific substrate in plasma: it has been obtained from both serum albumin and serum globulins when using human plasma fractioned by the method of Green & Bumpus (1954). Albumin yielded a slightly higher antidiuretic activity than hypertensinogen, but most of the experiments described up to date were carried out with extracts from hypertensinogen from different sources.

Using purified pig hypertensinogen* an antidiuretic substance is released even after removal of the hypertensin formed by previous incubation with renin. When this preparation is injected no vasoconstrictor effect is shown, but a slight and

* A highly purified sample generously supplied by M. F. Bumpus.

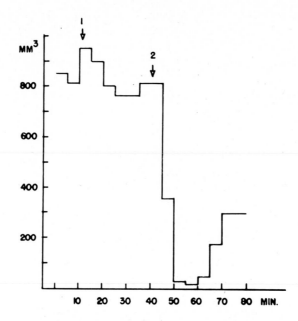

Figure 5

Rat anaesthetized with ethanol. Urine collected continuously and
the volume measured every 5 min.
1 = Injection of 0·1 ml. of an extract obtained from hypertensinogen. It was treated with renin, dialysed and incubated for 3
hours with chymotrypsin.
2 = Injection of the same preparation not incubated with chymotrypsin.

transient fall of blood-pressure is seen. From 5 to 10 mg. hypertensinogen an extract is
finally obtained with an antidiuretic potency equivalent to that of about 10 mU.
vasopressin (Venezian, 1955). Pepsanurin-containing extracts have oxytocic effects
of varying intensity. No extract free of oxytocic activity has as yet been prepared.

The antidiuretic principle differs from vasopressin since it has no pressor activity.
It is inactivated by chymotrypsin but the serum of pregnant women does not affect it
(Fig. 6) although it destroys vasopressin very easily (Croxatto, Barnafi & Ferrer,
1954*b*). This suggests a difference in the chemical composition of the two principles.

PEPSITOCIN

As reported before it seems possible that an oxytocic substance, different from the
antidiuretic principle, occurs in peptic hydrolysates. Thus, extracts with the same
antidiuretic activity may, depending on their origin, have a different oxytocic potency.
A higher yield of antidiuretic substance is obtained from the albumin fraction of
plasma, while higher oxytocic potency is obtained from the globulin fraction. The
oxytocic activity withstands the action of pepsin and trypsin but it is destroyed by
chymotrypsin and is more easily extracted from water by butanol than is pepsanurin.

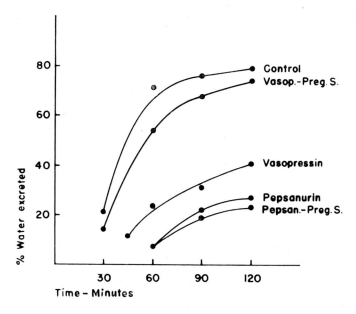

Figure 6

Antidiuretic effects in rats (Burn's test) injected with vasopressin and
pepsanurin both incubated and non-incubated with the serum of preg-
nant women (eighth month).
Control = rats injected with 0·9 per cent. NaCl solution.
Vasop.-Preg. S. = 50 mU. vasopressin incubated for 6 hours with 0·15 ml.
pregnancy serum.
Vasopressin = 50 mU. vasopressin.
Pepsanurin = 0·1 ml. extract obtained from human serum.
Pepsan.-Preg. S. = 0·1 ml. of the same extract incubated for 6 hours with
0·15 ml. pregnancy serum.

The oxytocic potency of hypertensinogen extracts is very slowly destroyed when
incubated at pH 7 to 7·2 with carboxypeptidase; this does not occur with oxytocin.

It can be assumed that pepsitocin is different from bradykinin or pepsitensin
(Venezian, 1955). When hypertensinogen is previously treated with renin so as to
exhaust hypertensin production and hypertensin is then eliminated by dialysis,
tryptic action does not produce bradykinin (Rocha e Silva, 1951); nor is pepsitensin
produced if digestion is accomplished by pepsin (pH 3·5) after prolonged treatment
with renin. If hypertensinogen preparations free of hypertensin, are submitted to a
long period of digestion with pepsin (pH 2·5), an extract having both oxytocic and
antidiuretic activity and with no vasoconstrictor activity can be prepared.

Hypertensinogen hydrolysates, previously treated with renin show less oxytocic
activity than untreated extracts. The contrary is observed with the antidiuretic
potency: When hypertensinogen is hydrolysed with pepsin for 11 hours and the
alcohol soluble polypeptides (pH 5·2) are removed, the denatured hypertensinogen
remaining forms neither an oxytocic nor an antidiuretic substance if submitted to a
second hydrolysis with pepsin (Venezian, 1955).

The purification of both pepsitocin and pepsanurin is still in a preliminary stage and it would therefore be premature to assume a relationship between them and the active peptides of the neurohypophysis or the albumin isolated by van Dyke, Chow, Greep & Rothen (1942). However, it can be claimed that they are not identical: pepsanurin differs from both vasopressin and van Dyke's protein, because it has no vasoconstrictor effect and resists the action of the vasopressinase contained in the serum of pregnant women. Pepsitocin also is not inactivated by pregnancy serum and it differs further from oxytocin because it is destroyed by carboxypeptidase, suggesting that it has free carboxyl groups.

GENERAL REMARKS

The substances released by the hydrolytic action of pepsin might be regarded as artefacts of pharmacological interest only. But if pepsin is able to liberate hypertensin-like substances from the same substrate as that for renin, one is tempted to consider the possibility that the blood proteins could also supply precursors for other peptides. Specific enzymes in the tissues or in the blood might react with circulating substrates to produce other active peptides. It is possible for example that hypothalamic nuclei and the hypophysis are capable of elaborating active peptides by hydrolytic mechanisms.

On the other hand, the presence of an antidiuretic substance among the peptides formed by the enzymatic action of pepsin could explain some controversial results of estimations of antidiuretic activity in blood: the antidiuretic effects of serum, plasma or blood when injected intraperitoneally into water-loaded rats, are due not only to the antidiuretic hormone but also to a different substance, presumably similar to pepsanurin. In our experience the antidiuretic activity of blood when measured with Burn's (1931) test is always higher than expected. In other words it is greater than could be accounted for by the amount of vasopressin contained in the blood and released by neurohypophysis under different conditions. This high antidiuretic potency is not due to some of the factors developed during coagulation (Croxatto, Pfister & Munizaga, 1955). It diminishes or disappears after incubation at 38° C. or after prolonged dialysis (Croxatto, Andrade & Barnafi, 1952). Recent experiments demonstrated that mere acidification (to pH 4) of plasma increases both antidiuretic and oxytocic potency whether the plasma had been dialysed for a few hours or not. We could show that the level of antidiuretic and oxytocic activity of the blood in hypophysectomized rats decreases slightly during the first week following the operation, but that it is then maintained even when the blood is obtained from rats during a period of polyuria.

When estimated by intraperitoneal injections both the oxytocic and the antidiuretic activity were as high in the blood of patients with diabetes insipidus as in normal subjects (Croxatto, Barnafi, Lopez & Andrade, 1954a) (Fig. 7). Moreover, we have found an antidiuretic substance in the blood of pregnant women which must be different from vasopressin since, as is well known (von Fekete, 1930; Page, 1946; Croxatto, Reyes & Croxatto, 1947; Croxatto, Vera & Barnafi, 1953), during pregnancy blood inactivates the antidiuretic hormone at a high rate. Nevertheless, during the last month of pregnancy the antidiuretic potency of plasma as measured by the intraperitoneal method is much higher than that in the plasma of non-pregnant women. All this leads to the assumption that a protein substrate in the

58

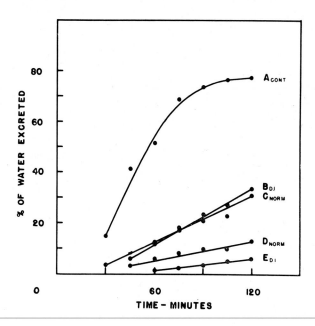

Figure 7

Percentage of water excreted by water-loaded rats (Burn's test). Water administered simultaneously with intraperitoneal injection: $A = 1$ ml. of 0·9 per cent NaCl solution; mean of 15 experiments, each performed on a group of 4 rats. $B = 0·5$ ml. per 100 g. body-weight of serum of 5 patients with diabetes insipidus; mean of 7 experiments. $C = 0·5$ ml. of serum of normal subjects per 100 g.; mean of 7 experiments. $D = 1$ ml. of serum of normal subjects per 100 g.; mean of 8 experiments. $E = 1$ ml. per 100 g. of serum of 5 patients with diabetes insipidus; mean of 8 experiments.

plasma which to some extent is protected from inactivating factors, gives rise to the substance which produces this antidiuretic effect. It is liberated by dialysis, and incubation at 37° destroys it. When plasma is injected into the intraperitoneal cavity of the rat, the active substance is liberated and the antidiuretic effect is produced.

When serum or plasma is deprived of its antidiuretic activity either by incubation or by prolonged dialysis and is then treated with pepsin, the antidiuretic action becomes even stronger than it was initially. Thus it would seem that there are at least three antidiuretic factors in the plasma: firstly the neurohypophysial antidiuretic hormone which can be rapidly removed by dialysis and which is easily inactivated by vasopressinase; secondly a substance linked with proteins and protected from the action of inactivating factors but which can be fairly well eliminated by dialysis or which can be destroyed by prolonged incubation and thirdly a factor which is liberated by the hydrolytic action of pepsin. The third factor is the substance for which we have provisionally coined the name 'pepsanurin'.

REFERENCES

BARNAFI, L., CROXATTO, H. & KRAUSE, J. (1956). Influencia de la Vasopresina y Ocitocina sobre el Indice renal de depuracion de la Creatinina en la rata. In press.

BURN, H. J. (1931). Estimation of the antidiuretic potency of pituitary (posterior lobe) extract. *Quart. J. Pharm.* **4**, 517–29.

BRUNN, F. (1921). Beitrag zur Kenntnis der Wirkung von Hypophysenextrakten auf den Wasserhaushalt des Frosches. *Z. ges. exp. Med.* **25**, 170–5.

CROXATTO, H. & CROXATTO, R. (1942). 'Pepsitensin'—a hypertensin-like substance produced by peptic digestion of proteins. *Science* **95**, 101–2.

CROXATTO, H., REYES, M. & CROXATTO, R. (1947). Actividad Ocitocinásica e Hipertensinásica del Plasma de la Mujer durante el embarazo. *J. chilenas Obst. Ginec.* **1**, 469–76.

CROXATTO, H., ROJAS, G. & BARNAFI, L. (1951). The liberation of an antidiuretic factor by the hypertensinogen pepsin reaction. *Acta Physiol. Latamer.* **1**, 178–86.

CROXATTO, H., ANDRADE, F. & BARNAFI, L. (1952). Antidiuretic action of human plasma. *Acta Physiol. Latamer.* **2**, 142–50.

CROXATTO, H., VERA, C. & BARNAFI, L. (1953). Inactivation of antidiuretic hormone by blood-serum of the pregnant woman. *Proc. Soc. exp. Biol.* (*N.Y.*) **83**, 784–6.

CROXATTO, H., BARNAFI, L., LOPEZ, R. & ANDRADE, F. (1954a). Antidiuretic potency of the blood in diabetes insipidus. *Metabolism* **3**, 32–43.

CROXATTO, H., BARNAFI, L. & FERRER, R. (1954b). The antidiuretic potency of pregnant women serum. *Acta Physiol. Latamer.* **4**, 166–70.

CROXATTO, H., PFISTER, N. & MUNIZAGA, J. (1955). Potencia Antidiurética de la Sangre. Influencia de la Coagulación y de algunos factores que en ella intervienen. Jornadas 25 Aniversario Escuela de Medicina Universidad Católica, Santiago. In press.

VAN DYKE, H. B., CHOW, B. F., GREEP, R. O. & ROTHEN, A. (1942). The isolation of a protein from the pars neuralis of the ox pituitary with constant oxytocic, pressor and diuresis-inhibiting activities. *J. Pharmacol.* **74**, 190–209.

ERSPAMER, V. (1952). Modificazioni delle azioni dell enteramina ad opera di farmaci simpaticomimetici e di farmaci simpaticolitici. *La Ricerca Scientifica* **22**, 1568–77.

VON EULER, U. S. (1936). Untersuchungen über Substanz P, die atropinfeste, darmerregende und gefässerweiternde Substanz aus Darm und Hirn. *Arch. exp. Path. Pharmak.* **181**, 181–97.

VON FEKETE, K. (1930). Beiträge zur Physiologie der Gravidität. *Endokrinologie* **7**, 364–9.

GREEN, A. A. & BUMPUS, F. M. (1954). The purification of hog renin substrate. *J. biol. Chem.* **210**, 281–6.

PAGE, E. W. (1946). The value of plasma pitocinase determinations in obstetrics. *Amer. J. Obst. Gynec.* **52**, 1014–21.

PICKERING, G. W. & PRINZMETAL, M. (1940). The effect of renin on urine formation. *J. Physiol.* (*Lond.*) **98**, 314–35.

POPENOE, E. A. & DU VIGNEAUD, V. (1953). Degradative studies on vasopressin and performic acid-oxidized vasopressin. *J. biol. Chem.* **205**, 133–43.

ROCHA E SILVA, M. (1951). *Bradicinina.* Thesis, Faculty of Medicine, University of Brazil, São Paulo: Ipsis.

SKEGGS, L. T., MARSH, W. H., KAHN, J. R. & SHUMWAY, N. P. (1955). Amino-acid composition and electrophoretic properties of hypertensin 1. *J. exp. Med.* **102**, 435–40.

VENEZIAN, S. (1955). *Polipéptidos activos derivados del Hipertensinógeno purificado.* Tesis de Grado, Universidad Católica, Santiago.

DU VIGNEAUD, V. RESSLER, C. & TRIPPETT, S. (1953). The sequence of amino-acids in oxytocin, with a proposal for the structure of oxytocin. *J. Biol. Chem.* **205**, 949–57.

DU VIGNEAUD, V., LAWLER, C. & POPENOE, E. (1953). Enzymatic cleavage of glycinamide from vasopressin and a proposed structure for this pressor-antidiuretic hormone of the posterior pituitary. *J. Amer. chem. Soc.* **75**, 4880–1.

WERLE, E. (1955). The chemistry and pharmacology of kallikrein and kallidin. In *Polypeptides which stimulate smooth muscle.* Ed. Gaddum, J. H. Edinburgh, London: Livingstone.

Discussion

Chairman : R. Gaunt

Gaunt. Are all your substances active intravenously?

Croxatto. Yes, they are active. However, the antidiuretic substance differs from vasopressin in being less active when given intravenously.

Noble. The findings presented, showing a marked reduction in the total output of urine in the rat after the injection of active fractions, raise the question of specificity of such action in the Burn method of assay. Although I would like to discuss this matter in more detail in my own paper we have felt that in the assay of urine extracts the test rats should excrete at least 50 per cent. of the administered water. If they excrete less we believe that antidiuretic values obtained are erroneous, and that non-specific toxicity or local vascular effects may be responsible for the antidiuretic action. Assays at different dose levels would be of interest and I wonder if Dr. Croxatto has run tests at other than the single dose level indicated on his slides?

Croxatto. Our antidiuretic assays were not confined to that described by Burn, and we found an antidiuretic effect with all methods. Neither toxic effects nor circulatory changes were found, even when the substances were injected intravenously. We got the same results with preparations of varying degrees of purity.

Gross. Did you notice any hypotensive activity with your peptide? It is well known that certain peptides, extracted from the plasma and also from the hypothalamus, have a long-lasting hypotensive activity.

Croxatto. In rats these extracts have no effect upon blood pressure except when given in very large amounts. They were not tested in cats.

van Dyke. Do these preparations have any effect on the renal circulation, i.e. on renal plasma flow and glomerular filtration rate?

Croxatto. We have estimated creatinine clearance, and we find the same effect as that obtained with vasopressin: with moderate doses there is no effect.

van Dyke. I doubt if anyone has really shown that vasopressin can be detected in peripheral blood of intact animals; the amount present is so minute that it can hardly be estimated accurately. Mirsky (Mirsky, Stein & Paulisch, *Endocrinology* **54**, 491, 1954) for instance finds the high figure of about 20 mU. 100 ml. in rats. His control experiments were done in dogs and would suggest extremely high levels of hormone.

The other factor I would like to comment on, is the alleged diuretic effect of oxytocin. We have studied purified synthetic oxytocin and the natural product, and we have invariably obtained an antidiuretic effect. Fraser (*J. Physiol. (Lond.)* **101**, 236, 1942) detected no diuretic effect after very large intravenous doses in dogs.

Croxatto. When blood is injected intraperitoneally we are quite certain that the effects seen are not solely due to vasopressin. Something else is contained in or liberated from the blood which increases the antidiuretic effect. This may explain why we have found no differences in the antidiuretic potency between the blood of normal subjects and patients with diabetes insipidus.

Concerning the diuretic and natriuretic effects obtained with our oxytocin preparation and the different results obtained with pure oxytocin, we can assume either that the former contain a contaminant substance or that we are dealing with species differences. In white rats natriuretic effects with oxytocin were always obtained, but this was not so in grey rats. Possibly this difference can be attributed to the fact that grey rats, being very excitable animals, respond to the injection with a release of vasopressin.

van Dyke. My remarks, of course, apply to highly purified oxytocin and not to your preparations.

Yoffey. I wonder if the different results after intraperitoneal and intravenous injections are partly explainable by lymphatic absorption. A protein injected into the peritoneum would be absorbed by lymphatics and we know that lymph glands can do strange things to proteins in a matter of 10 minutes or so. It might be worth while to see what happens when you incubate some of your preparations with lymphatic tissue.

Croxatto. We thought that perhaps the liver was involved but your suggestion requires consideration.

Walker. Are the activities of pepsitocin and pepsanurin retained after incubation with sodium thioglycollate, which is a substance often used by some of us to try to identify substances of pituitary origin?

Croxatto. This has not been tested.

Heller. With regard to the effect of oxytocin I believe that Professor van Dyke did not get a natriuretic effect after injecting it intravenously into dogs. I wonder if there may be a species difference: we have confirmed the reports of a natriuretic effect of oxytocin in the rat, and it seems possible that this is due to the renal vascular changes which can be produced by Pitocin in this species (Dicker & Heller, *J. Physiol.* (*Lond.*) **104**, 353, 1946) but so far nobody seems to have reported an increase of renal sodium excretion in the dog.

van Dyke. This is a possible explanation.

Pickford. We have sometimes found oxytocin to cause a sodium outpouring in the dog but this is not always so and may depend upon the size of the dose we used.

Sawyer. Whether one gets a diuretic effect with oxytocin in the rat seems to depend upon the sodium load (Sawyer, *Amer. J. Physiol.* 1952, **169**, 583). If the rat is excreting a large amount of sodium, oxytocin may increase this and thus produce an osmotic diuresis. The diet, therefore, might be important in determining whether one sees a diuretic response or not.

In Dr. Croxatto's experiments in which he showed the antidiuretic effect of whole serum injected intraperitoneally, did he exclude the possibility that the dialysable antidiuretic substance is 5-hydroxytryptamine rather than a polypeptide?

Croxatto. This is eliminated because the effect was not blocked by dibenamine and hydrogenated ergot alkaloids.

Eisen. Oxytocic activity is very readily produced in blood, plasma or serum from many mammalian species including man. Professor C. A. Keele and his collaborators have shown that such activity may result from mere contact with glass (Armstrong, Keele, Jepsen & Stewart; *Nature (Lond.)* **174**, 791, 1954). This uterine stimulation is ascribed to a substance provisionally called 'pain-producing substance' (PPS). It differs from 5-hydroxytryptamine in several aspects, and from bradykinin in its susceptibility to proteolytic enzymes. I have tested these substances in rats anaesthetized with ethanol and I found that their antidiuretic action is very variable when injected intravenously. For example, 5-hydroxytryptamine rarely produces a reduction in the urine flow in doses smaller than 5–10 μg./kg., often 20 μg./kg. or more are needed. When it is found that an antidiuretic substance is more potent by the subcutaneous than by the intravenous route, one should bear in mind that there are several ways in which the urine flow may be reduced such as pain, stress and nonspecific toxicity. I wonder also whether Professor Croxatto would have obtained oxytocic activity with less drastic extraction procedures.

Croxatto. Chymotrypsin destroys the oxytocic and antidiuretic activity of my extracts, which eliminates the possibility that it is due either to 5-hydroxytryptamine or to other non-peptide substances. We have found that simple treatment of plasma with hydrochloric acid (pH4) gives rise to oxytocic and antidiuretic activity.

Eisen. With regard to the specificity of this antidiuretic effect, I have noted that pain will produce an antidiuretic response in an animal with established diabetes insipidus following section of the supraoptico-hypophysial tract.

The storage and liberation of neurohypophysial hormones*

by

H. B. VAN DYKE, KARLIS ADAMSONS, Jr. and STANFORD L. ENGEL†

Department of Pharmacology, College of Physicians and Surgeons, Columbia University, New York

In all mammals the principal site of storage of the neurohypophysial hormones is in the posterior lobe of the pituitary body. Recently, as a result of the observations of Ranson and his co-workers, Verney, Harris and other investigators on the hypothalamic control of the liberation of the hormones as well as a renewed interest in the secretory activity of certain hypothalamic neurones (E. and B. Scharrer, Bargmann, and their collaborators), the distribution of the hormones in the hypothalamus has been carefully scrutinized, especially in the dog.

Early experiments suggested that differences among species may be considerable. Abel (1924) was perhaps the first to report that simple extracts of the hypothalamus contain vasopressor and uterine-stimulating substances. Abel used tissues of sheep. Later, van Dyke (1926) could detect only a minute amount of oxytocin in the tuber cinereum of the ox. In the same tissue of the dog Sato (1928) and Trendelenburg (1928) found more oxytocin than in the bovine tuber cinereum as well as a considerable amount of antidiuretic hormone; the quantities of both hormones in the tuber cinereum increased sharply after hypophysectomy. All subsequent work indicates that the hypothalamus of the dog contains more antidiuretic hormone than that of any other mammal. The information concerning other mammals is much less complete and includes observations, often fragmentary, on man, the macaque monkey, ox, camel, hog and rat. Table I summarizes these reports which are based upon assay-methods of varied reliability. The best-established figures are believed to be those for the dog. The proportion of total vasopressor-antidiuretic hormone in the hypothalamus is about 7 to 50 times as great in the dog as in other animals. A strikingly smaller proportion of the total oxytocin is in the canine hypothalamus which in this respect, although relatively rich in the hormone, resembles that of other mammals.

Peculiarities of the storage of the hormones in gross divisions of the hypothalamus are of interest. These are illustrated in Fig. 1 by a comparison between the dog and the camel based upon assays of the dissected tissues in our laboratory (van Dyke, Adamsons & Engel, 1955; Adamsons, Engel, van Dyke, Schmidt-Nielsen & Schmidt-Nielsen, 1956). All divisions of the hypothalamus of the dog were much

* The investigative work was supported by grants from the National Heart Institute of the National Institutes of Health (H-1788), U.S. Public Health Service and from the Lilla Babbitt Hyde Foundation.

† Research Assistant supported by a research grant (H-1788) from the National Heart Institute of the National Institutes of Health, U.S. Public Health Service.

TABLE I

The distribution of neurohypophysial hormones in the hypothalamus and posterior lobe of the pituitary*

Animal	Vasopressin		Oxytocin	
	Hypothal.	Post. lobe	Hypothal.	Post. lobe
	per cent.	per cent.	per cent.	per cent.
Dog	20·0	80	2·3	> 97
Dog [a]	15·0	85	8·0	92
Camel	0·4	> 99	1·2	> 98
Ox [a]	0·2	> 99	0·3	> 99
Hog [a]	0·5	> 99	0·5	> 99
Rat [b]	3·0	97	< 1·0	> 99
Monkey (Macaque)	0·4	> 99	——[c]	> 99
Man	0·7	> 99 [d]	——[c]	> 99 [d]
Man [a]	1·7	> 98	2·5	> 97

a Hild & Zetler, 1951 or 1952.
b S. Henry, unpublished.
c Less than 50 mU.; 6,700 mU. in posterior lobe of monkey.
d Two specimens; includes infundibular stem.

* Some results of Hild & Zetler are used in Table 1. The reliability of their methods of assay and the validity of their conclusion that vasopressin and antidiuretic hormone are different substances have not been accepted by van Dyke, Adamsons & Engel (1955). Their data alone are available for the hypothalamus of the ox and hog; their figures for vasopressin and antidiuretic hormone have been averaged on the assumption that the same substance had been assayed by two different methods.

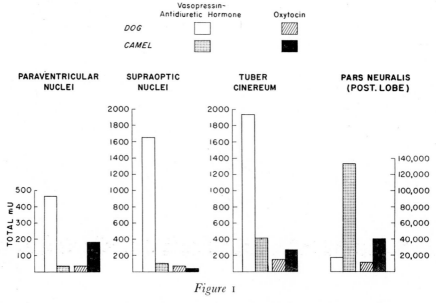

Figure 1

The distribution of vasopressin and oxytocin in the neurohypophysis of the dog and camel.
(Data of van Dyke *et al.* (1955) and of Adamsons *et al.* (1956).)

66

richer in vasopressin whereas, at least in the paraventricular nuclei, the camel tissue contained more oxytocin. The difference in the amount of oxytocin in the tuber cinereum of the dog and camel was not significant. The total amount of both hormones was, of course, much greater in the camel neurohypophysis owing to the much greater size of the posterior lobe (about 65 mg. after desiccation by acetone in comparison with 3·5 mg. for the dog).

The ratio of vasopressin to oxytocin in terms of the stored products in the hypothalamus and posterior lobe has an important bearing on theories concerning the secretion of the polypeptides. Information concerning the ratio of the two principles in several mammals is summarized in Table II; comparisons of the ratio in divisions

TABLE II

Approximate ratios (V/O) of vasopressin to oxytocin in the hypothalamus and posterior lobe

Animal	V/O in	
	Hypothal.	Post. lobe
Dog	17	1·5
Camel	1·1	3·3
Rat	5	1·3

V/O in the posterior lobe of the ox, hog, monkey and man (3 specimens) were 1·4, 1·1, 1·5 and 1·2 respectively.

TABLE III

Approximate ratios of vasopressin to oxytocin in divisions of the hypothalamus and posterior lobe

Animal	V/O in			
	Paraventric. nuclei	Supraoptic nuclei	Tuber cinereum	Posterior lobe
Dog	15	24	14	1·5
Camel	0·2	2·2	1·5	3·3

of the hypothalamus of the dog and camel will be found in Table III. The reader is warned that the ratios listed represent approximations, especially in the rat hypothalamus which contains only about 16 mU. of vasopressin and 3·4 mU. of oxytocin as average amounts.

According to the theory of neurosecretion, the neurones of the paraventricular and supraoptic nuclei secrete the hormones which migrate in or along their axones and are finally stored in the posterior lobe. It is said that a carrier substance, different from the hormones, serves for transport and is identified histologically by the chrome-alum-haematoxylin-phloxine stain (Hild & Zetler, 1953). Among the animals listed in Table II, the dog clearly differs from the other mammals in the very high ratio of vasopressin to oxytocin in the hypothalamus, 17, in comparison with the low ratio of 1·5 in the posterior lobe. (Vogt, 1953, reported V/O ratios of approximately 14 in the hypothalamus and of 1 in the posterior lobe of the dog.) No explanation of this discrepancy has been suggested by experiments. Miss Sarah Henry, working with canine or murine hypothalami and posterior lobes, incubated the tissues in various media but was unable to demonstrate a formation of either hormone or a conversion of one to the other *in vitro*. Great technical difficulties were encountered, especially in exact dissection. Vogt (1953) suggested that the site of elaboration of oxytocin might be in the posterior lobe or that its final synthesis might occur during its transfer in the axones terminating in the posterior lobe. Another possibility is that different neurones secrete vasopressin and oxytocin and that usually, except for vasopressin in the dog, final synthesis takes place in the posterior lobe. Lastly, it is conceivable that the transfer from the hypothalamus to the posterior lobe may be very rapid for oxytocin and slow for vasopressin in the dog whereas it is relatively rapid for both hormones in other mammals.

A comparison of the V/O ratios in the dog and camel in which estimates are based upon identical methods of assay is given in Table III. The very low ratio (0·2) in the paraventricular nuclei of the camel in comparison with about 15 in the dog suggests a high rate of secretion of oxytocin in these nuclei in the camel. This finding may be related to Olivecrona's (1954) conclusion, based upon briefly-described experiments, that the same nuclei in the rat 'regulate the production of oxytocin by the posterior lobe'. The V/O ratio in the posterior lobe of the camel pituitary, although clearly different from the dog and ox, is not exceptional. Ratios of 2 to 3 have been reported in the posterior lobe of the guinea-pig, rabbit, wallaby and finback whale and of 12·5 in the sperm whale. Even higher ratios have been found in foetal posterior lobes. (For references, see van Dyke, Adamsons & Engel, 1955.)

The investigations which have been made furnish no information concerning the rate of secretion of the hormones by hypothalamic neurones. A high rate of secretion could be associated with a rapid transfer to the posterior lobe and a low concentration in hypothalamic nuclei. Possibly a slow rate of transfer accounts for the exceptionally large quantity of vasopressor-antidiuretic hormone found in the dog's hypothalamus. If the quantity of hormone in the hypothalamus be taken as 1, the stored product in the posterior lobe is 4 for vasopressor-antidiuretic hormone and about 44 for oxytocin in the dog. In the camel, the corresponding figures are about 225 and 80 respectively. Other mammals appear to resemble the camel rather than the dog. Presumably the hormones found in the tuber cinereum represent secretions undergoing transfer to the posterior lobe.

The principal depot for storage is the posterior lobe. In only one mammal, the ox, is there information concerning stored hormones. Rosenfeld (1940), showed that the oxytocic and pressor activities of fluid pressed from posterior lobes behaved in the ultracentrifuge as if parts of one or more large molecules; after the fluid had been heated at a pH of about 4, the activities appeared to be small molecules sedimenting at a very much slower rate. A protein which could account for Rosenfeld's findings was isolated by van Dyke, Chow, Greep & Rothen (1942). It appeared to be a pure substance with a molecular weight of about 30,000. Constant antidiuretic, pressor and oxytocic activities were associated with this protein. One U.S.P. unit of each activity was about 60 micrograms or about one-thirtieth of the potency of the pure polypeptides isolated by du Vigneaud and his co-workers. It is not known what proportion of the total oxytocin and vasopressin in the posterior lobe of oxen is represented by this protein. The isolation of the pure substance was necessarily wasteful and only about 5 per cent. of the original activity could be recovered. Our present view is that a protein containing the polypeptides is stored in the posterior lobe of oxen. Antidiuretic hormone in the urine of dogs underwent sedimentation in the ultracentrifuge as if part of a large molecule; however, adsorption of the free hormone could not be excluded (Ames, Moore & van Dyke, 1950). The polypeptides are probably readily liberated from this protein by mild procedures. What proportions of the total active polypeptides are free or protein-linked is unknown although Rosenfeld's experiments suggest that the proportion of free oxytocin or vasopressin is low. The question of liberation of the hormones in response to physiological demands is another aspect of the problem.

How is the distribution of the hormones in the hypothalamus and posterior lobe modified by depletion of one or both hormones? Hild & Zetler (1953) and Zetler (1953) concluded that prolonged severe dehydration in the dog led to a marked depletion of vasopressin and antidiuretic hormone in both the hypothalamic divisions of the neurohypophysis and the posterior lobe. The reduction in the concentration of oxytocin was less striking. Their major conclusions from these and other experiments were (*a*) vasopressin, antidiuretic hormone and oxytocin are different hormones and (*b*) the rate of repletion in the hypothalamus is most rapid for oxytocin and slowest for antidiuretic hormone. Van Dyke, Adamsons & Engel (1955) criticized their methods of biological assay and disagreed with their conclusion that antidiuretic hormone differs from vasopressin. It is our belief that antidiuretic hormone and vasopressin are identical and that better confirmatory experiments will have to be performed before conclusions can be reached concerning the rates of repletion of oxytocin and vasopressin.

Dicker & Tyler (1953) reported that the ratio of vasopressin to oxytocin in the posterior lobe of several mammals rises during parturition and especially during lactation. For example in the dog V/O was found to be about 5·4 during lactation (4 dogs) in comparison with 1·0 in 8 normal dogs. We also have investigated the distribution and V/O ratio in the divisions of the neurohypophysis in lactating dogs. Results with 7 dogs were reported in 1955; recently the series has been expanded to 11 lactating dogs which as a group can be compared with a group of 12 normal dogs. Only in the posterior lobe was there a 'significant' fall in oxytocin (10,500 mU., normal, to 4,300 mU., lactating, $P = 0·0002$ and a rise in the V/O ratio (1.65, normal, to 3·52, lactating, $P = 0·002$). Antidiuretic hormone also was lower in the posterior lobe of lactating dogs (17,100 mU., normal, and 12,700 mU., lactating, $P = 0·05$). The amounts of hormones in divisions of the hypothalamus, *except* the supraoptic nuclei, fell in lactating dogs but the variability of the results prevented the reaching of satisfactory conclusions ($P = 0\cdot14$–$0\cdot18$ for oxytocin and $0\cdot10$–$0\cdot13$ for antidiuretic hormone). The ratio, V/O, was not altered in any division of the hypothalamus. The following conclusions are tentatively offered: (*a*) oxytocin and antidiuretic hormone are depleted from the posterior lobe of the lactating dog, (*b*) the depletion of oxytocin is the greater and (*c*) assays in sufficiently enlarged groups of normal and lactating dogs *might* demonstrate a depletion of antidiuretic hormone in the paraventricular nuclei and tuber cinereum but not in the supraoptic nuclei. Dicker & Tyler (1953) reported figures suggesting decreased storage of vasopressin in the posterior lobe of lactating rats, guinea-pigs and cats but not dogs.

Apart from experimental diabetes insipidus and extirpation of parts or the whole pituitary body, all other reports of depletion of the hormones experimentally are restricted to the posterior lobe. It appears that when severe depletion of one hormone is produced such as a fall in antidiuretic hormone with dehydration, the amount of the other hormone, oxytocin, also is greatly reduced.

Are both hormones liberated endogenously although the stimulus evoking their release appears to require only one? In a strict sense the answer appears to be affirmative and the evidence has been reviewed recently by Harris (1955). However, the liberated hormones, present in extremely minute amounts, are usually detected by their effects on target organs such as the kidney, the uterus or the lactating mammary gland. Exogenous vasopressin or oxytocin have been injected to mimic the effects of endogenous hormones. The estimates from such work suggest that although both hormones are liberated, the proportion of oxytocin released is very much higher despite the fact that teleologically vasopressin may be the hormone the organism requires under particular experimental conditions. Quantitative estimates of total amounts of released hormone or of the rate of release appear to be of little value if reliance be placed on assays of the hormones in the urine. No satisfactory experiments in which vasopressin and oxytocin have been simultaneously measured in blood, plasma or serum have been reported as a basis for deciding what amounts of the two hormones are liberated simultaneously. We have failed in numerous attempts to secure information from the blood plasma of the external or internal jugular veins of anesthetized dogs receiving intracarotid injections of large doses of drugs such as nicotine salicylate or morphine sulphate. Simple calculations reveal that relatively large quantities of hormones would have to be liberated if they are to be accurately determined in the jugular blood, even when this is restricted as far as possible to drainage of the brain. Blood of the cavernous sinus may contain a very high concentration of hormones (e.g. 16 mU. of antidiuretic hormone and 4 mU. of oxytocin per ml. of plasma), but a local injury of the posterior lobe or related structures has not been excluded.

New information is available concerning the mammalian distribution of the free neurohypophysial hormones which du Vigneaud and his colleagues isolated. The amino-acid sequences of oxytocin and the two vasopressins are shown in Fig. 2. In comparing the effects of lysine and arginine vasopressin, van Dyke, Engel & Adamsons (1956) discovered that purified natural lysine vasopressin, furnished by Professor du Vigneaud, differs from arginine vasopressin in only one important respect: it has a much lower relative potency as an *intravenous* antidiuretic agent than arginine

THE SEQUENCE OF AMINO ACIDS
IN NEUROHYPOPHYSIAL HORMONES

* $\overline{\text{CyS} \cdot \text{Tyr} \cdot \text{Ileu} \cdot \text{Glu}(\text{NH}_2) \cdot \text{Asp}(\text{NH}_2) \cdot \text{CyS}} \cdot \text{Pro} \cdot \text{Leu} \cdot \text{Gly}(\text{NH}_2)$

OXYTOCIN
Hog and Ox. Same in other mammals?

* $\overline{\text{CyS} \cdot \text{Tyr} \cdot \text{Phe} \cdot \text{Glu}(\text{NH}_2) \cdot \text{Asp}(\text{NH}_2) \cdot \text{CyS}} \cdot \text{Pro} \cdot \text{Arg} \cdot \text{Gly}(\text{NH}_2)$

ARGININE VASOPRESSIN
Camel, Cat, Dog, Macaque monkey, Man, OX, Rabbit, Rat & Sheep

* $\overline{\text{CyS} \cdot \text{Tyr} \cdot \text{Phe} \cdot \text{Glu}(\text{NH}_2) \cdot \text{Asp}(\text{NH}_2) \cdot \text{CyS}} \cdot \text{Pro} \cdot \text{Lys} \cdot \text{Gly}(\text{NH}_2)$

LYSINE VASOPRESSIN
Hog

* *Position of free amino group*

Figure 2

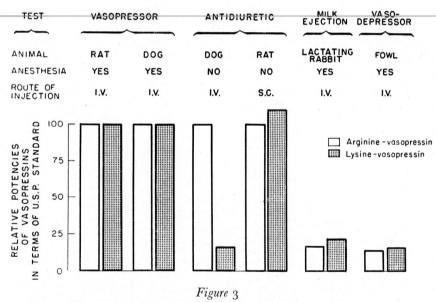

TEST	VASOPRESSOR		ANTIDIURETIC		MILK EJECTION	VASO-DEPRESSOR
ANIMAL	RAT	DOG	DOG	RAT	LACTATING RABBIT	FOWL
ANESTHESIA	YES	YES	NO	NO	YES	YES
ROUTE OF INJECTION	I.V.	I.V.	I.V.	S.C.	I.V.	I.V.

☐ Arginine-vasopressin
▨ Lysine-vasopressin

Figure 3

The relative potencies of arginine and lysine vasopressins. The vasopressor potency of each hormone in the rat or dog, in terms of U.S.P. standard, is given a value of 100 against which the other potencies are compared. Extracts of hog posterior lobe powder have the same relative potencies as highly purified lysine vasopressin.

vasopressin. The relative potencies of the two vasopressins are illustrated in Fig. 3. The highly purified vasopressins were obtained from the posterior lobes of cattle (arginine vasopressin) and hogs (lysine vasopressin) and there has been no similar product isolated from another species. By determining the relative potency of a posterior lobe extract as a vasopressor agent and as an intravenous antidiuretic agent, good pharmacological evidence can be presented that the vasopressin present behaves like arginine vasopressin or like lysine vasopressin. Such tests have been performed in extracts of the posterior lobe of the camel, cat, dog, hog, macaque monkey, ox, rabbit, rat and sheep, and of man. Only hog extracts had a relatively low antidiuretic potency when injected intravenously as if they contained lysine vasopressin; the extracts of all the other mammalian posterior lobes caused elevation of the blood-pressure and antidiuresis after intravenous injection as if they contained arginine vasopressin. Proof that the vasopressin of the mammals other than the hog is arginine vasopressin will have to await the isolation of the hormone from each species and the elucidation of its composition and structure as has been done for the arginine vasopressin of the ox.

SUMMARY

The distribution of neurohypophysial hormones in the hypothalamus and posterior lobe of the pituitary has been discussed. Such information can describe how the hormones are stored but does not indicate at what rate they are secreted or liberated. The dog, among the mammals studied up to this time, stores exceptionally large amounts of vasopressin (antidiuretic hormone) in the hypothalamus.

The stored hormones of the posterior lobe of the ox appear at least in part to be linked to a protein with a molecular weight of about 30,000. To what extent this is true of other mammals is unknown. The depletion of hormones stored in the posterior lobe, if severe, probably affects both hormones although the teleological requirement may be for only one hormone. Target-organ responses suggest that both hormones are always liberated but that the proportion of oxytocin is much higher. No successful simultaneous and quantitative determinations of both hormones in the blood have been reported.

One oxytocin and two vasopressins, one containing arginine, the other lysine, are known. Only the hog, among mammals investigated, appears to secrete lysine vasopressin.

REFERENCES

ABEL, J. J. (1924). Physiological, chemical and clinical studies on pituitary principles. *Bull. Johns Hopk. Hosp.* **35,** 305–28.

ADAMSONS, K. Jr., ENGEL, S. L., VAN DYKE, H. B., SCHMIDT-NIELSEN, B. & SCHMIDT-NIELSEN, K. (1956). The distribution of oxytocin and vasopressin (antidiuretic hormone) in the neurohypophysis of the camel. *Endocrinology* **58,** 272–8.

AMES, R. G., MOORE, D. H. & VAN DYKE, H. B. (1950). The excretion of posterior pituitary antidiuretic hormone in the urine and its detection in the blood. *Endocrinology* **46,** 215–27.

DICKER, S. E. & TYLER, C. (1953). Vasopressor and oxytocic activities of the pituitary glands of rats, guinea-pigs and cats and of human foetuses. *J. Physiol. (Lond.)* **121,** 206–14.

VAN DYKE, H. B. (1926). Die Verteilung der wirksamen Stoffe der Hypophyse auf die verschiedenen Teile derselben. *Arch. exp. Path. Pharmak.* **114,** 262–74.

VAN DYKE, H. B., CHOW, B. F., GREEP, R. O. & ROTHEN, A. (1942). The isolation of a protein from the pars neuralis of the ox pituitary with constant oxytocic, pressor and diuresis-inhibiting activities. *J. Pharmacol.* **74,** 190–209.

VAN DYKE, H. B., ADAMSONS, K. Jr., & ENGEL, S. L. (1955). Aspects of the biochemistry and physiology of the neurohypophyseal hormones. *Recent Progr. Hormone Res.* **11,** 1–41.

van Dyke, H. B., Engel, S. L. & Adamsons, K. Jr. (1956). A comparison of the pharmacological effects of lysine and arginine vasopressins. *Proc. Soc. exp. Biol.* (*N.Y.*) **91**, 484–6.

Harris, G. W. (1955). *Neural control of the pituitary gland.* London: Edward Arnold.

Hild, W. & Zetler, G. (1951) Über das Vorkommen der Hypophysenhinterlappenhormone im Zwischenhirn. *Arch. exp. Path. Pharmak.* **213**, 139–53.

Hild, W. & Zetler, G. (1952). Vergleichende Untersuchungen über das Vorkommen der Hypophysenhinterlappenhormone im Zwischenhirn einiger Säugetiere. *Dtsch. Z. Nervenheilk.* **167**, 205–14.

Hild, W. & Zetler, G. (1953). Über die Funktion des Neurosekrets im Zwischenhirn-Neurohypophysensystem als Trägersubstanz für Vasopressin, Adiuretin und Oxytocin. *Z. ges. exp. Med.* **120**, 236–43.

Hild, W. & Zetler, G. (1953) Experimenteller Beweis für die Entstehung der sog. Hypophysenhinterlappenwirkstoffe im Hypothalamus. *Pflügers Arch. ges. Physiol.* **257**, 169–201.

Olivecrona, H. (1954). Relation of the paraventricular nucleus to the pituitary gland. *Nature,* (*Lond.*) **173**, 1001.

Rosenfeld, M. (1940). The native hormones of the posterior pituitary gland: the pressor and oxytocic principles. *Bull. Johns Hopk. Hosp.* **66**, 398–403.

Sato, G. (1928). Über die Beziehungen des Diabetes insipidus zum Hypophysenhinterlappen und zum Tuber cinereum. *Arch. exp. Path. Pharmak.* **131**, 45–69.

Trendelenburg, P. (1928). Anteil der Hypophyse und des Hypothalamus am experimentellen Diabetes insipidus. *Klin. Wschr.* **7**, 1679–80.

Vogt, M. (1953). Vasopressor, antidiuretic and oxytocic activites of extracts of the dog's hypothalamus. *Brit. J. Pharmacol.* **8**, 193–200.

Zetler, G. (1953). Sind Adiuretin, Vasopressin und Oxytocin drei verschiedene Stoffe oder nur die Wirkungskomponenten eines einzigen Hormon-Moleküls? *Arch. exp. Path. Pharmak.* **218**, 239–50.

Discussion

Chairman : R. Gaunt

Dale. Did I understand Professor van Dyke to say that the ratio of vasopressin/ oxytocin for the ox gland was 1·5 : 1? This is difficult to understand, because by definition, one unit of vasopressin corresponds to the activity of 0·5 mg. of the standard dry preparation of ox pituitary posterior lobe; and the same amount corresponds to 1 unit of oxytocin; so that the ratio for the ox pituitary *must* be 1 : 1, and nothing else, unless it can be suggested that the International Standard Preparation does not contain and yield to extraction, oxytocin and vasopressin in the normal proportion.

van Dyke. Our conclusion depended upon the availability of pure, or nearly pure, oxytocin and vasopressin. Having these available we could then decide to what degree vasopressin has oxytocic activity and vice versa. Taking these facts into account we arrived at a ratio of 1·5 : 1.

Dale. It really involves re-definition of what is meant by a Unit?

van Dyke. That is correct.

Dale. That is a matter which quite frankly seems to me of rather serious importance.

Heller. Has Professor van Dyke compared the effects of intravenous injections of lysine and arginine vasopressin into rats as well as intravenous injections into dogs and subcutaneous injections into rats?

van Dyke. No. In our laboratory only Dr. Ames has had conspicuous success with intravenous rat assays. We find them too inconsistent and too time consuming.

Ginsburg. It would be interesting to see the effect of these vasopressins in the pig.

Dale. Could Professor van Dyke tell us whether he studied the residual oxytocic activity of his two vasopressins?

van Dyke. Both preparations have some activity when tested for milk ejection effect, and for vasodepressor activity in the fowl. There was no significant difference between the two preparations. They were not tested on the uterus.

Fromageot. Professor van Dyke said that the two vasopressins act differently: Lysine vasopressin depressed urine excretion very rapidly as compared with arginine vasopressin when tested on the same animals. Could this be an after-effect due to the arginine vasopressin being given first?

van Dyke. Usually there is a very abrupt fall in the first five minutes to maximum even if there have been preceding injections of either lysine or arginine vasopressin. The order of injections makes no difference.

O'Connor. Professor van Dyke has mentioned the probable nature of the material released from the neurohypophysis into the blood-stream, and referred to the findings of several different workers that it has a vasopressin-oxytocin ratio of 0·01 to 0·25. This is a possibility of great interest to those concerned with renal function as it would indicate that enough oxytocic activity may occur in the circulation to make the effect of oxytocin on the kidney of importance, particularly in relation to the excretion of sodium. It occurs to me that in all of the examples where this vasopressin-oxytocin ratio is so very low, the stimulus was one which produced the *rapid* release of large quantities of hormone, for example in dog the release of say 5 mU. in a minute, as opposed to the steady release of 0·1 to 0·3 mU. per minute which appears to be involved in the physiological control of renal function. Could Professor van Dyke tell us whether, at these slow steady rates of release, antidiuretic activity is set free into the blood-stream without contamination with something like a hundred times as much oxytocic activity.

van Dyke. The figures I quoted were from the literature and were not our own. We ourselves have found antidiuretic activity, together with oxytocic activity, in the blood drawn directly from the head; chiefly from the external jugular with other vessels tied off. The amounts produced are of little significance, because the doses of drugs used to cause release of hormones and injected into the carotid artery were unphysiologically high. I cannot answer your question, perhaps Dr. Walker can help us.

Walker. It is a little difficult to comment on your remark out of the context of my paper, but I think that the relatively high values which Dr. Bisset and I have been getting in the jugular venous blood of rats, may be partly due to the fact that we have taken rather large amounts of blood from both external jugulars and removal of blood has been shown by Ginsburg & Heller (*J. Endocr.* **9**, 274, 1953) to be a potent stimulus for the release of antidiuretic hormone.

Ginsburg. To return to Dr. O'Connor's point, there is another difficulty involved in the conception that oxytocin is always secreted in excess of vasopressin. Since the ratio of the hormones in the gland in undisturbed animals may be presumed to be constant, then the resynthesis of oxytocin would have to be many times faster than that of vasopressin, if it is released in larger amounts. This corollary to the proposition that small physiological stimuli also liberates excess of oxytocin is not easily accepted.

O'Connor. The amount of the hormone found in assays of the neurohypophysis is very large, representing several days' supply of hormone at the slow rates of release apparently involved in controlling renal function. This release may be only a small fraction of the total turnover in the gland and so whatever its vasopressin-oxytocin ratio, would have little effect in determining the nature of the material needed to maintain the hormone content in the gland.

Ginsburg. I do not agree with Dr. O'Connor. There must be a balance between the substances released and their repletion.

G. W. Harris. I wonder if Professor van Dyke would comment on the possibility that the different results we have heard, regarding the oxytocin-vasopressin content of the neurohypophysis in lactation, may be related to the suckling habits of the different species. Is it possible that the oxytocin-vasopressin relationships are not reduced in the cow or goat that are milked only once or twice a day, but are reduced in the rat and dog in which the litter is left with the lactating mother throughout the whole day and night? If the stimulus to release of oxytocin is, as seems likely, a sensory stimulus to the nipple by the suckling young, and perhaps also various conditioning reflexes set up by the presence of the young, then it might be feasible that more oxytocin is released if the litter is present with the maternal animal both day and night as compared with the release if milking is performed on only two occasions through the twenty-four hours.

van Dyke. I have no useful information to offer in reply to Professor Harris. It appears that the rather excessive depletion of hormones in our dogs represented the demand imposed by nursing. Our dogs and their litters were not carefully observed throughout the 24 hours of each day.

G. W. Harris. Were they with their litters continuously?

van Dyke. Yes.

Rossi. Unpublished experiments of Malandra (Istituto di Anatomia e Istologia Patologica, University of Pavia) have shown that, in water-loaded lactating rats, urine flow decreases significantly during the first hour after suckling and reaches normal levels after 3 hr. In lactating but non-suckling rats, with the same experimental treatment, there was no significant modification in urine excretion. It seems indicated therefore, when testing the neurohypophysial activity under these conditions, to consider carefully not only the duration of lactation but also the chronological relationship between the stimulus of suckling and the test.

Folley. Suckling under natural conditions by rats is not continuous but is interrupted by long periods of sleep, although of course, the suckling stimulus must be applied more frequently than in a goat. I would suggest that Professor Fromageot runs an experiment with two groups of rats, one with eight young and the other with say, only two young. In this way, the influence of varying degrees of suckling intensity could be studied.

Dale. Alternatively, the kids could be left with the goats all day.

Folley. In our herd we do not usually allow the kids to suckle after the first few days, but of course it could be done if necessary.

Dale. I think it pertinent to ask how these experimental goats are killed. Presumably they are not decapitated as is the case with the rat, so that one cannot, perhaps, be sure what is happening to the blood-supply of the head just at the time of killing.

Folley. In Mrs. Dodd's experiments the goats were killed with a humane killer, taking care to avoid damage to the pituitary.

Dale. That does not, of course, stop the supply of blood to the head immediately.

Folley. My colleagues who killed the goats will be able to answer that.

Fitzpatrick. In this connexion could we ask Professor van Dyke how his camel was killed. Could the procedure have influenced the results for the hypothalamus?

van Dyke. Possibly. The animal was killed by very rapid exsanguination: the great vessels near the heart were quickly severed.

Mrs. Dodd. I think it is important to consider the effect of the two forms of stimulation, namely demand-suckling by the pups and milking, on the vasopressin-oxytocin ratios. We wanted to know the influence of milking on the amount of oxytocin stored in the gland. As far as the goats were concerned, as soon as a humane killer was applied to the head, the carotid arteries were severed. The glands were dissected out extremely rapidly and were in acetone in 90 sec. to 4 min. from death.

van Dyke. In the dog we insert a needle into the heart, connect an indifferent electrode with the skin of the leg, and kill by inducing ventricular fibrillation with electrical stimuli.

The metabolism and fate of the neurohypophysial principles

by

H. HELLER
Department of Pharmacology, University of Bristol

In a paper published in 1909, H. H. Dale showed that the intravenous injection of posterior pituitary extracts into cats resulted in the excretion of a pressor substance and concluded that 'the active principle is excreted in the urine'. Twenty-six years later Larson (1935) in a short note in the *Journal of Pharmacology* reported that the oxytocic as well as the pressor activity of posterior pituitary extracts was eliminated by the kidneys of anaesthetized cats and dogs and Heller & Urban (1935) in the same year showed that the urine of conscious rats into which posterior pituitary extract had been injected intravenously acquired a pronounced antidiuretic action. Larson had found that amounts varying from 12·8 to 37·7 per cent. of the initial dose were excreted; and Jones & Schlapp (1936) in similar experiments on cats concluded that, on the average, 28 per cent. of the pressor activity appeared in the urine.

It was clear from these and later investigations (Heller, 1937; Ingram, Ladd & Benbow, 1939; Larson, 1939) that—irrespective of the species or dose used—only a part of the injected activity is eliminated. What is the fate of the unexcreted portion? Is it destroyed and if so in which organ or organs of the mammalian body? The solution of this problem which does obviously imply the quantitative estimations of the neurohypophysial principles, i.e. of peptide hormones in body fluids and tissues, meets formidable technical difficulties. Chemical estimation of the active octapeptides is—in spite of the great advances made by du Vigneaud, Fromageot and their co-workers—as yet hardly a practical possibility. The use of 'labelled' hormones has many limitations (discussed by Sonenberg & Money, (1955) in connexion with the anterior pituitary hormones). It remains therefore to measure distribution and inactivation of the posterior pituitary principles by biological assay. But it cannot be determined by biological assay of impure preparations whether one is dealing with small amounts of a very active substance or larger amounts of a less active derivative.

THE STATE OF ENDOGENOUS AND EXOGENOUS POSTERIOR PITUITARY PRINCIPLES IN BLOOD AND URINE

The form or forms in which the active polypeptides are secreted into the blood is unknown. Nor do we know in what form the native hormones circulate. There are several possibilities: Gomori-positive substance has been seen in the blood vessels of the posterior lobe of the giraffe (Hanström, 1952), the rat (Rothballer, 1953), and the dog (Scharrer & Scharrer, 1954). Do the hormones reach the blood linked with a

Gomori-stainable carrier substance? Or are they liberated into the circulation as the large-molecular compound which has been investigated by van Dyke, Chow, Greep & Rothen (1942) and Acher & Fromageot (1955)? Or is the inert protein to which —as Professor Fromageot told us this morning—the active peptides may be bound in the gland part of the secretory material? There is the further possibility that the peptides as such are released into the pituitary venous outflow. But the release of the free polypeptides would not necessarily mean that they also circulate as small-molecular compounds. Arrival in the blood may only involve a change of carrier—the peptides attaching themselves to one or the other of the plasma proteins. The work of Bennhold, Ott & Wiech (1950), Jancsó (1955), Goldstein (1949) and others has by now familiarized us with the carrier function of plasma protein and at least one other hormone, namely thyroxine has recently been shown to circulate bound to a plasma globulin (Albright, Larson & Deiss, 1955).

Binding of vasopressin and oxytocin by plasma protein is suggested by the finding (de Wesselow & Griffith, 1934; Broun & Scheiner, 1935; Levitt, 1936; Heller, 1937; Croxatto, Andrade & Barnafi, 1952) that the ultrafiltrability of the neurohypophysial principles is decreased when posterior pituitary extracts are mixed with blood. It would also appear (Ginsburg & Heller, 1953a) that in the living animal the diffusion of vasopressin into the extravascular fluid phase (other than into that of the kidneys or organs of the splanchnic vascular area) is very slow. This would not be expected of a compound of the molecular weight of about 1100. Moreover, Ames, Moore & van Dyke (1950) have found that the antidiuretic principle in the urine of dogs whose posterior pituitary had been stimulated by dehydration or the intracarotid injection of hypertonic sodium chloride solution, undergoes sedimentation in the ultracentrifuge and that it can only partially be removed by pressure dialysis. Similar results were obtained with urine of kangaroo rats (Ames & van Dyke, 1950). Ham & Landis (1942) may have also been dealing with this large-molecular compound or aggregate (see also Harris, 1948) and Aujard, Csanyi & le Breton (1955) have recently reported on the presence of a non-dialysable oxytocic substance in the urine of a variety of mammalian species. These findings suggest that some of the neurohypophysial activity released may reach the urine as a large-molecular compound. This compound may be the same as that isolated by van Dyke and by Fromageot from the posterior pituitary lobe but it has not been excluded that the small amounts of protein which normally escape into the urine (Rather, 1952) are sufficient to act as carrier for the neurohypophysial peptides.

Sufficient has been said to indicate that we are not certain whether injected vasopressin and oxytocin circulate in the same form or state as the endogenous hormones. And this in turn implies that results obtained with purified hormone preparations are not necessarily of physiological significance.

THE INACTIVATION OF THE POSTERIOR PITUITARY PRINCIPLES BY BLOOD

The inactivation of neurohypophysial extracts by 'blood' *in vitro* has been investigated by numerous investigators. The results are divergent and even contradictory, mainly perhaps because the difference between using whole blood or serum or plasma has not been realized. There are other factors which may have to be watched: for instance it has been shown (Jones & Schlapp, 1936; Page, 1946; Croxatto *et al.*, 1952) that lacked blood corpuscles inactivate the posterior principles; haemolysis may therefore influence the results. So may dilution of the medium, considering for example the recent finding of Miles & Wilhelm (1955) that simple dilution with isotonic sodium chloride solution causes the activation of a proteolytic system in guinea-pig serum. Nevertheless one important fact seems to emerge from all these investigations: *In vitro*, both the pressor-antidiuretic and the oxytocic activities of posterior pituitary preparations disappear much more rapidly from serum (Heller & Urban, 1935; Werle & Kalvelage, 1941; Birnie, Eversole, Boss, Osborn & Gaunt, 1950; Dicker & Ginsburg, 1950) than from plasma (Jones & Schlapp, 1936; Dicker & Ginsburg,

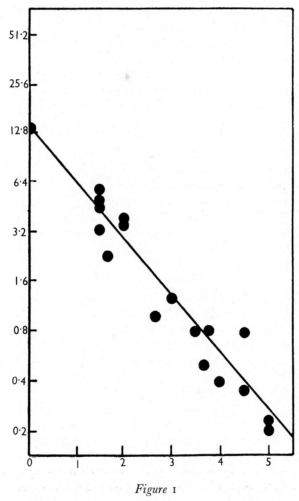

Figure 1

Concentration of vasopressin in arterial blood following the intravenous injection of 100 mU. Pitressin/100 g. into anaesthetized rats. Ordinate, concentration of vasopressin on a logarithmic scale (mU./ml.). Abscissa, time after injection in minutes. (Ginsburg & Heller, 1953*b*.)

1950; Sawyer, 1954). The endogenous activities behave similarly, i.e. they also are more stable in plasma than in serum (Birnie *et al.*, 1950; Ginsburg & Heller, 1953*a*).

It may be doubted whether these *in vitro* experiments with blood and its derivatives are of much physiological significance. Even if one disregards the fact that in many of them enzyme systems may have been at work which are not active in circulating blood, inactivation *in vitro* is too slow to account for the disappearance of a substantial fraction of neurohypophysial activities from the circulation. Figure 1 shows the rate of loss of injected antidiuretic activity from the circulation in the rat and Fig. 2 shows the results of incubating rat blood (containing 10 units of heparin per ml.) with vasopressin (Pitressin). Similar results had been obtained by Heller & Urban (1935) in rabbits, and in cats by Jones & Schlapp (1936) who measured both pressor and oxytocic activity. All these results were obtained in normal animals. It cannot be excluded that there are conditions in which the rate of inactivation in circulating blood is so high that a significant portion of injected or released posterior pituitary hormones is inactivated: Page (1946) has reported that an oxytocin-inactivating enzyme occurs in the plasma of women near term in such high concentration that 'half of any quantity of posterior pituitary hormone injected intravenously would be inactivated in 45 sec.'. His findings require confirmation.

INACTIVATION BY TISSUES AND TISSUE EXTRACTS IN VITRO

Since even the earliest investigators could show that the posterior pituitary activities were not or only very slowly inactivated by blood, it was reasonable to suspect that the hormones could be destroyed in the tissues. Experiments with suspensions and homogenates of organs of various laboratory species showed some loss of antidiuretic pressor or oxytocic activity in all instances (Heller & Urban, 1935; Larson, 1938; Christlieb, 1940; Birnie, 1953; Sawyer, 1954) but homogenates of small intestine, liver and kidney seem to be more potent than those of skeletal muscle, brain and non-pregnant uterus. Cell-free extracts of liver, kidney and spleen have also been shown to be effective (Heller & Urban, 1935; Jones & Schlapp, 1936; Eversole, Birnie & Gaunt, 1949; Miller & Townsend, 1954). Heating or boiling the tissue or extract decreased or stopped inactivation. Birnie (1953) has characterized the vasopressin inactivating system in liver homogenates to some extent; he found that its optimum activity was between pH 6·2 and 7·5, that the rate of inactivation increased appreciably with a rise in temperature from 0 to 37° C. but that it sharply declined when the temperature was raised further. The vasopressin inactivating principle was almost completely removed by adjustment to pH 5·2 or by half saturation with ammonium sulphate at pH 6·5. Addition of copper or zinc sulphate inhibited inactivation. Birnie made no claims as to the specificity of his inactivating principle and further work would be needed to establish it. The use of such terms as 'vasopressinase' or 'pitocinase' seems therefore premature. All the more so since *in vitro* the posterior pituitary principles can apparently be inactivated by several mammalian enzymes. Thus Croxatto and his co-workers (Croxatto, Croxatto, Illanes & Salvestrini, 1942–43) have shown that both vasopressin and oxytocin are inactivated by chymotrypsin and in the presence of cysteine by spleen aminopeptidase and kidney hypertensinase. Oxytocin is also destroyed by tyrosinase (de la Maza & Croxatto, 1944) and vasopressin by trypsin (Croxatto *et al.*, 1942–43; Lawler & du Vigneaud, 1953).

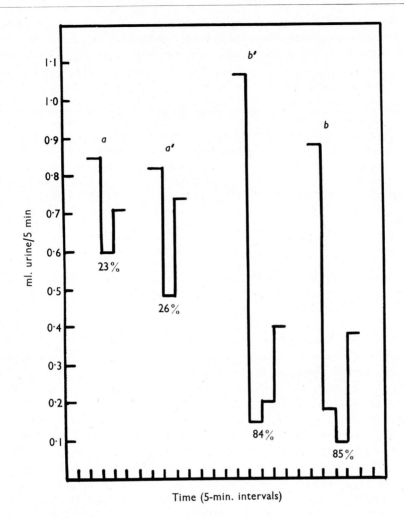

Time (5-min. intervals)

Figure 2

Incubation of rat blood (arterial) containing 10 units heparin and 1 mU. Pitressin per ml. for 30 min. at 38° C. Four-point antidiuretic assay of mixture by the method of Ginsburg & Heller (1953c): Unanaesthetized rat with jugular and bladder cannulae. *a* = i.v. injection of *non-incubated* mixture containing 100 μU. Pitressin; *a'* = same volume of *incubated* mixture; *b'* = i.v. injection of *non-incubated* mixture containing 300 μU.; *b* = same volume of *incubated* mixture. The figures above the abscissa indicate percentage antidiuresis. About 100 per cent. of the initial antidiuretic activity were recovered.
(Heller & Zaidi, unpubl.)

It may be worth stressing that results obtained with tissues *in vitro* may only have a very limited application to the fate of a substance in the intact animal. The reasons for this are not always sufficiently realized. Firstly, mechanical injury to cells by cutting, mincing or grinding is likely to release or activate enzymes. The rapid increase of amino-acid and peptide nitrogen recently demonstrated by Conway, Geoghegan & McCormack (1955) in ground rat kidney tissue may be mentioned as an example. Secondly, access and therefore perhaps velocity and/or completeness of inactivation of an added substance will, in the absence of transport by circulating blood or lymph, to some extent be dependent on the degree of dispersion of the isolated tissue, i.e. permeation of a test substance will differ in homogenates and in slices of the same tissue. Reaction velocity is probably also influenced by the release of permeability-increasing polypeptides liberated from tissues by short-term action of proteolytic enzymes (see Spector, 1951). Lastly the demonstration that an organ or tissue inactivates a substance *in vitro* can hardly be applied to the intact animal unless it has been shown that the substance whose fate one studies has access to that organ or tissue *in vivo*. That is to say, the organ or tissue 'clearance' for the substance has to be determined; for example there seems little sense in incubating a test substance with brain homogenates unless it can be shown that it penetrates the brain-blood barrier.

FATE OF THE NEUROHYPOPHYSIAL PRINCIPLES IN ORGANS IN SITU AND IN THE INTACT ANIMAL

Only one group of workers (Eser & Tüzünkam, 1950) seem to have estimated neurohypophysial activity after perfusion through an isolated organ. They reported that the antidiuretic activity of posterior pituitary extract in tyrode was reduced by 70 per cent. when circulated through guinea-pig liver for 3 hr.; less clear-cut results were obtained with kidneys. However, most workers interested in the fate of the posterior pituitary principles *in vivo* choose other techniques. Eversole, Birnie & Gaunt (1949) found that 40 mU. Pitressin injected into the spleen of hydrated rats inhibited water diuresis to a lesser degree than the same dose injected subcutaneously or intramuscularly; smaller doses failed to give clear results. Similarly, Møller-Christensen (1951) comparing the effects of intrajugular and intrasplenic injections of posterior pituitary extracts on the blood-pressure of anaesthetized rabbits and cats found that the latter were much less effective. These experiments are open to the objection that an injection into a tissue (even a parenchymatous one like the spleen) may not be comparable to an injection into the blood. It is therefore interesting that Mathe & Altman reported recently (1954) that small doses of vasopressin injected into the splenic vein of unanaesthetized dogs in water diuresis had the same effect on the urine volume and urine concentration as an injection into the saphenous vein. Figure 3 on the other hand shows an experiment of my colleague Dr. Ginsburg in which Pitressin had been injected directly into the portal vein. The doses used, although not influencing portal pressure significantly, raised the arterial pressure much less than the same doses injected into the femoral vein. It is difficult to believe that the dog and the rat handle vasopressin in so different a manner. More work is needed in both species.

In the rat evidence on the fate of exogenous and endogenous vasopressin obtained by a different approach is already available. Measuring vasopressin concentration in the blood by assays for antidiuretic activity, Ginsburg & Heller (1953*b*) could show in anaesthetized rats that tying of the coeliac and mesenteric arteries (which was demonstrated to cut the blood-flow through the liver by about 70 per cent.) retarded the removal of injected vasopressin from the circulation significantly. With the doses and under the experimental conditions used the splanchnic vascular area

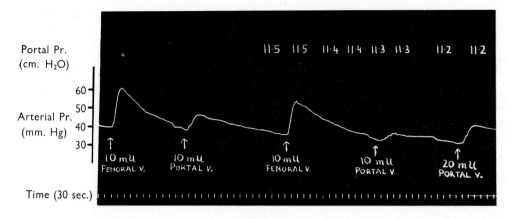

Figure 3

Comparison between the pressor effect of Pitressin injected into a femoral and into the portal vein. Rat, 250 g., urethane, dibenyline. Injection-needle inserted (not tied) into the portal vein. For further details, see text, p. 82. (Ginsburg, unpubl.)

accounted for at least 40 per cent. of the vasopressin cleared. These experiments did not make it clear which of the organ or organs of the splanchnic bed remove the hormone. But it would appear (Table 1) that the intestine removes none or very little of the endogenous antidiuretic principle and similar results (Ginsburg, 1956)

TABLE I

Antidiuretic activity of blood from the gastro-intestinal outflow
(Ginsburg, unpublished)

Experiment no.	Antidiuretic activity (mU./ml.) in blood from:	
	Abdominal aorta	Portal vein
1	0·30	0·32
2	0·19	0·14
3	0·37	0·52
4	< 0·04	< 0·04

All animals in pentobarbitone anaesthesia. Rat 4 was neurohypophysectomized. Vena cava tied below renal veins. Blood pressure maintained by compensation at 100 mm. Hg.

have been obtained with injected vasopressin. These results suggest strongly that in the rat the liver participates in the removal of vasopressin. However, it is not the only or perhaps not the main organ which 'clears' the neurohypophysial principles from the circulation. Experiments on nephrectomized rats (Ginsburg & Heller, 1953*b*) showed that the kidneys extracted about 50 per cent. of the injected antidiuretic activity. Crawford & Pinkham (1954) using a wide range of doses, and Dicker (1954) confirmed these results.

When both kidneys had been removed and the coeliac and mesenteric arteries had been tied, the clearance of injected vasopressin was only about 10 per cent. of that of intact rats (Ginsburg & Heller, 1953*b*) suggesting that organs other than the kidneys and those in the splanchnic circulation did not participate to any great extent in the removal of vasopressin. This agrees with results in animals whose blood level of endogenous vasopressin had been raised by ether anaesthesia: the antidiuretic potency of plasma obtained from the inferior vena cava below the renal and hepatic venous inflow was less than one-third of that of arterial plasma (Ginsburg & Heller, 1953*a*) which indicates that for the endogenous hormones also the kidneys and organs of the splanchnic vascular bed are major sites of clearance from the blood.

Assuming then that in the rat the kidneys and the liver remove the bulk of circulating vasopressin, how do these organs handle the hormones which they have cleared? There are obviously several possibilities. The hormone (either the polypeptide as such or a polypeptide-carrier complex) could be temporarily stored or reversibly bound, it could be excreted (into the urine or the bile), it could be

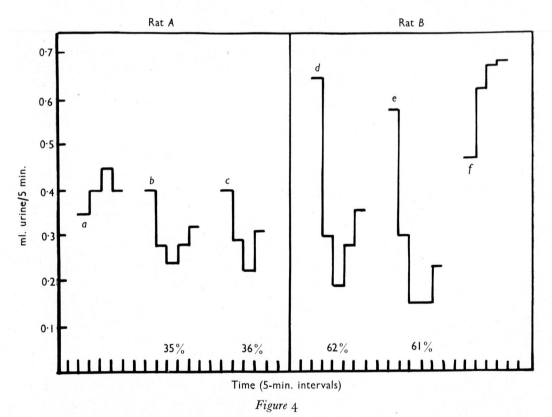

Figure 4

The antidiuretic effect of Pitressin added to 'acid ethanol' rat kidney extract. One ml. of extract was equivalent to 75 mg. wet kidney. Rat *A* : *a* = i.v. injection of 0·4 ml. kidney extract; *b* = 0·4 ml. extract containing 6·25 μU. Pitressin; *c* = 6·25 μU. Pitressin in 0·4 ml. 0·9 per cent. NaCl solution. Rat *B*: *d* = 100 μU. Pitressin in 0·3 ml. 0·9 per cent. NaCl solution; *e* = 100 μU. Pitressin in 0·3 ml. kidney extract; *f* = 0·3 ml. kidney extract. The figures above the abscissa indicate percentage antidiuresis. It will be seen that adding kidney extract did not alter the antidiuretic potency of Pitressin. (Heller & Zaidi, unpubl.)

irreversibly inactivated or a combination of these processes may apply. It has been mentioned that the injection of vasopressin results in the excretion of an antidiuretic (and pressor) substance in the urine, but experiments in rats (Ginsburg & Heller, 1953*b*) indicate that only a fraction of the activity cleared by the kidneys appears in the urine. Dr. S. M. A. Zaidi and I, in some recent experiments, have attempted to find an explanation for this descrepancy. We first extracted the kidneys of 'normal' rats, i.e. adult male animals which were not in water diuresis and which had been killed by decapitation, either with acid saline or by a method employing acid ethanol similar to that used by Vogt (1953) for the hypothalamus and Bisset & Walker (1954) for blood. It has the advantage that—when tested in rats—the depressor effect commonly obtained with aqueous extracts, is no longer seen. The antidiuretic effect of a given dose of vasopressin remains unchanged when added to such kidney extracts (Fig. 4) thus excluding the presence of antagonistic or potentiating substances. The mean recovery of vasopressin added to rat kidney homogenate (as estimated by 4-point assays for antidiuretic activity using a modification of the method of Ginsburg & Heller (1953*c*) was 79·7 ±3·49 per cent. with aqueous extracts, and 73·9 ±3·40 per cent. with alcoholic extracts. The mean recovery of small amounts (5 mU/kidney) of vasopressin injected into a kidney immediately after death was 90·9 ±8·23 per cent. However, as shown in Table II, no antidiuretic effect could be obtained with the

TABLE II

Antidiuretic assays of acid ethanol extracts of kidneys of normal rats

No. of extract	Sensitivity of assay rat to Pitressin in μU./animal	Volume injected* without antidiuretic effect (in ml.)	Maximum antidiuretic activity in both kidneys (in terms of mU. Pitressin)
I	6·25	0·8	< 0·23
2	6·25	0·8	< 0·23
3	6·25	0·4	< 0·46
4	6·25	0·3	< 0·62
5	6·25	0·3	< 0·62
6	6·25	0·3	< 0·62
7	6·25	0·4	< 0·46
8	6·25	0·4	< 0·46
9	3·13	0·4	< 0·23

* Total volume of each extract = 30 ml.

extracts of normal rat kidney. That is to say when expressed in terms of the limits of sensitivity of the assay, the kidneys contained much less than the equivalent of 220μU. (corrected for incomplete recovery) vasopressin per gramme kidney tissue. This does not suggest that the antidiuretic hormone is stored for long after it has been cleared by the kidney. Nor could any accumulation of activity be demonstrated in the kidneys of rats whose blood concentration of endogenous vasopressin had been artificially raised by ether anaesthesia (Fig. 5).

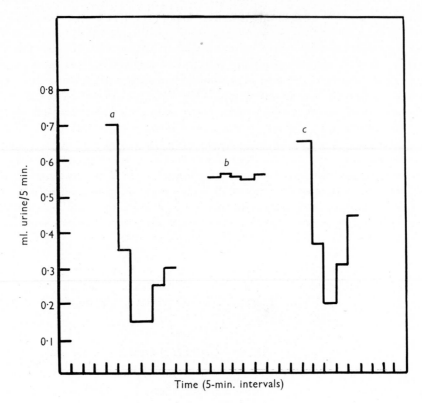

Figure 5

Absence of demonstrable antidiuretic activity in the extract of the kidneys of a rat anaesthetized with ether for 10 min. and injected with Pitressin (100 mU./100 g. body-weight) during the 7th min. of anaesthesia. Recipient rat unanaesthetized, jugular and bladder cannulae. *a* = 50 μU. Pitressin in 1·0 ml. 0·9 per cent. NaCl solution i.v.; *b* = 1·0 ml. kidney extract; *c* = 25 μU. Pitressin in 1·0 ml. 0·9 per cent. NaCl solution. Total volume of kidney extract = 20 ml. Hence, kidneys contained the equivalent of less than 0·5 mU. Pitressin. (Heller & Zaidi, unpubl.)

TABLE III

Unanaesthetized rats injected with 100 mU. Pitressin/100 g.
Antidiuretic activity of acid ethanol extracts of kidneys

Min. killed after injection	Percentage recovery of injected dose			
I	< 0·12,	< 0·12,	< 0·24,	< 0·24
3	0·20,	0·26,	< 0·12,	< 0·12
6	< 0·45,	< 0·20,	< 0·45	
12	< 0·50,	< 0·25,	< 0·25	
15	< 0·50,	0·09		

To study the fate of vasopressin in the kidney further, 100 mU. Pitressin per 100 g. rat—the same dose as that used by Ginsburg & Heller (1953*b*) in their clearance experiments—was intravenously injected into unanaesthetized rats, the animals killed at given times after the injection and the antidiuretic activity in their kidneys estimated. Table III shows the recoveries expressed as percentage activity of the dose injected: some small amounts of an antidiuretic principle could sometimes be recovered from the kidneys of animals killed 1 to 3 min. after they had been injected, but only traces from those killed after a longer interval. It appears then that the bulk of the 100 mU. or so which the kidneys of our 200 g. rats are likely to have removed from the blood was either excreted or inactivated or both within the first few minutes after injection. It would seem that both mechanisms are involved and that both operate with great rapidity: The results shown on Table III referred to extracts of kidneys from which pelvic tissue and ureters had been carefully removed. But when, post mortem, the ureters were tied at their junction with the bladder and

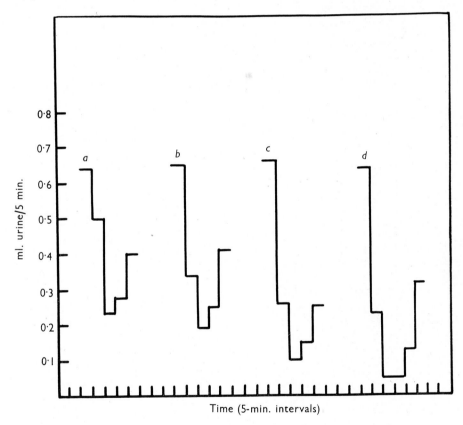

Figure 6

Antidiuretic assay of extract of kidneys (including pelves and ureters) of an unanaesthetized rat killed 3 min. after the injection of 100 mU. Pitressin/100 g. $a = 50 \mu$U. Pitressin i.v.; $b = 0\cdot2$ ml. kidney extract i.v.; $c = 100 \mu$U. Pitressin i.v.; $d = 0\cdot4$ ml. kidney extract i.v. All injections made up to same volume. The kidney extract contained antidiuretic activity equivalent to 4·1 per cent. of the dose of Pitressin injected into the donor rat. (Heller & Zaidi, unpubl.)

extracts were made of kidneys including 'pelvis' and ureter (i.e. when the dead space of the kidney was considered), quite substantial amounts of antidiuretic activity could be recovered. Figure 6 shows the results of such an experiment in which the rat was killed 3 min. after the injection of vasopressin. Further experiments showed that in that time small amounts of antidiuretic activity (0·39, 0·64 and 0·53 per cent. of the injected dose in 3 experiments) had also reached the bladder. The total recovery from renal tissue, ureters and bladder was equivalent to about 5 per cent. of the injected dose at a time when 25 per cent. or more of the injected dose had been removed by the kidneys. The very great rapidity of inactivation of vasopressin in the rat kidney thus indicated (which would be faster than the rate of inactivation observed *in vitro*; Dicker & Greenbaum, 1954; Zaidi, 1955; Heller & Zaidi, 1956) is perhaps less startling if one considers that 200 mU. of vasopressin (the order of total dose injected into our rats) represent only about 0·4 μg. in terms of the pure octapeptide. We cannot say in which tissue element the inactivating process occurs but experiments in which vasopressin was incubated with homogenates of the 'glomerular' and the 'tubular' fraction of rat kidney (prepared by

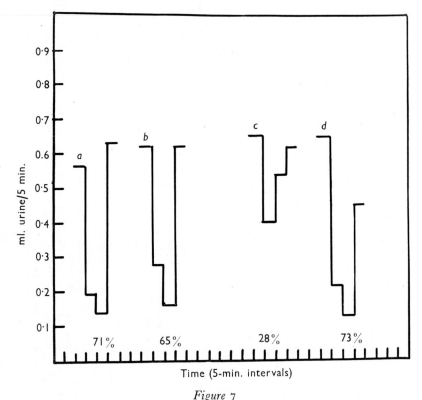

Figure 7

Effect of incubating Pitressin with the 'glomerular' and the 'tubular' fractions of rat kidney (see text p. 89) for 30 min. at 38° C. Antidiuretic assay. *a* = i.v. injection of 200 μU. Pitressin in glomerular fraction *after* incubation; *b* = 200 μU. Pitressin in glomerular fraction *before* incubation; *c* = 220 μU. Pitressin in tubular fraction *after* incubation; *d* = 220 μU. Pitressin in tubular fraction before incubation. The figures above the abscissa indicate percentage antidiuresis. The amount of Pitressin added to the fractions was proportional to the weight of suspended renal tissue. (Heller & Zaidi, unpubl.)

differential centrifugation of kidney suspensions according to Lowell, Greenspon, Krakower & Bain, 1953) suggest that the glomeruli are not implicated (Fig. 7).

Similar experiments as with kidney extracts were also done with extracts of rat liver. The mean recovery of vasopressin added to liver suspension was $88\cdot2 \pm4\cdot46$ per cent. Figure 8 shows that endogenous activity was also recoverable. However, no antidiuretic effects were obtained with extracts of the liver of normal animals indicating that the storage of antidiuretic hormone (if any) was less than about $70\,\mu U./g.$ liver. Table IV shows the results of antidiuretic assays of liver extracts of unanaesthetized rats injected with 100 mU./Pitressin/100 g. The animals were killed at intervals varying from 1 to 15 min. after the intravenous injection. Some small amounts of antidiuretic activity (equivalent to less than 1 per cent. of the dose given) were found in the livers of rats killed up to 3 min. after the injection but extracts of livers of

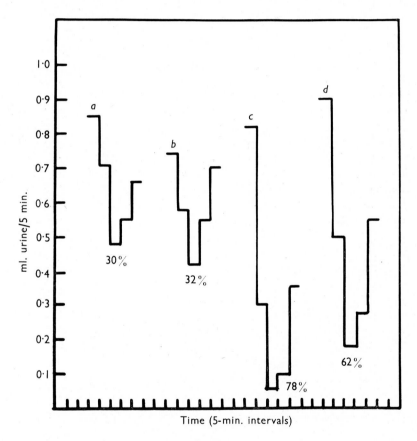

Figure 8

Recovery of endogenous antidiuretic hormone in rat plasma when added to rat liver suspension and extracted by the acid ethanol method. The plasma concentration of antidiuretic hormone was raised by anaesthetizing the donor rat with ether. Antidiuretic assay. a = o·2 ml. jugular plasma of rat anaesthetized with ether i.v.; b = o·2 ml. of extract of liver homogenate mixed with the jugular plasma (1 ml. extract was equivalent to 200 mg. liver plus 1 ml. plasma); c = o·4 ml. plasma; d = o·4 ml. extract. Percentage recovery of antidiuretic activity = 88·4. (Heller & Zaidi, unpubl.)

TABLE IV

Unanaesthetized rats injected with 100 *mU. Pitressin*/100 *g.*
Antidiuretic activity of acid ethanol extracts of liver

Min. killed after injection	Percentage recovery of injected dose			
1	< 0·47,	< 0·46		
3	0·61,	0·46,	< 0·43,	< 0·12
6	< 1·0,	< 0·43,	< 0·48	
9	< 0·48,	< 0·48		
12	< 0·50,	< 0·50		
15	< 0·52			

animals killed after 6 min. and later had no antidiuretic effect. If therefore—as indicated by the experiments of Eversole, Birnie & Gaunt (1949), Ginsburg & Heller (1953*b*) and the recent work of Ginsburg (Fig. 3)—the liver of our rats had cleared a substantial fraction of the injected hormone within that period it must be inferred that the retained vasopressin was rapidly inactivated.

It would thus appear from these investigations that in the rat, the kidneys and perhaps the liver are not only the main organs of vasopressin clearance but also major sites of the metabolic degradation of the hormone. Whether the kidney in addition to 'clearing' and inactivating vasopressin also excretes the unchanged polypeptide cannot be answered as long as we do not know whether inactivation in the tissue does give rise to breakdown products of the hormone with lower biological activity. The renal excretion of such a derivative has been postulated by Dicker & Greenbaum (1954).

The main basis of their claim is as follows: they infused vasopressin into rats anaesthetized with ethanol and found that the antidiuretic activity of urine collected from such animals remained unchanged after incubation with rat kidney slices but that it was almost entirely destroyed when incubated with liver slices. When the urine of a rat injected with vasopressin was infused into a second rat, the antidiuretic activity of the urine of the recipient 'was only about half that present in the infused urine'. They suggest that the kidneys and the liver in the intact rat behave like slices of these organs *in vitro*; in other words that half of the antidiuretic activity in the urine was destroyed by the liver and that the other half passed unchanged through the kidneys. Since rats infused with Pitressin excrete, according to Dicker (1954), only 3–28 per cent. of the injected dose the results of these experiments would be strongly in support of their thesis. They were therefore repeated. Table v shows one of our experiments. It will be seen that the recipient excreted 11 per cent. of the activity in donor's urine, i.e. the animal excreted much the same amount as if it had been infused with Pitressin. These results do not support Dicker's & Greenbaum's hypothesis.

TABLE V

Amount of antidiuretic activity excreted by a rat infused with
urine collected from another rat injected with vasopressin

Rat A:		
500 mU. Pitressin, i.v.	0·1 ml. urine A*	0·544 mU.
	Thus: 3·3 ml. urine infused into rat B had a	
	total antidiuretic activity equivalent to ..	17·952 mU.
Rat B:		
3.3 ml. urine of Rat A, i.v.	0·1 ml. urine B	0·056 mU.
	Thus: 3·55 ml. urine excreted by rat B had	
	an antidiuretic activity equivalent to ..	1·992 mU.

Result: Rat B excreted 11 per cent. of the infused activity.

* The volume of urine collected from rat A during and for one hour after the infusion was 4·0 ml. The urine was then made isotonic with a 0·9 per cent. NaCl solution which involved dilution to 5·0 ml. One portion (i.e. 1·3 ml.) of the diluted urine was used to estimate antidiuretic activity by the method of Ginsburg & Heller (1953c). It was found that rat A had excreted the equivalent of 27·2 mU. vasopressin or 5·44 per cent. of the infused activity. The remaining portion (= 3·3 ml.) was infused into rat B.

In view of our findings it seems preferable for the present to assume that the injection or the release of vasopressin results in the rapid excretion of small amounts of the unchanged hormone. But be this as it may, the problem of the intermediary metabolism of the posterior pituitary principles remains and is a challenge for future work. Such work is—in our opinion—desirable not only because of its intrinsic interest but also because the increasing number and importance of biologically active polypeptides raises the question of a common metabolic path of these compounds. Only one of them, namely insulin, has been investigated to a similar extent as vasopressin. The results indicate that as in the case of vasopressin, the kidneys and the liver are major sites of clearance and inactivation for intravenously injected insulin (Haugaard, Vaughan, Haugaard & Stadie, 1954; Elgee & Williams, 1954). The renal excretion of insulin, on the other hand, seems to be of much less importance than that of the posterior pituitary hormones.

There is a further reason for work on the metabolism and fate of the neurohypophysial hormones: some years ago, several groups of workers suggested that the impaired water diuresis, the oedema and the ascites in patients with liver cirrhosis were due or partly due to decreased inactivation of the antidiuretic hormone by the diseased liver. They based their hypothesis on the demonstration that liver homogenates or extracts inactivate vasopressin. They did not consider that it had also been shown (Jones & Schlapp, 1936; Larson, 1938; Christlieb, 1940) that homogenates of other tissues do this as well. Moreover, there seems to have been no hesitation to apply *in vitro* results with animal tissues to intact human beings. It seems to us that if an increase in the blood level of a posterior pituitary principle (or perhaps of any hormone) is to be ascribed to decreased inactivation, the organs or tissues which remove and metabolize the endogenous active principle should be known and that the quantitative aspect of the problem should not be neglected. Our results suggest that organs like kidney and liver *in situ* inactivate large doses of injected vasopressin with great rapidity. Pathological changes in these organs would presumably have to be very pronounced before their capacity to deal with relatively small quantities of the endogenous principle is critically lowered. It will also have to be seen to what degree a gradual decrease in the clearing and inactivating capacity of a diseased organ can be compensated in another site. I submit that only if approached in this comprehensive manner, can studies in the fate and metabolism of the neurohypophysial hormones be expected to be a valid aid to clinical research.

REFERENCES

ACHER, R. & FROMAGEOT, C. (1955). Chimie des hormones neurohypophysaires. *Ergebn. Physiol.* **48**, 286–327.

ALBRIGHT, E. C., LARSON, F. C. & DEISS, W. P. (1955). Thyroxine binding capacity of serum alpha globulin in hypothyroid, euthyroid and hyperthyroid subjects. *J. clin. Invest.* **34**, 44–7.

AMES, R. G., MOORE, D. H. & VAN DYKE, H. B. (1950). The excretion of posterior pituitary antidiuretic hormone in the urine and its detection in the blood. *Endocrinology* **46**, 215–27.

AMES, R. G. & VAN DYKE, H. B. (1950). Antidiuretic hormone in the urine and pituitary of the Kangaroo rat. *Proc.Soc. exp. Biol. (N.Y.)* **75**, 417–20.

AUJARD, C., CSANYI, E. & LE BRETON, E. (1955). Recherches sur l'activité ocytocique des urines. *Arch. Sci. physiol.* **9**, 71–82.

BENNHOLD, H., OTT, H. & WIECH, M. (1950). Uber den Bindungsunterschied lebergängiger und nierengängiger Substanzen an die Serumeiweisskörper. *Dtsch. med. Wschr.* **75**, 11–15.

BIRNIE, J. H. (1953). The inactivation of posterior pituitary antidiuretic hormone by liver extracts. *Endocrinology* **52**, 33–8.

BIRNIE, J. H., EVERSOLE, W. J., BOSS, W. R., OSBORN, C. M. & GAUNT, R. (1950). Antidiuretic substance in blood of normal and adrenalectomized rats. *Endocrinology* **17**, 1–12.

BISSET, G. W. & WALKER, J. (1954). Assay of oxytocin in blood. *J. Physiol. (Lond.)* **126**, 588–95.

BROUN, D. & SCHEINER, H. (1935). Contribution a l'étude de l'état physicochimique des hormones dans le sang. Diffusion du principe ocytocique hypophysaire dans le sérum du chien et des bovides. *C. R. Soc. Biol. (Paris)* **119**, 1379.

CHRISTLIEB, M. (1940). Über den Abban von Oxytocin und Vasopressin in vitro. *Arch. exp. Path. Pharmak.* **194**, 44–51.

CONWAY, E. J., GEOGHEGAN, H. & McCORMACK, J. T. (1955). Autolytic changes at zero centigrade in ground mammalian tissues. *J. Physiol. (Lond.)* **130**, 427–37.

CRAWFORD, J. D. & PINKHAM, B. (1954). The removal of circulating antidiuretic hormone by the kidney. *Endocrinology* **55**, 699–700.

CROXATTO, H., ANDRADE, F. & BARNAFI, L. (1952). Antidiuretic action of human plasma. *Acta physiol. Latinoamer.* **3**, 142–9.

CROXATTO, H., CROXATTO, R., ILLANES, G. & SALVESTRINI, H. (1942–43). *Rev. med. aliment.* (Chile) **5**, 300. Cited from Acher & Fromageot (1955).

CROXATTO, H., ILLANES, G., SALVESTRINI, H. & CROXATTO, R. (1942–43). *Rev. med. aliment.* (Chile) **5**, 226. Cited from Acher & Fromageot (1955).

DALE, H. H. (1909). The action of extracts of the pituitary body. *Biochem. J.* **4**, 427–47.

DICKER, S. E. (1954). The fate of the antidiuretic activity of Pitressin in rats. *J. Physiol. (Lond.)* **124**, 464–75.

DICKER, S. E. & GINSBURG, M. (1950). Some observations on the antidiuretic activity of rat serum. *Brit. J. Pharmacol.* **5**, 497–504.

DICKER, S. E. & GREENBAUM, A. L. (1954). The degree of inactivation of the antidiuretic activity of vasopressin by the kidneys and the liver of rats. *J. Physiol. (Lond.)* **126**, 116–23.

VAN DYKE, H. B., CHOW, B. F., GREEP, R. O. & ROTHEN, A. (1942). The isolation of a protein from the pars neuralis of the ox pituitary with constant oxytocic, pressor and diuresis-inhibiting activities. *J. Pharmacol.* **74**, 190–209.

ELGEE, N. J. & WILLIAMS, R. H. (1954). Degradation of Insulin—I^{131} by liver and kidney in vivo. *Proc. Soc. exp. Biol. (N.Y.)* **87**, 352–55.

ESER, S. & TÜZÜNKAM, P. (1950). La foie et l'hormone antidiuretique. *Ann. Endocr. (Paris)* **11**, 124–30.

EVERSOLE, W. J., BIRNIE, J. H. & GAUNT, R. (1949). Inactivation of posterior pituitary antidiuretic hormone by the liver. *Endocrinology* **45**, 378–82.

GINSBURG, M. (1956). Unpublished experiments.

GINSBURG, M. & HELLER, H. (1953a). Antidiuretic activity in blood obtained from various parts of the cardiovascular system. *J. Endocr.* **9**, 274–82.

GINSBURG, M. & HELLER, H. (1953b). The clearance of injected vasopressin from the circulation and its fate in the body. *J. Endocr.* **9**, 283–91.

GINSBURG, M. & HELLER, H. (1953c). The antidiuretic assay of vasopressin by intravenous injection into unanaesthetized rats. *J. Endocr.* **9**, 267–73.

GOLDSTEIN, A. (1949). Interactions of drugs and plasma proteins. *Pharmacol. Rev.* **1**, 102–65.

HAM, G. C. & LANDIS, E. M. (1942). A comparison of pituitrin with the antidiuretic substance found in human urine and placenta. *J. clin. Invest.* **21**, 455–70.

HANSTRÖM, B. (1952). Transportation of colloid from the neurosecretory hypothalamic centres of the brain into the blood vessels of the neural lobe of the hypophysis. *Kgl. Fysiogr. Sällsk. Förhandl. (Lund)* **22**, 1–5.

HARRIS, G. W. (1948). The excretion of an antidiuretic substance by the kidney after electrical stimulation of the neurohypophysis in the unanaesthetized rabbit. *J. Physiol. (Lond.)* **107**, 430–35.

HAUGAARD, N., VAUGHAN, N. M., HAUGAARD, E. S. & STADIE, W. C. (1954). Studies on radioactive labelled insulin. *J. biol. Chem.* **208**, 549–63.

HELLER, H. (1937). The state in the blood and the excretion by the kidney of the antidiuretic principle of posterior pituitary extracts. *J. Physiol. (Lond.)* **89**, 81–95.

HELLER, H. & URBAN, F. F. (1935). The fate of the antidiuretic principle of postpituitary extracts *in vivo* and *in vitro*. *J. Physiol. (Lond.)* **85**, 502–18.

HELLER, H. & ZAIDI, S. M. A. (1956). Unpublished experiments.

INGRAM, W. R., LADD, L. & BENBOW, J. T. (1939). The excretion of antidiuretic substance and its relation to the hypothalamico-hypophyseal system in cats. *Amer. J. Physiol.* **127**, 544–51.

JANCSÓ, N. (1955). *Speicherung. Stoffanreicherung im Retikuloendothel und in der Niere.* Budapest: Akadémiai Kiadó.

JONES, A. M. & SCHLAPP, W. (1936). The action and fate of injected posterior pituitary extracts in the decapitated cat. *J. Physiol. (Lond.)* **87**, 144–57.

LARSON, E. (1935). Tolerance and fate of posterior lobe pituitary extract. *J. Pharmacol.* **54**, 151.

LARSON, E. (1938). Tolerance and fate of the pressor principle of posterior pituitary extracts in anaesthetized animals. *J. Pharmacol.* **62**, 346–62.

LARSON, E. (1939). Fate of the injected oxytocic principle of posterior pituitary in anaesthetized cats and dogs. *J. Pharmacol.* **67**, 175–85.

LAWLER, C. H. & DU VIGNEAUD, V. (1953). Enzymic evidence for intrinsic oxytocic activity of the pressor-antidiuretic hormone. *Proc. Soc. exp. Biol. (N.Y.)* **84**, 114–16.

LEVITT, G. (1936). Problem of antidiuretic substance in the blood of patients with eclampsia and other hypertensive diseases with observations on spinal fluid. *J. clin. Invest.* **15**, 135–41.

LOWELL, D. J., GREENSPOON, S. A., KRAKOWER, C. A. & BAIN, J. A. (1953). Metabolic activity of renal cortical tubular epithelial cells. *Amer. J. Physiol.* **172**, 709–17.

MILES, A. A. & WILHELM, D. L. (1955). Enzyme-like globulins from serum reproducing the vascular phenomena of inflammation. I. An active permeability factor and its inhibition in guinea-pig serum. *Brit. J. exp. Path.* **36**, 71–81.

MILLER, G. E. & TOWNSEND, C. E. (1954). The *in vitro* inactivation of Pitressin by normal and cirrhotic human liver. *J. clin. Invest.* **33**, 549–54.

MATHE, G. & ALTMAN, J. (1954). Contribution experimentale a l'étude de l'inactivation hépatique de la Pitressin. *Presse Méd.* **62**, 983–5.

MAZA, J. DE LA, & CROXATTO, H. (1944). *Bol. Soc. Biol. (Santiago)* **2**, 23. Cited from Acher & Fromageot (1955).

MØLLER-CHRISTENSEN, E. (1951). Investigations on the inactivation of vasopressin in the liver. *Acta endocr. (Kbh.)* **6**, 153–60.

PAGE, E. W. (1946). The value of plasma pitocinase determinations in obstetrics. *Amer. J. Obstet. Gynec.* **52,** 1014–21.

RATHER, L. J. (1952). Filtration, reabsorption and excretion of protein by the kidney. *Medicine (Baltimore)* **31,** 357–80.

ROTHBALLER, A. B. (1953). Changes in the rat neurohypophysis induced by painful stimuli with particular reference to neurosecretory material. *Anat. Rec.* **115,** 21–41.

SAWYER, W. H. (1954). Inactivation of oxytocin by homogenates of uteri and other tissues from normal and pregnant rats. *Proc. Soc. exp. Biol. (N.Y.)* **87,** 463–65.

SCHARRER, E. & SCHARRER, B. (1954). Hormones produced by neurosecretory cells. *Recent Progr. Hormone Res.* **10,** 183–240.

SONENBERG, M. & MONEY, W. L. (1955). The fate and metabolism of anterior pituitary hormones. *Recent Prog. Hormone Res.* **9,** 43–82.

SPECTOR, W. G. (1951). The role of some higher peptides in inflammation. *J. Path. Bact.* **63,** 93–110.

VOGT, M. (1953). Vasopressor, antidiuretic and oxytocic activities of extracts of the dog's hypothalamus. *Brit. J. Pharmacol.* **8,** 193–6.

WERLE, E. & KALVELAGE, A. (1941). Über die Vasopressin inaktivierende Kraft des Blutes von Schwangeren und die Natur des inaktivierenden Prinzips. *Biochem. Z.* **308,** 405–12.

DE WESSELOW, O. L. V. S. & GRIFFITH, W. J. (1934). On the question of pressor bodies in the blood of hypertensive subjects. *Brit. J. exp. Path.* **15,** 45–52.

ZAIDI, S. M. A. (1955) Inactivation of vasopressin by the kidney. *J. Endocr.* **12,** 1P.

Discussion

Chairman: J. M. Yoffey

de Wardener. I am a little puzzled by the rapid disappearance of antidiuretic activity from the blood and the kidney parenchyma. The antidiuretic activity on the functioning kidney goes on 20–30 min. and even longer, yet the substance which is producing this change has disappeared from the blood and kidney in from six to seven minutes.

Dale. That applies to the pressor effect which also lasts for much longer than six or seven minutes.

Heller. I think there may be two explanations. We have been investigating the fate of relatively large doses of vasopressin but the amount needed to produce a biological effect—as has already been said this morning—is very likely to be measured in micro-units. Such small amounts of the hormone may still have been present in the tissues but we would not have been able to demonstrate them. Another explanation, of course, for which however I have no evidence, would be that the biological effect persists after the agent which elicited it has disappeared.

Gross. In connexion with other work on nephrectomized rats, we injected Pitressin and found an increase and prolongation of the pressor effect. Another polypeptide—angiotonin—did not give this reaction. We regard this as evidence in support of the view that Pitressin is inactivated by the kidneys.

Ginsburg. This is extremely interesting and odd because I have observed pressor responses to Pitressin in nephrectomized rats and did not get a prolongation of the effect.

I thought that the reason might be that a significant part of the vasopressor effect of the Pitressin was due to vasoconstriction in the kidneys, and although I had eliminated one of the organs by which the Pitressin is cleared, I had also removed one through which its pressor effect is exerted.

Gross. How long was this after you had taken out the kidneys?

Ginsburg. Less than 30 min.

Gross. We did it the day before.

Ginsburg. It does not make it any clearer.

Grose. Which dose did you use?

Ginsburg. About 10 or 15 mU.

Fromageot. There are several reactions by which the antidiuretic hormone may be inactivated. It may be subject to proteolysis or deamination, or to inactivation by the oxidation of SH groups or the tyrosine residues. I would like to ask Professor Heller about the conditions of his inactivation experiments. Were they carried out in the presence or absence of air? If air was present, was the supply of it adequate to permit oxidation?

Heller. We have not investigated the chemistry of the inactivation process but we have considered some of the possibilities you have mentioned. With regard to your second question, most of the *in vitro* experiments were done at 37° to 38° C. under aerobic conditions, but the tubes were neither shaken nor were their contents stirred with oxygen.

Croxatto. I would like to put a question regarding the vasopressinase and oxytocinase. When you are referring to extracts of tissues, I agree that you are not dealing with specific enzymes, but it is a different thing when we are dealing with the blood of pregnant women. In this case the inactivating potency may be due to a specific enzyme. We have seen only small change in the hypertensinase activity although the vasopressinase and oxytocinase activities increase very much in the last month of pregnancy.

Heller. I think perhaps that Professor Croxatto has misunderstood me. There can be no doubt about the physiological significance of the enzymes or enzyme systems mentioned, and it may be convenient to talk of vasopressinase, but I would rather reserve this name for an enzyme whose specificity has been clearly demonstrated. As to calling an enzyme 'Pitocinase': I don't believe that Nature has gone to the trouble to produce an enzyme with inactivates solely a preparation of Parke, Davis and Co.

Wirz. I have a question which I might as well ask here as it doesn't fit in with any other topic to be discussed. I have been asked for advice in Basle about a case of diabetes insipidus which does not respond to Pitressin. One might think of an increased rate of destruction of the Parke, Davis preparation, but does Professor Heller or anyone else know what to do about such a patient? What is the explanation for this condition and what are the therapeutic possibilities? It is an infant of five months which has to be maintained on a constant infusion. If the infusion stops for some reason the child is quite feverish the next morning.

Heller. These cases are rare but a number of them have been described and they seem to be genetically determined. Williams & Henry (*Ann. int. Med.* **27**, 84, 1947) have investigated the possibility of increased inactivation of vasopressin, but I don't think that their experiments were quite decisive. Judging from the amount of hormone which can be inactivated in normal rats in a very short time, it seems unlikely that increased inactivation is the trouble. It seems much more likely that the defect is in the kidney which cannot respond to vasopressin in the normal manner.

Gaunt. Has the steroid production been determined in this infant? One can get high Pitressin resistance from chronic administration of steroids.

Lloyd. We have studied a child like this. I think first one must establish that a Pitressin-fast individual does not respond to a large dose given intravenously. We have seen a number of cases of diabetes insipidus in which the patient became refractory to intramuscular or intranasal administration, but responded when it was given intravenously. As Dr. Gaunt says, we have studied one patient in particular who had a corticosteroid excretion which was three times higher than normal when he was requiring very large amounts of Pitressin. A year later, for some reason, he was requiring much less and corticosteroid secretion was then within the normal limits. The major problem in the child with 'nephrogenic' diabetes insipidus is that posterior pituitary substance is ineffective. A decrease in solute intake will produce a modest decrease in urine volume. Apart from this all you can do is to keep them on water day and night.

Ginsburg. I have often wondered whether the uptake of Pitressin by the kidney is related to its antidiuretic action. It might be a good idea to test this in a case such as we are now discussing by finding out whether a higher proportion of the injected dose is excreted in the urine.

Heller. Dr. Darmady tells me that he has dissected the tubules in a case of vaso-pressin-resistant diabetes insipidus and that, at least, microscopically, he could find no difference between the tubules of such a child and those of a normal child. That of course does not necessarily mean that they were functionally normal.

de Wardener. One thing about these children is that if they do get very dehydrated they can apparently concentrate the urine to a specific gravity of 1,023.

Wirz. No, in our case it was not as high as that, about 1,016, but I don't know how far they went with the dehydration.

Yoffey. I wonder if anyone has ever tried coupling the polypeptides with a fluorescent molecule?

Heller. No, this has not been done with posterior pituitary hormones but it seems a very useful suggestion.

The excretion of posterior pituitary principles in the urine

by

R. L. NOBLE

Collip Medical Research Laboratory, University of Western Ontario, London, Canada

ONE of the less direct approaches for obtaining evidence of the participation of the neurohypophysis in physiological processes has been the study of the excretion of antidiuretic substance (ADS) in the urine. From a consideration of the numerous conflicting reports in the literature of the multiplicity of clinical conditions which reputedly are associated with large amounts of antidiuretic hormone in the urine, one forms the impression that either the posterior pituitary is associated with innumerable metabolic processes in the body, or more reasonably, that the methods used for extraction of the urine have been highly inadequate and non-specific. Some years ago various extraction methods were attempted in the laboratory in London of Sir Charles Dodds. At this time it was found that such procedures as dialysis or precipitation yielded extracts which gave highly erratic and poor recoveries (Noble, Rinderknecht & Williams, 1938). These inconsistencies are now realized to be related to whether or not the active molecule will dialyse at a uniform rate through various membranes, and if it can be quantitatively extracted off the membrane when it does not dialyse (Walker, 1939; Schaffer, Cadden & Stander, 1941; Ames, Moore & van Dyke, 1950). As a result, however, of such unsatisfactory studies, a new method of extraction of urine was explored and published in 1939 (Noble, Rinderknecht & Williams).

This method, employing the principle of adsorption of the active principle on zinc ferrocyanide, was found to yield a good recovery of antidiuretic hormone after it was added to urine; but the method was not used in serious attempts to study posterior lobe function.

More recently a continuation of the study of extraction methods has been made by Dr. Taylor and Dr. Jessup, and these have been applied in the study of neurohypophysial function. Initially, I would like to discuss the zinc ferrocyanide method of extraction and later include some preliminary observations on what we believe is a new improved method. During the years which we have been using this first method of extraction we have realized that we were stumbling over obstacles of an ill-definable nature, hidden in a morass of impurities which could not be clarified until an appreciation of the properties of the isolated and identified active principles was accomplished. These more primitive observations therefore left us exposed to the criticism of non-specificity of the extraction method. These shortcomings have been appreciated to the extent that these experiments have had to be stripped down and the results expressed in the barest and most conservative form. They are familiarly referred to in the laboratory as the 'BVD' or 'BDV' type of experiment—implying of course their crudity and non-specificity, since they were 'Before van Dyke' and 'Before du Vigneaud'.

The zinc ferrocyanide method, which can only be profitably applied to urine, consists of the formation of a voluminous flocculent precipitate resulting from the addition and interaction of sodium ferrocyanide and zinc sulphate, which at an acid pH adsorbs posterior lobe hormones. They can then be eluted from the separated precipitate by ammoniacal ethanol. After concentration, impurities may be precipitated by high concentrations of ethyl alcohol. The final aqueous extract, when concentrated to 5 or 1 per cent. of the original volume of urine, (which is always adjusted to a constant specific gravity of 1,010) is a dark brown homogeneous mixture from which the only thing we have isolated is urea. Surprisingly enough, however, the recovery by this method of antidiuretic hormone added to urine is satisfyingly constant and gratifyingly high. (Noble & Taylor, 1953.)

In an experiment to depict the effectiveness of this extraction process, from 1 to 10 U. of the vasopressor principle may be added to 3 l. of urine (Noble, Plunkett & Taylor, 1950). For comparative results extraction is made of this urine sample as well as from a control aliquot of urine but without added antidiuretic hormone. The hormone preparation is then added to the final extract of the control urine and the samples assayed. Using the Burn method of assay and administering the extracts by either subcutaneous or intraperitoneal injection it is found that the difference between the activities of extracts to which antidiuretic hormone was added before and after extraction is about 15 per cent. A recovery of over 80 per cent. therefore, is consistently experienced.

Such an experiment in addition demonstrates a curious feature which is consistently shown with extracts of urine. When tested by subcutaneous injection the total apparent recovery is found to be increased by a factor up to 5. This effect is apparently related to augmenting substances in the extract which, by prolonging absorption, result in an increased sensitivity of the method by some 5 times. Fortunately, this augmentation is constantly shown by urine extracts, so that by using suitable control urine solutions with graded amounts of antidiuretic hormone added after extraction it is still possible to obtain quantitative data. Intraperitoneal injections are not followed by such marked augmentation and may be used for a direct comparison with a standard dose response curve for approximate quantitative assays (Noble, Plunkett & Taylor, 1950).

Concentrated extracts of urine, however, when injected either intraperitoneally or subcutaneously may, because of their high salt content or general toxicity, result in a non-specific antidiuresis. This is presumably due to liberation of endogenous antidiuretic hormone or to renal circulatory changes. Such fractions will not cause non-specific antidiuresis if tested in the small doses required for intravenous techniques. Comparative tests of this nature have led to the belief that results obtained by using subcutaneous injections in rat assay methods are open to serious criticism.

For an accurate interpretation of results, therefore, it is necessary to appreciate that extracts containing antidiuretic hormone will show erroneously high activity if given subcutaneously when compared with a standard dose response curve for antidiuretic hormone (instead of a curve established using a control extract with added antidiuretic hormone). In addition, intraperitoneal or subcutaneous injections of a concentrated extract devoid of antidiuretic hormone may be followed by an anti-diuresis due to toxic substances, or a high salt content. Because of such factors van Dyke (van Dyke, Adamsons & Engel, 1955) has stressed that all assays of extracts or body fluids not rich in antidiuretic hormone should be assayed by an intravenous technique. One property of urine extracts, however, has suggested that they may not be suitable for intravenous assay of the antidiuretic hormone. When such extracts of urine from any source are given intravenously they show a marked and sustained pressor action similar to that shown by vasopressin. The degree of pressor activity, when compared with antidiuretic activity, precludes the possibility that the action is due to the antidiuretic hormone and in addition, the pressor substance is resistant to heat at pH = 10 (Noble, Plunkett & Taylor, 1950). It is possible that this pressor contaminant may be piperidine (von Euler, 1945), or more likely, the substance studied by Dekanski (1951). Since extracts of urine therefore exert a pressor effect when given intravenously it was feared that this would result in an antidiuresis from a non-specific effect on renal circulation. It is possible that this belief is ill-founded, and Dr. Taylor and his collaborators are presently engaged in testing urine extracts by a modified Dicker (1953) technique.

Assays to be reported in this paper, therefore, have all been performed on the basis of the method of Burn (1937) and the rats injected by the subcutaneous or intra-peritoneal route. An adapted modification in the use of the fed rather than the starved rat is, however, of some interest (Jessup & Taylor, 1954). Apparently the starved animal, even though having access to water, becomes partially dehydrated and has endogenous liberation of antidiuretic hormone. As a result the induced water diuresis starts more slowly and is more variable than that obtained by using fed animals, and in addition the preparation is less sensitive to antidiuretic hormone. An added feature of using fed animals is that they may be used every second or third day for assay purposes.

Using the described extraction method and means of assay, what is the evidence which led us to believe that it would be possible to use the results of urine assays in an interpretation of posterior lobe function, even though the active substance could not be positively identified as the active factor of the extracts? Again, one may question whether because antidiuretic hormone added to urine may be recovered by a certain extraction method, there is any assurance that the hormone excreted under physiological conditions is in the same form so that it also would be extracted? Certainly Heller (1937) has demonstrated that posterior lobe hormone may be 'bound' or adsorbed in some fashion by body fluids, and something of a similar nature might occur in urine. Information on these problems may be derived from two differ-ent types of experiments. The first concerns the appearance of extractable ADS in the urine of humans immediately after the intravenous injection of the hormone, and the second the gradual increase of antidiuretic activity in the urine of rats and human subjects with increasing dehydration. The study of such conditions associated with an excretion of ADS in the urine is of course in no way an original contribution, but is now an accepted conclusion drawn from published experiments in which many of you here today have collaborated.

In the first experiments Dr. Taylor was fortunate in being able to collaborate with

Dr. O. G. Edholm, who was studying the effects of injections of posterior pituitary extracts and of haemorrhage under various controlled conditions on certain cardiovascular responses in man. In 9 cases 'Pitressin' in doses of 2 to 5 units was given intravenously. The equivalent of 200 to 400 c.c. of urine from these individuals before injection was found to have no antidiuretic activity when extracted by the zinc ferrocyanide method. Following the intravenous injection of Pitressin, however, all subjects showed extractable antidiuretic activity in the urine over the next 4 hr. Quantitatively, the amount of antidiuretic activity excreted and extracted averaged approximately 13 per cent. of that injected, but varied in different individuals from 4·5 to 30 per cent (Noble & Taylor, 1953). Others have obtained a 5 per cent antidiuretic activity from extracts of urine prepared by the zinc ferrocyanide method after the intravenous administration of up to 1·5 units in humans, and believed that the method recovered 81 per cent of antidiuretic hormone when added to urine (Burn & Singh Grewal, 1951).

Following mild dehydration in humans which follows the withholding of free fluid in the diet, there is an excretion of ADS in the urine. Again, it was found that the urine from hydrated subjects did not show such activity, but withholding fluids for periods of 24 up to 65 hr. caused an increased excretion of antidiuretic substance which could be extracted from the urine. Perhaps more striking is the effect of withdrawing all fluids from groups of rats and extracting the collected urine at different intervals. At 24, 48 or 72 hr. of dehydration a marked and increasing amount of antidiuretic substance is found in the urine. From such studies on dehydration the amount of antidiuretic substance excreted can be calculated. If an approximate figure of 13 per cent. urinary excretion of injected posterior lobe hormone is taken from the previously described recovery experiments, then it can be estimated that during the third 24-hr. period of dehydration rats secreted 'assumed' antidiuretic hormone at an average rate of approximately 0·515 mU./min./kg. body-weight. In the human cases, after much less severe dehydration, the maximum rate of secretion was only 0·005 mU./min./kg. (Noble & Taylor, 1953).

If one can assume from the preceding evidence that the antidiuretic substance extracted from urine by the zinc ferrocyanide method is one of the posterior lobe hormones, then it should be possible to employ this method in a study of posterior lobe function. Of the various conditions which we have studied perhaps one of the most interesting is fainting. In the experiments of Dr. Edholm, of 14 patients from whom various amounts of blood were withdrawn and then reinfused, half fainted at some stage of the experiment, although this was not related to the amounts of blood withdrawn. Dr. Taylor was able to show that, whereas the urine did not contain appreciable amounts of ADS in specimens before fainting, nor at any time in those who did not faint, there was always a considerable amount of ADS extractable from urine specimens voided after fainting. Furthermore, 3 subjects who fainted from psychic causes showed ADS in urine specimens immediately after the faint, but not in samples obtained after recovery. From a quantitative point of view the equivalent of 85 to 372 mU. of antidiuretic hormone was extracted after fainting, indicating a liberation of from 0·7 to 3·0 units by the posterior pituitary. Curiously enough, individuals who lost consciousness associated with black-out during acceleration did not excrete more antidiuretic hormone in response to this reaction (Noble & Taylor,

1953). Again using the zinc ferrocyanide extraction we found an appreciable increase in ADS in the urine of individuals after emotional trauma induced by various 'practical jokes', but not after nightmares apparently involving equally severe emotional conflicts. Electro-convulsive therapy in mental cases is consistently associated with the excretion of ADS in the urine, whereas insulin shock therapy is not (Rechnitzer & Noble, 1950).

Others have effectively used the zinc ferrocyanide method with apparent success. Just recently Goldman & Luchsinger (1956) in recovery experiments were apparently somewhat surprised to obtain a yield of 109 per cent. of Pitressin added to urine. They obtained values indicating an average excretion of 51 mU. of antidiuretic hormone over 16 hours in normal individuals. In most of our experiments which have been cited the doses of extract from normal or control urines have been adjusted so that they contain only trace amounts of antidiuretic activity. For every 100 c.c. of starting urine of the specific gravity of 1,010, the extract was concentrated to 5 ml. or 5 per cent. of the initial volume. This was given to rats in doses of 0·5 c.c./100 g., i.e. the equivalent of 10 ml. of urine/100 g. body-weight was administered. Since the assay method used requires at least 1·0 mU./100 g. body-weight, an antidiuretic response could not be expected unless the urine contained more than 10 mU./100 ml. which would be equivalent in humans to an excretion of approximately 200 mU./day. However, Taylor & Jessup (1954) have studied the 24-hr. excretion of antidiuretic hormone in normal persons, using extracts concentrated to 1 per cent. of the starting urine volume. They have reported that they could extract activity equivalent to 25–75 mU. of antidiuretic hormone daily; values very similar to those found by Dekanski (1951). Also, Taylor & Walker (1951) were able to show from studies on urine that one of the less dangerous but more consistently predictable perils of cigarette smoking was a stimulation of posterior lobe secretion with the liberation of 0·2 to 1·0 unit of antidiuretic hormone, of which 50 mU. found its way into the urine. Burn & Singh Grewal (1951) have confirmed this finding and, using the zinc ferrocyanide method, extracted the equivalent of 75 to 100 mU. from urine obtained after cigarette smoking.

Many of these experimental findings have been a fitting epilogue to earlier observations that the same various stimuli led to an inhibition of water diuresis in the donor through stimulation of the neurohypophysial system. The work of Verney (1946) and Gilman & Goodman (1937) on osmotic stimulation and dehydration; Brun, Knudsen & Raaschou (1945) on fainting, and Burn, Truelove & Burn (1945) on cigarette smoking may be cited. In experiments of a similar nature, Dr. Taylor (1956), who has continued his interest in studies of posterior lobe function at the Defence Medical Research Laboratories in Toronto, has been able to correlate to a high degree an inhibition of water diuresis to susceptibility to motion sickness in humans. At present he is studying the excretion of antidiuretic hormone in the urine of susceptible individuals after exposure to motion. The finding of antidiuretic activity in the urine in experiments of the type described have strengthened the evidence of endogenous liberation of posterior lobe hormones in such conditions, although it must be admitted that conversely it has been doubted whether the appearance of antidiuretic activity in the urine at such appropriate times favours the probability of the active urinary principles being of posterior lobe origin.

The suggested implication of neurohypophysial stimulation under conditions of altered osmotic pressure of the blood, fainting, emotional stress, electro-convulsive therapy, cigarette smoking, vestibular stimulation due to motion and to which should be added suckling in rabbits (Cross, 1951) and sexual intercourse in humans (Friberg, 1953), is sufficient to suggest that an endocrinologist is not entirely suited even to attempt to indicate tentatively a common factor or new nervous pathway which might ultimately allow all these various stimuli to reach the neurohypophysis: rather, I shall leave this to the neurophysiologists.

I feel somewhat remiss for presenting so many of our results using the zinc ferro-cyanide adsorption method of urine extraction, especially as some of these results may be familiar to you. However, most of our experience has been with this method and it seemed necessary to review this before attempting to consider some newer studies. The main drawback of the zinc ferrocyanide method is the high degree of impurity of the final extract, especially in concentrated extracts such as may be necessary to determine small amounts of antidiuretic activity. These impurities may lead to toxic side effects in the assay animals. The publication of an apparently improved adsorption method by Grollman & Woods in 1949 was therefore viewed with considerable interest. In this procedure activated charcoal was used to adsorb the activity at pH 5. The activity was extracted from the dried charcoal precipitate by glacial acetic acid and from this it was precipitated by 10 volumes of ethanol–petroleum ether mixture. The resulting product was reported to yield a 90 per cent. or higher recovery of posterior lobe hormone. Dr. Jessup has studied this method extensively when applied to saline solutions or urine and has found that it leaves a great deal to be desired. The final extract, it is true, contains only about 1/50 the amount of total solid (6·5 mg. from 100 ml. of urine of the specific gravity of 1,010) when compared with the zinc ferrocyanide product (310 mg. from 100 ml. of urine of the specific gravity of 1,010), but unfortunately, it contains only about one-tenth of the expected yield of antidiuretic activity (Jessup, Taylor & Noble, 1956).

When the charcoal adsorption method was applied to either saline or urine to which concentrations of Pitressin up to 200 mU./100 c.c. had been added, the recovery was negligible. For concentrations above 200 mU. and up to 1 unit per 100 c.c. the recovery rate was approximately 10 per cent. In experiments run in parallel to compare with the zinc ferrocyanide method, it was noted that this method extracted 80 per cent. of the antidiuretic activity when Pitressin was added to urine in concentrations as low as from 10 to 100 mU. per 100 c.c. of urine. If the charcoal method is examined step by step, and the residues extracted by the zinc ferrocyanide method and then assayed, Dr. Jessup has found that approximately 25 per cent. of the total activity was not adsorbed on the charcoal. About 50 per cent. of the activity remained in the acetic acid eluate and was not precipitated by petroleum ether and alcohol. Since 10 per cent. only was recovered in the eluate the remaining 15 per cent. was probably not eluted by acetic acid from the charcoal. This discrepancy in the results obtained by us and those reported by Grollman & Woods is more apparent than real. Actually, our recoveries of 10 per cent. using their method appear to be equally as inadequate as those reported by them, but this is not obvious because their calculations of recovery were made from a dose response curve in rats which required 10 times the amount of antidiuretic hormone to give excretion times, which we find with one-tenth of the quantity. In Grollman's & Woods' curve the doses required to show antidiuresis extended from 10 to 100 mU. whereas most workers under comparable conditions find a dose range of 1 to 10 mU. sufficient to show maximum antidiuresis. The error of the 10 per cent. recovery was therefore corrected by the application of another error of a factor of times 10, giving a satisfying 100 per cent. recovery. We have been somewhat reluctant to publish this marked discrepancy in results which we believe invalidates accurate studies using the charcoal method, especially since the method has been used by others with such success and without comment (Stein, Jinks & Mirsky, 1952).

Having examined the charcoal adsorption method with such devastating findings, it is with some temerity and reluctance that we venture to put forward a new method of extraction for your criticism, particularly since further work on it is obviously required. However, this method has so many features apparently in its favour that we believed it would be justified to bring it to your attention. The method is essentially an extraction technique rather than one using adsorption and is based on a method which Dr. Carroll had used in a different project while working in the laboratory of Sir Alexander Todd at Cambridge. Urine which may be concentrated to one-fifth of its original volume for ease in handling, is adjusted to pH 5. It is then extracted three times with equal volumes of concentrated phenol solution saturated with water. The phenol fraction contains the activity, which may then be recovered from the phenol solution by the addition of ether and back extraction with water. The aqueous fraction is taken to dryness and the dried residue may be extracted with absolute alcohol to remove impurities. The final extract has a total solid content of approximately one-seventh of the comparable extract prepared by the zinc ferrocyanide method (57·5 mg. per 100 ml. of urine of the specific gravity of 1,010) (Jessup, Carroll & Noble, 1956).

The recovery of antidiuretic hormone added to urine or saline by the phenol method has been consistently better than 85 to 90 per cent. When aliquots of the same urine were extracted by this method and that using zinc ferrocyanide the recovery was always equal to or better than that found with the adsorption method. The phenol method has also been applied to the urine of rats obtained during progressive dehydration. Apparently the endogenously produced antidiuretic hormone when excreted can also be extracted by this method. Similarly, the method has been used, and is particularly suited, for determining the excretion of antidiuretic hormone by normal humans. Unfortunately, phenol also extracts the pressor substance previously referred to in normal urine, which is not posterior lobe hormone. Initial tests, however, indicate that such extracts contain only approximately one-half the pressor activity of extracts made by the zinc ferrocyanide method from the same urine samples.

Perhaps the most useful contribution of the phenol method may be in its application to the extraction of antidiuretic hormone from blood. It is obviously beyond the scope of this paper to review this particular field, but it may be mentioned that the addition of the phenol to plasma or serum acts as a protein precipitant at the same time as it extracts the posterior lobe hormone. When antidiuretic hormone is added to plasma it may be recovered equally as well as from urine, by the phenol method. A single experiment was performed to compare the pooled blood drawn by heart puncture from 5 normal rats under ether anaesthesia, with that removed from 5 animals dehydrated for 72 hr. The extracted plasma drawn from rats by this exsanguination technique showed a marked antidiuresis on assay, and when compared with a standard of Pitressin, indicated a level of 1·2 mU. per c.c. The animals previously dehydrated yielded a plasma containing 4·8 mU. per c.c. under comparable conditions. These values are obviously high, since they have not been corrected for the augmenting action of the serum. On the other hand, following exsanguination and ether anaesthesia a value of 1·2 mU. per c.c. for rat serum was obtained on intravenous assay by Ginsburg & Heller (1953).

The evidence which has been presented from the study of results obtained for the antidiuretic activity of urine using extraction procedures, the errors of which are recognized, strongly supports the contention that it is the antidiuretic hormone in the urine which is being extracted. Thus the quantitative recovery of antidiuretic hormone added to urine, the immediate appearance of antidiuretic activity in the urine following the intravenous injection of posterior pituitary extract, the increasing activity of the urine paralleling increasing dehydration, and the amounts of antidiuretic activity obtained in urine extracts after smoking or fainting, are indicative that the antidiuretic hormone is being excreted. Furthermore, the quantitative data which have been obtained in these experiments, using Burn's method of assay, are in close agreement with those reported by others using different assay techniques.

It would perhaps be convincing if one concluded at this time that the antidiuretic substance extracted from urine represented a secretion by the neurohypophysis. However, since this paper was designed to present some of the difficulties encountered and criticisms levelled at this experimental approach, it is only fitting to record some recent findings which are perhaps at variance with the concept so far developed: in general the properties of the active substance in urine extracts correspond closely to those of the pituitary antidiuretic hormone and we have been impressed with observations on the stability to heat at various pH levels. It has been found repeatedly, for example, that at pH 10 rapid inactivation of active extracts takes place on heating (Noble, Plunkett & Taylor, 1950). The use of thioglycol to inactivate antidiuretic hormone has been advocated repeatedly by van Dyke, but curiously enough, Ames & van Dyke (1951) found that sodium thioglycollate would cause an antidiuresis *per se* and was toxic if administered subcutaneously to rats. However, it was well tolerated if given intravenously and did not cause a complicating antidiuresis, so that it proved to be an efficient inactivator of antidiuretic hormone if intravenous assay methods were used. Since the assay method used in our laboratory involved the subcutaneous injection of the test extract we had not attempted to inactivate urine extracts with thioglycol until recently. Rather to our surprise Dr. Jessup failed to find antidiuresis or other toxic manifestations when sodium thioglycollate was given subcutaneously to fed or fasted rats of the Sprague-Dawley strain. This is in keeping with the earlier observations of Ralli, Raisz, Leslie, Dumm & Laken, 1950). On the other hand, approximately 85 per cent. inactivation by thioglycollate of antidiuretic hormone in saline, or extracts of urine prepared by the zinc ferrocyanide or the phenol method, was found by assays employing subcutaneous injection. When however the activity of extracts was presumably due to endogenously produced posterior pituitary hormone no inactivation could be produced by thioglycol. This has been demonstrated in single experiments for the antidiuretic activity found in zinc ferrocyanide extracts of normal human urine and also for the activity extracted by the phenol method from the urine of dehydrated rats. Before one concludes that the antidiuretic activity of such extracts is not due, therefore, to the antidiuretic hormone it should be mentioned that in our experience thioglycol is not effective against posterior lobe hormones in the presence of large amounts of impurities such as in crude pituitary extracts. The finding remains, however, that although it is not difficult to destroy posterior lobe hormone added to urine extracts with thioglycol, it has not been possible to destroy presumed posterior pituitary hormone of endogenous origin in similar extracts. In view of the evidence previously presented it would appear probable that the antidiuretic activity in urine extracts *is* of pituitary origin, so that it would seem that endogenous posterior pituitary hormone may be present in the urine in some form which is protected from the action of thioglycol but is yet extractable and active on injection into the test animal.

It is probably fitting, therefore, to conclude this paper with the warning that any suggestion that the antidiuretic activity obtained with any method of extraction respresents a stimulation and liberation of hormones by the neurohypophysis should be regarded as speculation until the time when chemical identification methods are practical. The cautious and critical approach to the whole problem of the antidiuretic activity of urine would still seem to be justified in case erroneous conclusions as to hypophysial function are drawn, which would further complicate an already difficult field of neurophysiology.

REFERENCES

AMES, R. G. & VAN DYKE, H. B. (1951). Thioglycollate inactivation of posterior pituitary antidiuretic principle as determined in the rat. *Proc. Soc. Exp. Biol. (N.Y.)* **76,** 576–8.

AMES, R. G., MOORE, D. H. & VAN DYKE, H. B. (1950). The excretion of posterior pituitary antidiuretic hormone in the urine and its detection in the blood. *Endocrinology* **46,** 215–27.

BRUN, C., KNUDSEN, E. O. E. & RAASCHOU, F. (1945). Post-syncopal oliguria. *Acta med. scand.* **122,** 381–95.

BURN, G. P. & SINGH GREWAL, R. (1951). The antidiuretic response to and excretion of pituitary (posterior lobe) extract in man, with reference to the action of nicotine. *Brit. J. Pharmacol.* **6,** 471–82.

BURN, J. H. (1937). *Biological Standardization.* Oxford: University Press.

BURN, J. H., TRUELOVE, L. H. & BURN, I. (1945). The antidiuretic action of nicotine and of smoking. *Brit. med. J.* i, 403–6.

CROSS, B. A. (1951). Suckling antidiuresis in rabbits. *J. Physiol. (Lond.)* **114,** 447–53.

DEKANSKI, J. (1951). A pressor substance in urine. *Brit. J. Pharmacol.* **6,** 351–6.

DICKER, S. E. (1953). A method for the assay of very small amounts of antidiuretic activity with a note on the antidiuretic titre of rats' blood. *J. Physiol. (Lond.)* **122,** 149–57.

VAN DYKE, H. B., ADAMSONS, K. & ENGEL, S. L. (1955). Aspects of the biochemistry and physiology of the neurohypophyseal hormones. *Recent Progr. Hormone Res.* **11,** 1–41.

VON EULER, U. S. (1945). The occurrence and determination of piperidine in human and animal urine. *Acta pharmacol. (Kbh.)* **1,** 29–59.

FRIBERG, O. (1953). The antidiuretic effect of coitus in human subjects. *Acta endocr. (Kbh.)* **12,** 193–6.

GILMAN, A. & GOODMAN, L. (1937). The secretory response of the posterior pituitary to the need for water conservation. *J. Physiol. (Lond.)* **90,** 113–24.

GINSBURG, M. & HELLER, H. (1953). Antidiuretic activity in blood obtained from various parts of the cardiovascular system. *J. Endocr.* **9,** 274–82.

GOLDMAN, R. & LUCHSINGER, E. B. (1956). Relationship between diurnal variations in urinary volume and the excretion of antidiuretic substance. *J. clin. Endocr. Metab.* **16,** 28–34.

GROLLMAN, A. & WOODS, B. (1949). A new procedure for the determination of the antidiuretic principle in the urine. *Endocrinology* **44,** 409–14.

HELLER, H. (1937). The state in the blood and the excretion by the kidney of the antidiuretic principle of posterior pituitary extracts. *J. Physiol. (Lond.)* **89,** 81–95.

JESSUP, D. C. & TAYLOR, N. B. G. (1954). A sensitive method of assay for antidiuretic hormone. *Rev. canad. Biol.* **13,** 474–5.

JESSUP, D. C., CARROLL, K. K. & NOBLE, R. L. (1956). A new method for the extraction of posterior lobe antidiuretic hormone from body fluids. *Rev. canad. Biol.* **15,** 260–61.

JESSUP, D. C., TAYLOR, N. B. G. & NOBLE, R. L. (1956). A comparison of methods for extracting pituitary antidiuretic substance from urine. *Endocrinology.* In press.

NOBLE, R. L. & TAYLOR, N. B. G. (1953). Antidiuretic substances in human urine after haemorrhage, fainting, dehydration and acceleration. *J. Physiol. (Lond.)* **122,** 220–37.

NOBLE, R. L., PLUNKETT, E. R. & TAYLOR, N. B. G. (1950). Factors affecting the control of the pituitary gland. *Recent Progr. Hormone Res.* **5,** 263–304.

NOBLE, R. L., RINDERKNECHT, H. & WILLIAMS, P. C. (1938). Clinical hyperfunction of the posterior lobe of the pituitary. Suggested by a pressor and antidiuretic substance obtained from the urine. *Lancet* i, 13–5.

NOBLE, R. L., RINDERKNECHT, H. & WILLIAMS, P. C. (1939). The apparent augmentation of pituitary antidiuretic action by various retarding substances. *J. Physiol. (Lond.)* **96,** 293–301.

RALLI, E. P., RAISZ, L. G., LESLIE, S. H., DUMM, M. E. & LAKEN, B. (1950). Evidence for more than one antidiuretic substance in Pitressin. *Amer. J. Physiol.* **163,** 141–7.

RECHNITZER, P. A. & NOBLE, R. L. (1950). The excretion of an antidiuretic substance in the urine of humans who have convulsed. *Proc. roy. Soc. Can.* **44,** 243–4.

SCHAFFER, N. K., CADDEN, J. F. & STANDER, H. J. (1941). Measurement of antidiuretic activity as applied to eclamptic urine and properties of antidiuretic substances in rat urine, pituitary and beef liver. *Endocrinology* **28,** 701–6.

STEIN, M., JINKS, R. & MIRSKY, I. A. (1952). The bioassay of Pitressin and antidiuretic substances in blood and urine. *Endocrinology* **51,** 492–503.

TAYLOR, N. B. G. (1956). Personal communication.

TAYLOR, N. B. G. & JESSUP, D. C. (1954). Antidiuretic substance in the urine of healthy human subjects. *Fed. Proc.* **13,** 152.

TAYLOR, N. B. G. & WALKER, J. M. (1951). Antidiuretic substance in human urine after smoking. *J. Physiol. (Lond.)* **113,** 412–8.

VERNEY, E. B. (1946). The absorption and excretion of water: the antidiuretic hormone. *Lancet* ii, 781–3.

WALKER, A. M. (1939). Experiments upon the relation between the pituitary gland and water diuresis. *Amer. J. Physiol.* **127,** 519–40.

Discussion

Chairman: J. M. Yoffey

van Dyke. I feel that if Professor Noble could perform intravenous antidiuretic assays, he might be more satisfied. For that reason I should like to ask him how much antidiuretic activity the extract contained. How many milli-units were present in addition to this pressor substance?

Noble. The pressor activity was actually in an extract of normal hydrated human urine, which would not have enough antidiuretic activity to show at all by our ordinary methods. The 2 c.c. of 1 per cent. extract which would be equivalent to

200 c.c. of normal urine would be expected to contain about 5 mU. of antidiuretic activity.

van Dyke. I was thinking of approximately 10–20 mU.; that would be 10 or 20 times the dose you would need for a single intravenous antidiuretic injection in the dog. Such assays may be worth trying if the phenol method continues to hold promise.

Our experiments with thioglycollate were performed because Ralli and her co-workers (*Amer. J. Physiol.* **163**, 141, 1950) reported that there are two antidiuretic substances in Pitressin one of which is active in the rat but not in the dog. Her conclusions for the rat were based upon the fact that thioglycollate appeared not to inactivate the hormone causing antidiuresis in the rat. Unfortunately she did not do control experiments with thioglycollate itself. We found that thioglycollate is quite toxic subcutaneously in the doses Dr. Ralli had employed. In many cases we observed haematuria and obvious evidence of renal damage. I wonder whether you used doses as large as Ralli had employed in her experiments.

Noble. We used the same dose which you found to be toxic and we increased considerably above it, and to be on the safe side we also went considerably below. We are at a complete loss to explain this difference in results. There was no suggestion of toxicity or antidiuresis at all in the Sprague-Dawley strain of rats: good inhibition of posterior lobe activity by thioglycollate was found when tested against standard extracts using subcutaneous injections.

Dale. I do not want to complicate matters by suggesting another technique, but I wonder if Dr. Noble has ever tried what seems to me to be a very elegant and useful process which my late colleague Dudley used. After preliminary purification and neutralization of the posterior lobe extract, Dudley added sodium benzoate, and then, on acidification with hydrochloric acid, obtained a finely crystalline precipitate of benzoic acid to which the active hormones adhered. This precipitate was collected, washed and dried. Place in a thimble, extract the benzoic acid with dry ether, and you are left with a very small intensely active residue. I don't know whether it would work with urine, but it might be worth trying. Somebody in Toronto tried it I think at a certain stage of insulin isolation; but of course they eventually found better methods for that particular separation.

Noble. I think that we explored that method. It did extract some activity but at that time we were not trying to do quantitative experiments. It would be interesting to try the method you suggest.

Dale. If it works, the benzoic acid method might have great advantages. The activity is separated on a crystalline precipitate of benzoic acid, which is soluble in organic solvents and these do not dissolve the active material.

Cole. I would like to ask Professor Noble if he has tried feeding a high sodium diet to see its effect on the excretion of antidiuretic hormone in the urine.

Noble. No.

Eisen. With regard to the nature of the antidiuretic substance in urine, I should like to mention some studies carried out by Dr. A. A. G. Lewis and myself (Eisen &

Lewis, *Lancet* ii, 361, 1954) with the urines of post-operative patients collected during the twenty-four hours following surgical procedures of various extent. Acidified, filtered urines, kept in the deep freeze and diluted 5–20 times, were assayed by intravenous route in ethanol-anaesthetized rats and in a well-trained dog with established experimental diabetes insipidus. The antidiuretic activities found ranged from 0·05 to 2·5 mU./ml. Our reasons for believing that this was due to posterior pituitary hormones were the following: the responses in the two species of test animals were mostly of the same order of magnitude in terms of Pitressin activity. In the dog, the antidiuretic responses occurred without changes in the endogenous creatinine excretion and could be ascribed to tubular water reabsorption. In rats, the slopes of the log-dose response curves of urinary activity and Pitressin were highly similar. Urinary activity was destroyed by boiling in alkali and by contact with sodium thioglycollate.

I can confirm Professor Noble's observations that sodium thioglycollate occasionally does not destroy posterior pituitary factors. We found that destruction is more successful when the salt is freshly prepared and contact is maintained for at least 30 minutes. Some rats showed, after one or more intravenous injection containing sodium thioglycollate, a greatly reduced responsiveness to Pitressin.

Reiss. Professor Noble, did you test your extracts for the presence of anterior pituitary hormones?

Noble. The phenol extraction method would extract certain of the anterior pituitary hormones but we did not test for them as a routine. It is curious that preliminary tests indicate that it will apparently extract FSH from post-menopausal urine, but not chorionic gonadotrophin.

Chalmers. Lewis and I some time ago observed antidiuresis after fainting and we found that the duration of the antidiuresis was matched by intravenous injections of Pitressin of the order of 0·5 to 2·0 U. which I think agrees very well with what Professor Noble found.

The effects of haemorrhage and plasma hypertonicity on the neurohypophysis

by

M. GINSBURG *and* L. M. BROWN

Department of Pharmacology, University of Bristol

IN this symposium so far we have been concerned mainly with the morphology of the neurohypophysial system, the chemistry and the fate of neurohypophysial hormones. Most of the papers we are to hear during the remainder of the symposium deal with the action of the hormones in regulating and controlling bodily function. The hormonal control of body functions is usually achieved by a sequence of three events. First a change within or on the surface of the organism affects sensory receptors which are either part of the gland or connected to it; secondly, a response by the gland to stimulation alters the rate at which hormones are liberated into the circulation; and thirdly, cellular activity in target organs is affected by blood-borne hormones.

Much of our work aims at revealing the nature of the initiating stimuli and the action of the hormones, for where a hormone's effect is related to a change which provokes its liberation, a self-correcting, physiological mechanism may be involved. While there can be no doubt that the antidiuretic, milk-ejecting and possibly oxytocic actions of posterior pituitary hormones participate in such mechanisms, it is usually denied that the vasopressor action of the antidiuretic hormone has physiological significance. This assertion is usually based on the argument that the amounts of the hormone required to affect blood vessels are much greater than are commonly believed to be liberated from the gland. However, it has been shown that haemorrhage provokes an antidiuretic response and so we undertook further study of this phenomenon to see firstly, whether during haemorrhage there was a discharge of the antidiuretic hormone from the posterior pituitary in amounts great enough to suggest that it aided the maintenance of blood pressure and secondly, if we were successful, to determine how the body changes during haemorrhage affect the neurohypophysis.

There are two ways in which such a problem can be approached. First, by study of changes in the function of a target organ in an animal subjected to manœuvres which may alter the rate of secretion of the hormone. Observations of this kind were made by Rydin & Verney (1938) who found that removal of small volumes of blood from an artery (sufficient to lower blood pressure by 10 mm. Hg) in water-loaded dogs, brought about a marked inhibition of urine flow, and that this response to haemorrhage did not depend on the innervation of the kidneys or the secretion of adrenaline. However, in experiments in man, Lewis (1953) found that removal of as much as 1,200 ml. of blood by venesection did not affect water diuresis.

The second approach, which we have adopted, is to measure the changes in the amounts of the hormone in body fluids. Noble & Taylor (1953) estimated the antidiuretic hormone content in urine in men after blood withdrawal; they found antidiuretic activity in urine of only those subjects who fainted during blood withdrawal and none in the urine of subjects who remained conscious.

In the experiments I am about to describe we have followed the changes in antidiuretic activity in blood during haemorrhage. A disadvantage inherent in this type of experiment is that the effect is observed of only that fraction of the liberated hormone which is present in a sample of blood, and therefore only great changes in hormone secretion can be detected. On the other hand, the demonstration of increased amounts of the hormone in blood gives the most direct and unequivocable evidence of increased hormone secretion.

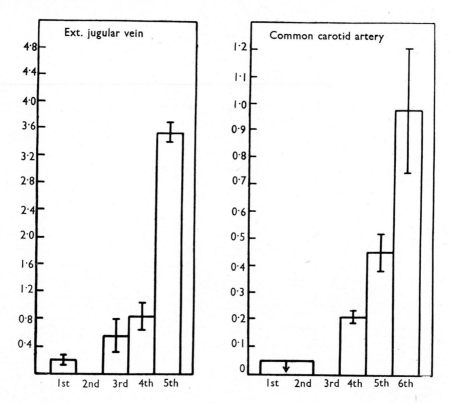

Figure 1

Effect of haemorrhage in rats anaesthetized with ether on the antidiuretic potency of external jugular and common carotid blood. The interval between the withdrawal of each ml. was 90 sec.

Ordinate: Antidiuretic poteney of blood (mU. vasopressin/ml.).
Abscissa: ml. of blood.

(Ginsburg & Heller, 1953).

Figure 1 shows the antidiuretic potency of successive millilitres of blood withdrawn at 90-sec. intervals from a common carotid artery or an external jugular vein in rats anaesthetized with ether. The antidiuretic potency of the blood from both sources increased so that in the fifth millilitre it was at least 10 times greater than that of the first millilitre withdrawn. The activity in blood coming from the head was 4–6 times greater than that of arterial blood and the absolute difference between external jugular and arterial blood antidiuretic activity increased from 0·2 mU./ml. in the first millilitre to 3·0 mU./ml. in the fifth millilitre of blood withdrawn. The antidiuretic substance must therefore enter the circulation in the head. Later experiments showed that this substance could not be detected in the blood of neuro-hypophysectomized rats and that the antidiuretic activity was abolished by treatment with thioglycollate, so it may be concluded that posterior pituitary antidiuretic hormone was liberated in increased amounts during haemorrhage.

It has been suggested that the antidiuretic response to haemorrhage is a consequence of emotional disturbance, but since in the present experiments the blood was withdrawn from anaesthetized animals, it is improbable that emotional stimuli were involved.

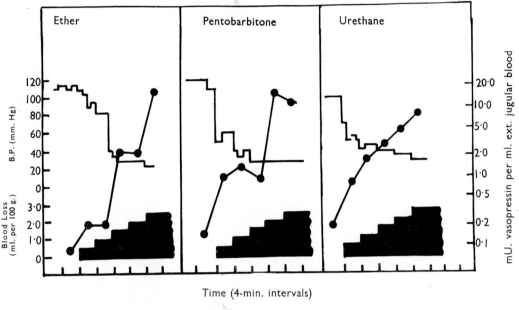

Time (4-min. intervals)

Figure 2

Effect of slow haemorrhage upon blood pressure and antidiuretic activity in external jugular blood in rats anaesthetized with ether, pentobarbitone and urethane. 0·5 ml. blood/100 g. was withdrawn at 4-min. intervals.

●——● mU. vasopressin/ml. blood.
———— blood pressure, mm. Hg.

In Fig. 2, the results are shown of typical experiments in which blood was withdrawn more slowly, from rats anaesthetized with ether, pentobarbitone and urethane. Blood, 0·5 ml. per 100 g. body-weight, was withdrawn at 4-min. intervals from an external jugular vein, and when a sample of blood was taken for antidiuretic assay an equal volume of rat blood was simultaneously returned to the animal via a femoral vein. The blood pressure was recorded from a femoral artery. In these experiments, we observed up to 100-fold increases in the antidiuretic potency of external jugular blood. Before haemorrhage, in the first sample, the antidiuretic activity was 0·1–0·3 mU. vasopressin/ml. blood. The first big increase in antidiuretic activity (about 5–10-fold) seemed to occur after the first pronounced fall in blood pressure, i.e. a fall of 50 mm. Hg or more. In some experiments, the blood pressure fell and the antidiuretic activity rose after the first haemorrhage, but in others neither change occurred until after three withdrawals of blood. This was followed by a continuous increase in the antidiuretic activity of the blood or the activity remained unchanged until 8–12 min. after the first increase, when it again rose abruptly. In experiments with these anaesthetics (ether, pentobarbitone and urethane) concentrations equivalent to 10–20 mU. vasopressin per ml. blood were usually found after 5 haemorrhages and the highest concentration we recorded was 26 mU./ml. blood.

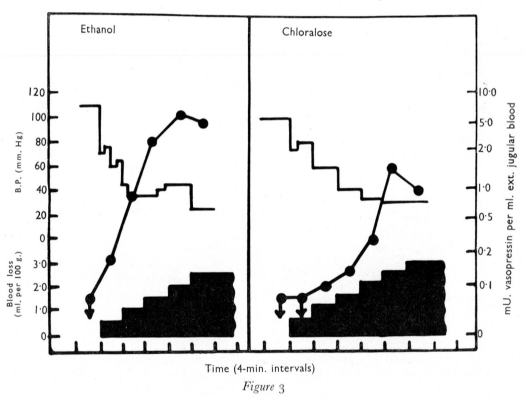

Figure 3

Effect of slow haemorrhage upon blood pressure and antidiuretic activity in external jugular blood in rats anaesthetized with (*a*) ethanol and (*b*) chloralose. 0·5 ml. blood/100 g. was withdrawn at 4-min. intervals.
●——● mU. vasopressin /ml. blood.
———— blood pressure mm. Hg.

Figure 3 shows results of similar experiments in rats anaesthetized with ethanol and chloralose. With both of these anaesthetics no antidiuretic activity could be detected in the first sample of external jugular blood. In all experiments with ethanol anaesthesia, the antidiuretic potency of the blood increased during haemorrhage, reaching 5–10 mU. vasopressin per ml. Three experiments were performed on rats anaesthetized with chloralose; in two, no antidiuretic activity (i.e. less then 200 μU./ml.) could be detected in the external jugular blood even after removal of 3·0 ml. blood/100 g. body-weight. In the other rat (the experiment illustrated), the highest antidiuretic activity was less than 2·0 mU./ml. blood. The blood pressure fell by 20 mm. Hg or less each time blood was withdrawn from rats anaesthetized with chloralose, whereas with other anaesthetics, sooner or later, the blood pressure fell suddenly by 40 mm. Hg or more, and the increase in blood antidiuretic activity was associated with this fall in blood pressure. It is possible therefore, that the lower activity in blood during haemorrhage in chloralose anaesthesia is due to an altered pattern of blood pressure change rather than a specific effect upon the neurohypophysial system or peripheral receptors linked to that system.

The antidiuretic activity of blood during haemorrhage in ethanol anaesthesia was only slightly lower than that found in experiments when ether, pentobarbitone or urethane were used. Ethanol can prevent the release of antidiuretic hormone in other circumstances but it does seem that the description of ethanol anaesthesia as 'functional neurohypophysectomy' (Dicker, 1953) is not justified in this connexion.

Figure 4 shows the changes in antidiuretic activity of external jugular blood following a single rapid removal of approximately 40 per cent. of the blood volume in a rat anaesthetized with pentobarbitone; 5·5 ml. of blood was withdrawn in 2 min. from a femoral artery and the artery was then connected to a blood reservoir in which the blood level was 44·5 cm. (equivalent to approx. 36 mm. Hg) above the animal's heart. During the subsequent 25 min. a further 0·5 ml. of blood transfused out of the animal but the blood pressure did not change. The antidiuretic activity in a sample of external jugular blood taken 4 min. after the removal of blood was 25 times greater than that before haemorrhage. The antidiuretic hormone concentration then fell rapidly and 12 min. later was of the same order as that found in blood before haemorrhage. This fall was followed by a second rise in the blood antidiuretic activity. The essential features are similar to those of the 'slow' haemorrhage experiments. The liberation of antidiuretic hormone, in the first place, followed closely upon the fall in blood pressure and there was a second increase in the hormone concentration in the blood (in this case) after 20 min. of hypotension.

These findings indicate the liberation of very large amounts of antidiuretic hormone from the pituitary during haemorrhage and that the discharge of the hormone is more closely related to the fall in blood-pressure than to changes in blood-volume. This may, of course, apply only to the massive discharge of the hormone under our experimental conditions. Concentrations of antidiuretic hormone in the venous effluent from the head, of the order of 10–20 mU./ml. blood are certainly high enough to suggest that the hormone could have a sustaining effect on blood-pressure during haemorrhage. This conclusion is supported by the findings of Frieden & Kellar (1954) who measured the volume of blood which it is necessary to remove from dogs in order to lower the blood pressure to 70 mm. Hg and found that, in dogs with experimental diabetes insipidus, this volume of blood was significantly less than in normal animals. It has been suggested that the liberation of antidiuretic hormone in response to a fall in blood pressure might account for the antidiuresis associated with syncope and with vomiting (Andersson & Larson, 1954). Administration of histamine and veratrum alkaloids also provoke the liberation of antidiuretic hormone and these too may be responses to the fall in blood pressure.

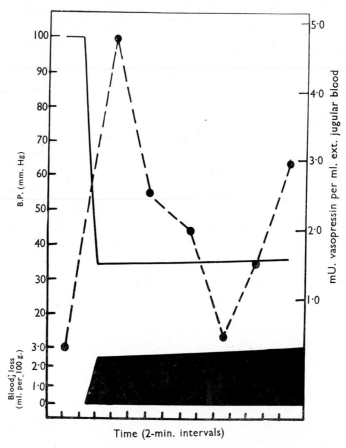

Figure 4

Effect of rapid haemorrhage on blood pressure and antidiuretic activity in external jugular blood. 5·5-ml. blood was withdrawn in two minutes and the blood-pressure maintained at 33–37 mm. Hg.
●------● mU. vasopressin/ml. blood.
———— blood pressure, mm. Hg.

In view of the evidence that following electrical stimulation of the vagus nerve, there is liberation of posterior pituitary hormones (Chang, Chia, Huang & Lim, 1939; Andersson, 1951), an obvious way in which this response could be mediated is through an increase in chemoreceptor or baroreceptor impulse activity in afferent vagal fibres. However in experiments on rats in which both vagi had been divided in the neck; the increase in antidiuretic activity in blood during haemorrhage was not prevented, and was again associated with a sharp fall in blood-pressure. During haemorrhage in rats in which the carotid sinuses were denervated in addition to bilateral vagotomy, the amounts of antidiuretic hormone were lower than those found in rats with these nerves intact. However, in these experiments, every time blood was withdrawn, the blood pressure fell in steps of less than 40 mm. and the characteristic sudden collapse of blood pressure was not observed. It is therefore not possible to conclude that in this experiment we had destroyed a specific nervous pathway through which changes in blood pressure are transmitted to the pituitary, since the pattern of blood pressure change during haemorrhage had been altered. However, the results obtained with vagotomized rats may be peculiar to this species. Blood, Kosman & d'Amour (1955) have shown recently that although pulmonary depressor reflexes can be elicited in rats, the responses are not abolished (as in other species) by section of the vagus nerves.

A connexion between stretch receptors in the left auricle and pulmonary veins with urine flow has been demonstrated by J. P. Henry, O. Gauer and their co-workers (Gauer, Henry, Sieker & Wendt, 1954; Henry, Gauer & Reeves, 1956; Henry & Pearce, 1956). If these changes in urine flow which are associated with the state of filling of intrathoracic blood-vessels are indeed determined by the neurohypophysial antidiuretic hormone, such receptors could be involved in the release of the hormone during haemorrhage. The present experiments have not given decisive information on this point, possibly because of the peculiarity of the rat mentioned above. However a few years ago, Professor Heller and I (Ginsburg & Heller, 1953), found that blood taken by heart puncture from anaesthetized rats had greater antidiuretic activity than could be accounted for by the activities in venous blood. We thought then that this might have been due to the release of antidiuretic hormone by puncture of the myocardium or alterations of the pressures within the intrathoracic circulation.

These findings of a connexion between intrathoracic stretch receptors and urine flow are not entirely consistent with some older observations. For example, electrical stimulation of the central vagus liberates hormones from the neurohypophysis, while activation of the intrathoracic stretch receptors which increases impulse activity in vagal fibres, has, what would appear to be, the opposite effect—it induces a diuresis. Indeed, at present, there is little or no evidence for the view that the changes in urine flow associated with these stretch receptors are determined by posterior pituitary antidiuretic hormone—although an alternative might be hard to find.

After we had shown that during haemorrhage in rats large amounts of antidiuretic hormone are liberated from the posterior pituitary, we investigated the effect of haemorrhage upon vasopressin and oxytocin contents of the neurohypophysis. The oxytocic and vasopressor activities in extracts of glands from rats anaesthetized with ether, ethanol and chloralose were not different from those from unanaesthetized rats which had been killed by decapitation, and 'slow' haemorrhage of the anaesthetized rats did not affect the hormone contents in the glands. The ratio of pressor to oxytocic activity in all extracts was not significantly different from 1·0. Figure 5 shows the results of similar experiments in rats anaesthetized with pentobarbitone and urethane. In the extracts of glands from rats anaesthetized with urethane, the vasopressin content was less and the oxytocin content was more than in those from unanaesthetized rats, and the ratio of pressor to oxytocic activity was of the order of 0·5; again, bleeding did not affect the activities of the gland extracts.

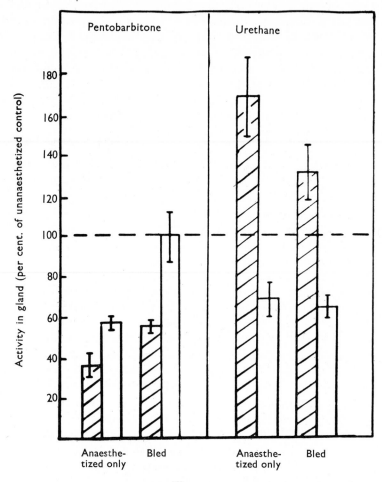

Figure 5

Effect of anaesthesia with pentobarbitone and urethane, and the effect of haemorrhage on the oxytocin and vasopressin contents of rat neurohypophyses.

[////////] oxytocin.

[_____] vasopressin.

In rats anaesthetized with pentobarbitone, the oxytocin and vasopressin contents of the gland extracts were less than in the unanaesthetized controls, with greater depletion of oxytocin so that the ratio of pressor to oxytocic activity was now of the order of 2·0. In gland extracts from rats which had been bled under pentobarbitone anaesthesia, both the oxytocin and vasopressin contents were significantly greater than in glands from animals which were only anaesthetized, although the ratio of pressor to oxytocic activity remained at about 2·0. Since haemorrhage under these conditions undoubtedly causes liberation of antidiuretic hormone into the blood, this finding can be explained only by increased repletion of the hormones stored in the gland. It may therefore be necessary to distinguish between *tropic* stimuli which affect the posterior lobe so that the hormones are transferred in increased amounts from the gland into the circulation and *trophic* stimuli which increase the amounts of biologically active material in the gland. Ames & van Dyke (1950) found an increased vasopressin content in the posterior pituitaries of rats which had been deprived of fluid for 3 days, but in most investigations the hormone content of the neurohypophysis has been found to decrease under conditions or after treatment which would increase liberation of hormones from the gland. However, close examination of some of these results leads to the conclusion that trophic stimulation of the neurohypophysial-hypothalamic system also occurred. The normal rate of antidiuretic hormone secretion has been estimated in dogs to be of the order of 1–5 mU./hr. (Shannon, 1942) and 0·3–1·2 mU./hr. in rats (Dicker, 1954); assuming that the vasopressin content of the posterior lobe does not vary greatly from day to day, this rate must be approximately equal to that at which the hormone store is normally replenished. In Hild & Zetler's (1953) experiments, after restoration of access to water in dogs which had been thirsted for 14 days, the vasopressor potency of neurohypophyses increased at a rate of 2·7 units/day, i.e. the rate of repletion was 20–100 times greater than normal. More striking, perhaps, are the results of Dexter, Stoner & Green (1954) who showed that following depletion by ATP injection, the antidiuretic activity of rat posterior pituitaries was restored by over 200 mU. (one-third of the content of a normal gland) in 30 min., i.e. 330–1,300 times faster than the normal rate. Similarly, Rothballer (1953) found that painful stimuli in rats caused almost complete depletion of neurosecretory substance in the neurohypophysis within a few minutes; after 2 hr. the normal content of neurosecretory material was restored. Since the activity in the hypothalamus is small compared with that in the pituitary, repletion at such rates cannot be explained solely on the basis of increased rate of flow of the axoplasm current (Scharrer & Scharrer, 1954). Such stimuli must also increase the rate at which active material is formed in hypothalamic nuclei. The amounts of active substances in the neurohypophysis are determined by the rate of repletion as well as by the rate of hormone release, and the turnover of hormones by the gland may be independent of the level at which they are stored. Change in the hormone content of the gland is therefore not a reliable index of secretion.

The liberation of antidiuretic hormone during haemorrhage appeared to occur in two stages. The first discharge of the hormone was associated with a fall in blood pressure and the second one occurred after 10–20 min. of sustained hypotension. We thought that the second increase in the concentration of antidiuretic hormone in blood might be due to the liberation of substances such as ATP or ferritin which could stimulate the further release of antidiuretic hormone.

To test this hypothesis, blood was taken from a rat during sustained hypotension, and its antidiuretic effect when given into an internal carotid artery was compared with its effect after intravenous administration. We found that the antidiuretic effect was the same when the blood was given by either route. However, when 0·5 ml. of 4·5 per cent. NcCl solution was injected into the carotid there was no inhibition of the diuresis. This disturbing observation demanded further investigation.

The injections were given to unanaesthetized rats through an exteriorized polyethylene cannula inserted into an external carotid artery between the origins of the occipital and superior thyroid arteries. The tip of the cannula was placed close to the carotid bifurcation and its wall blocked the origin of the occipital artery. Injections made into this cannula are driven into the internal carotid by the force of the arterial pressure. The cannulae were inserted, under ether anaesthesia, 4–5 hr. before the experiment.

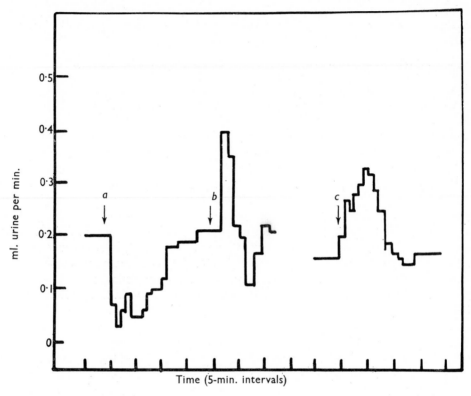

Figure 6

Effect of rapid injections (5 sec.) of hypertonic NaCl solution on urine flow in unanaesthetized rat.
    (a) 300 μU. vasopressin in 0·4 ml. 0·9 per cent. NaCl i.v.
    (b) 300 μU. vasopressin in 0·4 ml. 3·6 per cent. NaCl i.v.
    (c) 0·4 ml. 3·6 per cent. NaCl into right internal carotid.

Figure 6 shows the results of one of our first experiments. In a rat with cannulae in the bladder, external jugular vein and an external carotid artery, a high water load was maintained by intravenous infusion of a 1 per cent. solution of dextrose. Intravenous injection of 300 μU. of Pitressin in 0·9 per cent. NaCl given in 5 sec. had a typical antidiuretic effect lasting 10–15 min. When the same dose of Pitressin was given in 3·6 per cent. NaCl solution, the antidiuretic effect was masked. During the two minutes following the injection, the urine flow was almost doubled and thereafter fell to slightly below the initial rate to which it returned about 10 min. after the injection. When hypertonic NaCl solution was given into the right internal carotid the urine flow increased for about 10 min. without any indication of an antidiuretic effect.

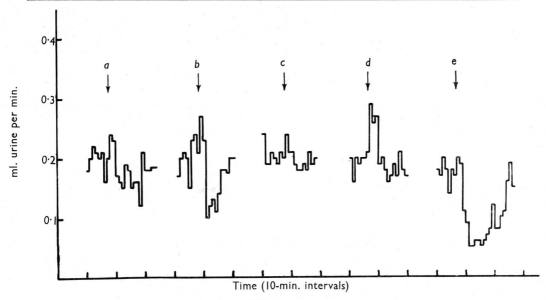

Figure 7

Effect of slow injection (30 sec.) of hypertonic NaCl solution on urine flow in unanaesthetized rat.

   (*a*)   30 μU. vasopressin in 0·3 ml. 0·9 per cent. NaCl i.v.
   (*b*)   30 μU. vasopressin in 0·3 ml. 4·5 per cent. NaCl i.v.
   (*c*)   0·3 ml. 0·9 per cent. NaCl into left internal carotid.
   (*d*)   0·3 ml. 4·5 per cent NaCl into left internal carotid.
   (*e*)   60 μU. vasopressin in 0·3 ml. 4·5 per cent. NaCl i.v.

When hypertonic solutions were injected more slowly, the interference with administered Pitressin was absent or not prominent. Figure 7 shows the results of an experiment in which the water load was maintained by water administration by mouth. When 30 or 60 μU. of Pitressin were given in 4·5 per cent. NaCl solution, and the injection given over 30 sec., there was no interference with the antidiuretic responses but again, when a hypertonic NaCl solution was injected into an internal carotid, a brief enhancement of the diuresis occurred without any indication of an antidiuresis. In this experiment, the absence of an antidiuretic response cannot be attributed to interference with the effect of the hormone on the kidney.

These findings, in rats, are not in agreement with those of Verney (1947) in his experiments on dogs. Verney did not investigate the effect of rapid intravenous injection of hypertonic solutions on the antidiuretic responses to injected vasopressin in his dogs, but judging from the effects he obtained following intracarotid injection of hypertonic solutions, the amounts and rates of his injections did not interfere with antidiuretic responses.

The effect of continuous intracarotid infusion of hypertonic NaCl solution is shown on Fig. 8. The urine flow increased during intracarotid infusion of 1·8 per cent. NaCl. When the hypertonic salt solution was infused intravenously together with Pitressin, the antidiuretic effect of the Pitressin was masked so that the urine flow recovered even while the Pitressin administration continued, but there was a definite antidiuretic effect during the first ten minutes of infusion. In this experiment, NaCl

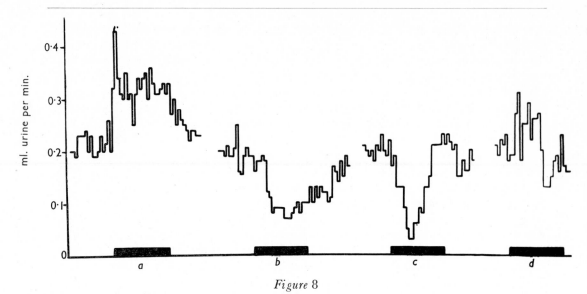

Figure 8

Effect of continuous infusion of hypertonic NaCl solution on urine flow in unanaesthetized rat.

    (*a*) 1·8 per cent. NaCl at 0·2 ml./min. into right internal carotid.
    (*b*) 40 μU. vasopressin in 0·2 ml. 1 per cent. dextrose/min. into left external jugular vein.
    (*c*) 40 μU. vasopressin in 0·2 ml. 1·8 per cent. NaCl/min. into left external jugular vein.
    (*d*) 1·8 per cent. NaCl at 0·2 ml./min. into left external jugular vein.

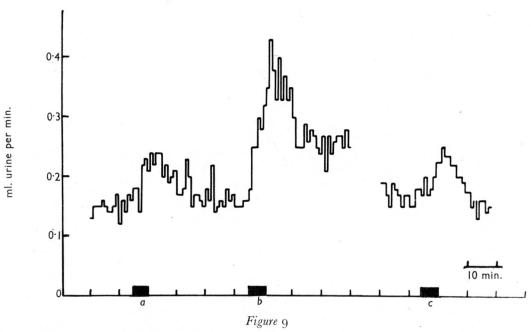

Figure 9

Effect of continuous infusion of hypertonic sucrose solution on urine flow in unanaesthetized rat.

    (*a*) 10·6 per cent. sucrose at 0·17 ml./min. into right internal carotid.
    (*b*) 31·8 per cent. sucrose at 0·17 ml./min. into right internal carotid.
    (*c*) 31·8 per cent. sucrose at 0·06 ml./min. into right internal carotid.

was infused at the rate of 12·5 mg./kg./min. increasing the osmotic pressure of the internal carotid blood by 15·5 per cent. For comparison when Verney, in one of his experiments infused a hypertonic NaCl solution into a common carotid in a dog giving 11·0 mg. NaCl/kg./min. and increasing the osmotic pressure of the blood by 18·0 per cent., profound and long-lasting inhibition of urine flow was produced.

Figure 9 shows that results essentially similar to those obtained during infusion of NaCl solution were also obtained during intracarotid infusion of hypertonic solutions of sucrose. In this experiment an isotonic sucrose solution was infused into the right internal carotid for 10 min. causing a slight enhancement of the diuresis. This was followed by an intracarotid infusion of 31·8 per cent. sucrose at the same rate which we calculated would increase the osmotic pressure of the carotid blood by 14·5 per cent. The rate of urine flow was more than doubled. The third intracarotid infusion given in this experiment was also 31·8 per cent. sucrose but the infusion rate was reduced so that the animal received the same total quantity of sucrose as during the first, isotonic, infusion. The increase in osmotic pressure here was 3·0 per cent. Again there was a slight enhancement of the diuresis, very similar to that obtained during the infusion of isotonic sucrose.

These findings appear to be in direct contradiction to the findings in dogs by Verney (1947), Ames, Moore & van Dyke (1950) and Abrahams & Pickford (1954). At first we considered the possibility that the injections were not in fact entering the internal carotid artery and the cerebral circulation. During intracarotid injection or infusion of strongly hypertonic solutions the rats showed signs of excitement and discomfort; rotation of the head and jaw movements reminiscent of chewing, were frequently observed. These effects did not occur after intravenous administration of hypertonic solution. About 2–3 seconds after intracarotid injection of Evans Blue in albino rats, the retina was seen to be momentarily suffused with blue dye. The best evidence that the injections entered the internal carotid was obtained by injecting [24]Na: 0·3 ml. of a 0·9 per cent. NaCl solution containing 200 micro-curies of [24]Na was injected into an internal carotid or an external jugular vein in 30 sec.; immediately after the completion of the injection, the rat was decapitated. The brain was divided medially and the distribution of radio-activity was determined in each half. When [24]Na was injected, as we believed, into the right internal carotid artery, the radio-activity on the right side of the brain was greater than on the left side. The biggest differences were found in the temporal lobes and the least in the medulla. When intravenous injections were given, much smaller amounts of radio-sodium were found in the brain and there were no marked differences between the right and left sides. Whatever else these results mean, they do indicate that injections given by our technique do enter the internal carotid artery, and so reach the brain before general mixing with the circulating blood.

The explanation of our findings is a formidable task and we have always considered that they may be artefacts without physiological significance. For example, it is possible that osmoreceptors in the bed of the internal carotid artery are not responsive to stimulation under the conditions of our experiments. The animals had been operated under ether anaesthesia only 4–5 hr. before the experiment and this could have altered the sensitivity of the osmoreceptors. When the animals were water-loaded it was noted, as might be expected, that the delay before the onset of water diuresis was greater than normal, indicating that antidiuretic hormone had been liberated during the anaesthesia and operation. The antidiuretic hormone content of the posterior pituitaries of such operated animals was not less than normal, at the time of the experiment, but it is possible that the hormone is not in a physical state or position in a gland which has been recently depleted to permit its discharge into the circulation.

A second possibility concerns the concomitant secretion of oxytocin. Abrahams & Pickford (1954), found that following intracarotid injection of hypertonic NaCl in dogs, the amounts of antidiuretic hormone liberated were only about one-thirtieth of the oxytocin simultaneously released. Fraser (1937; 1942) has shown that oxytocin preparations increase the diuresis rate in water-loaded rats (but not in dogs) and that oxytocin (given in excess) can prevent the antidiuretic response to administered vaso-pressin. If, after osmotic stimulation in rats there is preponderance of the oxytocic principle in the secretion from the pituitary, then it is possible that an antidiuretic response may be obscured.

Other effects due to the injection of hypertonic solution in water-loaded rats may prevent the secretion of antidiuretic hormone or prevent the hormone from affecting urine flow. For example, as we have shown, intravenous administration of hypertonic solutions interferes with antidiuretic responses, but this alone cannot account for the failure of the intracarotid injections to cause antidiuresis. However, in experiments of this type, elevation of osmotic pressure in one arterial bed and not in others is entirely contrived by the experimental situation and could not occur normally. It must be shown, I think, that increases in the osmotic pressure of renal arterial blood do not impair antidiuretic responses to identical and simultaneous increases in caro-tid blood osmotic pressure. Such conditions must come perilously close to those which have been found by del Greco & de Wardener (1956) to result in the production of a diuresis of hypotonic urine which is not inhibited by Pitressin. Such a diuresis may be responsible for the interference with antidiuretic responses which we observed during infusion of hypertonic solutions, although it is just as likely that increases in the tonicity of the urine and changes in GFR are involved.

The experiments of Chambers, Melville, Hare & Hare (1945) in which they showed that intravenous injections of very large amounts of NaCl in hypertonic solution cause greater increases in urine volume in diabetes insipidus dogs than in normal dogs go some way to meeting these criticisms. However, in experiments of this type, in normal animals or human subjects, there seems to be an unduly great delay between the administration of hypertonic solutions and the onset of antidiuresis. An osmotic diuresis induced by the salt does not seem to be the sole explanation since for example, in experiments by Kleeman, Rubini, Lamdin & Epstein (1955) the free-water clearance was not reduced in water-loaded subjects until 30 min. after cessation of an intravenous infusion of 5 per cent. NaCl solution of 1 hr. duration.

During the last five years, numerous investigators have shown that diuresis of a hypotonic urine is not solely dependent on the dilution of electrolytes in plasma and may be induced even by administration of slightly hypertonic solutions. For example Borst and his co-workers (Blombert, Gerbandy, Molhuysen, de Vries & Borst, 1951) found that the first effect of infusing slightly hypertonic solutions into recumbent subjects was the production of a hypotonic urine similar to that obtained after simple water loading. Such observations cannot be explained by the osmoreceptor theory and it has been proposed that there are 'volume' receptors which are sensitive to changes in the circulating blood volume. Secretion of hypotonic urine can be induced by procedures which increase the effective circulating blood volume, while antidiuretic effects are produced when the effective circulating blood-volume is reduced, without increasing the plasma osmotic pressure. It was at first difficult to conceive the nature of these 'volume' receptors but it is possible that they may be the intrathoracic stretch receptors described by Henry and his colleagues (Henry, Gauer & Reeves, 1956; Henry & Pearce (1956). They point out that volume changes could be sensed by some part of the circulatory system with greater than average distensibility and suggested that the low-pressure parts of the intrathoracic circulation could play such a role. Many of the procedures which, without changes in tonicity, result in increased urine flow, and for which volume receptors had been postulated, lead to engorgement of the intrathoracic vessels and conversely, that procedures which cause antidiuresis lead to reduced filling of these vessels. However, as I pointed out earlier, there is as yet no evidence that the changes in urine secretion associated with activation of these stretch receptors are dependent upon the antidiuretic hormone.

Following the injection of hypertonic solutions, according to one theory the increase in plasma osmotic pressure will tend to increase antidiuretic hormone output while according to another view, the expansion of the extracellular fluid volume will affect the intrathoracic receptors in such a way as to enhance diuresis. In the physiological counterpart—water deprivation—this paradox is not encountered; the plasma osmotic pressure will tend to increase without a simultaneous expansion of the extracellular fluid volume.

REFERENCES

ABRAHAMS, V. C. & PICKFORD, M. (1954). Simultaneous observations on the rate of urine flow and spontaneous uterine movements in the dog and their relationship to posterior lobe activity. *J. Physiol. (Lond.)* **126,** 329–46.

AMES, R. & VAN DYKE, H. B. (1950). Antidiuretic hormone in the urine and pituitary of the kangaroo rat. *Proc. Soc. exp. Biol. (N.Y.)* **75,** 417–20.

AMES, R., MOORE, D. H. & VAN DYKE, H. B. (1950). The excretion of posterior pituitary antidiuretic hormone in the urine and its detection in the blood. *Endocrinology* **46,** 215–27.

ANDERSSON, B. (1951). Further studies on the milk ejection mechanism in sheep and goats. *Acta physiol. scand.* **23,** 24–30.

ANDERSSON, B. & LARSON, S. (1954). Inhibitory effect of emesis on water diuresis in the dog. *Acta physiol. scand.* **32,** 19–27.

BLOMBERT, G., GERBANDY, J., MOLHUYSEN, J. A., DE VRIES, L. A. & BORST, J. G. G. (1951). Diuretic effect of isotonic saline solution compared to that of water. *Lancet* ii, 1011–5.

BLOOD, F. R., KOSMAN, M. E. & D'AMOUR, F. E. (1955). Pulmonary depressor chemoreflex in the rat. *Amer. J. Physiol.* **182,** 180–2.

CHAMBERS, G. H., MELVILLE, E. V., HARE, R. S. & HARE, K. (1945). Regulation of the release of pituitrin by changes in the osmotic pressure of plasma. *Amer. J. Physiol.* **144,** 311–20.

CHANG, H. C., CHIA, K. F., HUANG, J. J. & LIM, R. K. S. (1939). Vagus-post-pituitary reflex; antidiuretic effect. *Chin. J. Physiol.* **14,** 161–72.

DEXTER, O., STONER, H. B. & GREEN, H. M. (1954). The release of posterior pituitary antidiuretic hormone by adenosine triphosphate. *J. Endocr.* **11,** 142–59.

DICKER, S. E. (1953). A method for the assay of very small amounts of antidiuretic activity with a note on the antidiuretic titre of rats' blood. *J. Physiol. (Lond.)* **122,** 149–57.

DICKER, S. E. (1954). The fate of the antidiuretic activity of Pitressin in rats. *J. Physiol. (Lond.)* **124,** 464–75.

FRASER, A. M. (1937). The diuretic action of the oxytocic hormone of the pituitary gland and its effect on the assay of pituitary extracts. *J. Pharmacol.* **60,** 89–95.

FRASER, A. M. (1942). The action of the oxytocin hormone of the pituitary gland in urine secretion. *J. Physiol. (Lond.)* **101,** 236–51.

FRIEDEN, J. & KELLAR, A. D. (1954). Decreased resistance to haemorrhage in neurohypophysectomized dogs. *Circulation Res.* **2,** 214–20.

GAUER, O. H., HENRY, J. P., SIEKER, H. O. & WENDT, W. E. (1954). The effect of negative pressure breathing on urine flow. *J. Clin. Invest.* **33,** 287–96.

GINSBURG, M. & HELLER, H. (1953). Antidiuretic activity in blood from various parts of the cardiovascular system. *J. Endocr.* **9,** 274–82.

DEL GRECO, F. & DE WARDENER, H. E. (1956). The effect on urine osmolarity of a transient reduction in glomerular filtration rate and solute output during a 'water' diuresis. *J. Physiol. (Lond.)* **131,** 307–16.

HENRY, J. P., GAUER, O. H. & REEVES, J. L. (1956). Evidence of the atrial location of receptors influencing urine flow. *Circulation Res.* **4,** 85–90.

HENRY, J. P. & PEARCE, J. W. (1956). The possible role of cardiac atrial stretch receptors in the induction of changes in urine flow. *J. Physiol. (Lond.)* **131,** 572–85.

HILD, W. & ZETLER, G. (1953). Experimenteller Beweis fur die Entstehung der sog Hypophysen-hinterlappenwirkstoffe im Hypothalamus. *Pflügers Arch. ges. Physiol.* **257,** 169–201.

KLEEMAN, C. R., RUBINI, M. G., LAMDIN, E. & EPSTEIN, F. H. (1955). Studies on alcohol diuresis. II. The evaluation of ethyl alcohol as an inhibitor of the neurohypophysis. *J. Clin. Invest.* **34,** 448–55.

LEWIS, A. A. G. (1953). The control of the renal excretion of water. *Ann. roy. Coll. Surg. Engl.* **13,** 36–54.

NOBLE, R. L. & TAYLOR, N. B. G. (1953). Antidiuretic substances in human urine after haemorrhage, fainting, dehydration and acceleration. *J. Physiol. (Lond.)* **122,** 220–37.

ROTHBALLER, A. B. (1953). Changes in the rat neurohypophysis induced by painful stimuli with particular reference to neurosecretory material. *Anat. Rec.* **115,** 21–42.

RYDIN, H. & VERNEY, E. B. (1938). The inhibition of water diuresis by emotional stress and by muscular exercise. *Quart. J. exp. Physiol.* **27,** 343–74.

SCHARRER, E. & SCHARRER, B. (1954). Hormones produced by neurosecretory cells. *Recent Progr. Hormone Res.* **10,** 183–240.

SHANNON, J. A. (1942). The control of the renal excretion of water. II. The rate of liberation of the posterior pituitary antidiuretic hormone in the dog. *J. exp. Med.* **76,** 387–99.

VERNEY, E. B. (1947). The antidiuretic hormone and the factors which determine its release. *Proc. roy. Soc.* B **135,** 25.

Discussion

Chairman : G. W. Harris

Lloyd. We have a few experiments on the injection of hypertonic solution in rats which were done quite differently from those of Dr. Ginsburg. These were in animals which had been dehydrated for 48 hr. With moderate dehydration of this degree we found an increase in antidiuretic activity in the hypothalamus. When the animals were given hypertonic saline very rapidly—so rapidly indeed that a number had convulsions—we found a decrease in the antidiuretic hormone content of the neuro-hypophysis. I wonder if it was a question of the animals being anaesthetized or a question of the very rapid injection not permitting mixing with the rest of the circulating blood or else acting as a non-specific stress.

Jewell. Dr. Ginsburg has given us many possible reasons why the results he got should differ from those of Verney and it is quite clear there are an enormous number of factors involved here, making it very difficult to find one's way amongst them. A few points did occur to me while Dr. Ginsburg was talking. The first relates to the blood distribution. We ought to be quite sure that the blood was reaching the brain. There is great variation between animals in this regard. In the dog, for example, usually only the most anterior part of the hypothalamus receives carotid blood and the rest of the brain posterior to it is supplied by the vertebrals. In the goat on the other hand, as Dr. Andersson and I have recently discovered, the whole of the brain is supplied by blood from the carotids. I believe the rat has quite a good vertebral supply so that there might be something here that should be looked at further, although your experiments with radio-active sodium did suggest that carotid blood was reaching the hypothalamus, and hence this argument is met. I wonder whether the dextrose may be responsible for the discrepancy. It will be remembered that Verney found that dextrose failed to release hormone when used to raise the osmotic pressure of the blood, and I believe he did entertain the idea that there may actually be an interference with the output of the hormone or its release directly due in some way to the dextrose or to the insulin released by it, in addition to the dextrose being an ineffective osmotic stimulant. Could this factor affect your experiments? Those unanaesthetized rats, I suppose, must be restrained in some way. I wonder if emotional disturbance and release of adrenaline might be interfering at the hypothalamic or renal level. In experiments on the dog, using intracarotid infusions of sodium chloride, I think you could get a masking of the effect of the antidiuretic hormone, when the quantities released are very small, by a direct osmotic or filtration effect upon the kidney. Sometimes during the period of infusion of hypertonic solutions into the carotid, the urine flow rises during the ten minutes' infusion period, and antidiuresis only appears, if at all, after you stop the infusion. Under your experimental conditions these factors might be of greater importance. Finally there is the question of the water load. In the experiments which I showed the other afternoon when Dr. Andersson and I had kept a dog hydrated for ten days, we didn't actually do that to look at the neurosecretory material, for we are novices in the study of neurosecretion. We really wanted to see whether the responses to intracarotid infusion of hypertonic solutions were the same before and after this period of hydration. We found when we gave a previously effective intracarotid injection, that there was no response after the prolonged period of hydration.

Ginsburg. To deal first with Dr. Lloyd's point. I think that the conditions of his experiments are so much different from ours that little can be gained by comparing them at the present moment. To turn to Dr. Jewell's point about the distribution of the injection in the brain, we did find more radio-sodium in the right hypothalamus than in the left side when the injection was made into the right internal carotid artery; also I think that Daniel, Dawes & Pritchard (*Philos. Trans.* B **237**, 173, 1953) have shown that in the rat the anastomotic arteries are absent and thus internal carotid injections in rats have a better chance of reaching intracranial receptors than in dogs. Rats produce urine rather quickly, and after oral administration of water it is very difficult to keep a sufficient water load in the animal. That is why we used dextrose infusions. However, we did a number of experiments with water-loading by mouth which showed that the dextrose was not interfering; we used water loads ranging from 2–8 per cent. of the body weight and the results obtained didn't seem to depend on the water load. The animals were not restrained in any way; they were placed in wooden boxes with Perspex lids which do not quite cover the whole of the box top so that there is a little slit at one side; the tubes connected to the various cannulae in the animal pass out through this slit and the rats can turn round and move about inside the box as they wish. I was very interested to hear, however, that in dogs you have occasionally obtained results rather like ours.

Pickford. I thought that was a very fascinating account and if you really have found a use for vasopressin *per se* it is really important and interesting. Dr. Jewell has already made some of the points that I had in mind and a number of others as well. There is one on which I have personal experience and that is on the question of anaesthetizing animals only a few hours before making observations. When I was wanting to make observations on water diuresis under light choralose anaesthesia with the pituitary exposed so that I could manipulate it, first of all I exposed the pituitary under ether in the morning and then I proceeded to make the observations in the afternoon, but I found that urine secretion and the responses of the pituitary simply were not normal within a few hours of administering ether, so I then started doing my preliminary operation on the previous day, leaving a good twentyfour hours for recovery. I think your suggestion correct that ether anaesthesia may have something to do with the difference between your results and those obtained in dogs. The other question concerns these intrathoracic receptors, which are probably baroreceptors. We have a small bit of evidence that they are concerned in antidiuresis; it is based on the results of injecting 5-hydroxytryptamine into different parts of the circulation. If you inject 5-hydroxytryptamine into a fore-limb vein so that it reaches the intra-thoracic viscera first, then it produces its greatest antidiuretic effect.

Ginsburg. It is always possible that the recent operation and anaesthesia interfered with the responses of the pituitary; but we found, as you could see, that at least the urine flow and the responses to injected Pitressin were not abnormal in the recently operated animals.

Cole. I would like to mention two points from my own work which may have some interest in connexion with Dr. Ginsburg's paper. I have been using rats with an indwelling cannula in the external jugular vein and gave them constant infusions of isotonic Krebs-bicarbonate solution over a period of eight hours. These animals develop a very marked increase of urine flow and sodium excretion. This increased urine flow is slightly reduced by giving Pitressin intravenously in doses up to 200 mU. This, to my mind, tends to suggest that a diuresis caused by an expansion of the body-fluid volume is not inhibited by the antidiuretic hormone.

The second point is that a similar infusion of twice isotonic Krebs solution caused a significant increase of urine volume, and naturally, sodium excretion. Clearly, there was a marked diuresis under conditions where an increased output of antidiuretic hormone would be expected.

de Wardener. I am a little bit confused about these experiments in which the activity of Pitressin is measured by the rate of urine flow, because unless the rate of solute output is known it is impossible to deduce whether a change in urine flow is due to a change in the level of circulating antidiuretic hormone or to a change in solute output. Usually these tests are done with the understanding that solute output remains unchanged. If this assumption is false then changes in urine flow cannot be used as an indication of posterior pituitary hormone activity. It is then necessary to measure both the solute output and the concentration of the urine over a range of the former which is the same both before and after the experimental situation under study.

Sloper. Dr. Ginsburg's suggestion that haemorrhage may provoke the liberation of large quantities of vasopressin is of great interest to me, because it may explain a curious finding which Dr. Adams and I have made in the human hypothalamus after hypophysectomy. Now it is known that in a wide variety of animals neurosecretory material accumulates above the cut pituitary stalk. This accumulation is rarely marked before about the fourth day after operation—Dr. Stutinsky has a particularly wide experience in this field—but in the human, only 32 hr. after hypophysectomy we have found a marked accumulation of neurosecretory material above the cut pituitary stalk. Now in man there is a good deal of haemorrhage during the hypophysectomy, and I wonder if the severity of this haemorrhage could account for the apparent rapidity of the mobilization of this neurosecretory material.

O'Connor. I would like to refer to the earlier part of Dr. Ginsburg's paper—that dealing with the effects of haemorrhage and refer to experiments on the dog. Rydin & Verney (*Quart. J. exp. Physiol.* **27**, 343, 1938) found that bleeding about 40 ml. from the femoral artery produced inhibition of water diuresis. That was in dogs in which the kidneys were denervated involving a partial destruction of the sympathetic nervous system. Certainly the splanchnic nerves had been cut and I do not remember whether also the lumbar sympathetic chains were also removed. Some years ago I tried to experiment on the effect of haemorrhage on water diuresis in dogs with sympathetic system intact and found that bleeding up to 150 ml. from the jugular vein had no effect on water diuresis. I have not gone any further than this, as there seemed to be no problem to investigate.

I can also say that occlusion of both carotid arteries in the conscious dog does not produce an inhibition of water diuresis—rather in fact a small increase in urine flow—so that it appears that release of antidiuretic hormone cannot be mediated through the carotid sinus baroreceptors.

Ginsburg. I wonder whether withdrawal of even as much as 100 ml. of blood from a vein in a conscious dog would have much effect upon blood pressure.

O'Connor. I don't know anything about the change of blood pressure, the pulse rate fell rather than increased.

Heller. When Dr. Ginsburg removed relatively small volumes of venous blood, one or two millilitres in rats, he couldn't show any increase of antidiuretic activity in the blood. He had to remove quite considerable volumes which are not comparable to those in Rydin & Verney's experiments on dogs or perhaps even to those in Lewis's (*Ann. roy. Coll. Surg. Engl.* **13**, 36, 1953) experiments in man.

Chalmers. Lewis, Pawan and I (Chalmers, Lewis & Pawan, *J. Physiol., Lond.* **117,** 218, 1952) did some experiments in man in which we put venous cuffs on the legs removing from the effective circulation about 700 ml. of blood by trapping it in the legs: we never had any evidence of antidiuretic hormone release except when the subjects fainted.

Heller. That is the same result as that obtained by Professor Noble.

Chalmers. Yes. In man, short of fainting, we did not get any release of antidiuretic hormone. With regard to the effect of hypertonic saline infusion in man under the conditions of the Hickey and Hare test, that is 2·5 per cent. sodium chloride intravenously up to a total of 700 ml. in about 40 min., you usually get an antidiuretic effect although this is opposed by a sharp rise of G.F.R. and by the osmotic diuresis.

Walker. Did I understand Dr. Ginsburg correctly that after ether when you bleed out a rat you get an increase in the vasopressor activity in the neurohypophysis?

Ginsburg. That happens in pentobarbitone anaesthesia. It did not change in ether.

Walker. Dr. Martini and I have been doing some experiments and we have found in dogs rather higher figures for antidiuretic activity in the pituitary than say Dicker & Tyler (*J. Physiol., Lond.* **120**, 141, 1953). These dogs happened to have been bled out under ether and I was hoping that that might be the explanation.

Garrod. When Dr. Cates and I were using the Hickey and Hare test we encountered a case of primary polydipsia who showed only a minimal antidiuretic response to the infusion. This patient was excreting enormous quantities of chloride at the time and we discovered later that she had been on a very high salt intake. It is possible for an osmotic diuresis to mask liberation of antidiuretic hormone or the effect of Pitressin. A few days later the patient responded quite normally to Pitressin.

Sawyer. I would just like to add something along these lines as far as the rat is concerned. There the filtration rate is extremely labile and a very slight change in G.F.R. will change the sodium load to the distal tubules tremendously. Have you determined sodium or osmotic excretion during these diuresis? In a rat loaded with lots of hypertonic sodium, large doses of antidiuretic hormone will give you an enhancement of diuresis and not an antidiuresis.

Ginsburg. I am quite sure that one of the possibilities, as I have mentioned, is that changes in tonicity of the urine or the G.F.R. obscure antidiuretic effects. In our experiments we were measuring urine flow at one minute intervals and the very rapid changes which occurred did not permit the use of clearance techniques. In any case, we failed to observe antidiuresis following intracarotid injection of hypertonic solutions in animals in which we could show that identical salt loading did not abolish the antidiuretic effect of Pitressin, although it was modified. Therefore I do not think that our failure to get antidiuretic responses during the intracarotid infusion can be entirely attributed to the effect of salt-loading, on either the solute concentration in urine or on G.F.R.

Croxatto. I was very interested in Dr. Ginsburg's observations. We were able to show in cats which were under the influence of a continuous infusion of hypertonic sodium chloride solution that when they were given a rather high dose of Pitressin there was an enhancement of the diuresis which was dependent upon an increase in blood pressure.

Morel. We have done some experiments in rats in which we followed the changes in urine flow and the changes in sodium output by measuring radio-sodium in the urine by a continuous method. We injected hypertonic sodium chloride solution rapidly followed by a volume of distilled water to make the whole injection isotonic. We observed an antidiuretic effect with an enormous increase in sodium concentration, typical of antidiuretic hormone release. When the sodium chloride was given as a single isotonic injection there was a diuretic response without an increase in the sodium concentration in the urine. We have done the same experiments in animals with diabetes insipidus produced by hypothalamic lesions and they did not show this response and we think that we have stimulated the neurohypophysis by the increase in osmotic pressure.

Ginsburg. I was aware of and rather worried by Dr. Morel's (*Bull. biol. France Belg. Suppl.* **39**, 1955) experiments as his results seemed not to agree with our own. We repeated Dr. Morel's experiments and when the experimental conditions were exactly the same as his we got the same results. That is, in rats anaesthetized with pento-barbitone, rapid intravenous injection of 9·0 per cent. NaCl solution followed by distilled water produced an antidiuretic response (Morel also found that ammonium chloride solutions produced greater antidiuretic effects than those following injection of NaCl solutions of the same tonicity.) However, in unanaesthetized rats we found that the rapid intravenous injection of 9·0 per cent. NaCl followed by distilled water had a diuretic effect which was not distinguishable from that obtained after a single slow injection of the same amount of NaCl in an isotonic solution. Also, we found in the unanaesthetized rats that while isotonic NH_4Cl injected slowly increased the urine flow, injection of strongly hypertonic NH_4Cl induced a series of violent convulsions.

On the other hand, when we repeated these experiments in rats anaesthetized with pentobarbitone, the rapid intravenous injection of hypertonic NaCl was followed by an antidiuresis. In the anaesthetized rats there were some respiratory changes following the injection. The animal either stopped breathing for a few seconds, or the respiration became so rapid and shallow that we could not see respiratory movements. We thought it would be interesting to see what happened to the blood pressure under these conditions. Firstly, in unanaesthetized rats, after rapid injection of hypertonic NaCl solution, the blood pressure rose by about 10 mm. The rats were then an-aesthetized and the injection of hypertonic NaCl solution now caused a sharp fall in blood pressure of about 45 mm. I would suggest then that the antidiuresis under these conditions is indeed due to antidiuretic hormone but that the hormone is released as a result of the fall in blood pressure and not by osmotic stimulation.

Martini. In connexion with what Dr. Ginsburg said about the relationships between buffer nerves and antidiuretic hormone secretion, I want to emphasize that we have observed that in dogs after bilateral vagatomy and section of both carotid sinus nerves, the amount of antidiuretic activity in the cerebospinal fluid is increased. This augmentation of antidiuretic hormone secretion maybe of some importance in maintaining the rise of blood pressure generally observed in debuffered dogs.

Polydipsia, antidiuresis and milk ejection caused by hypothalamic stimulation

by

BENGT ANDERSSON

Department of Physiology, Veterinärhögskolan, Stockholm

During the last half-century it has become more and more obvious that the hypothalamo-neurohypophysial system plays a very important role in the regulation of water metabolism. Most of the experimental work and the majority of clinical observations made, have stressed its importance in the control of the conservation of water by the kidney, but the possibility that the hypothalamus may also control water intake has been considered much more rarely. Thus the polydipsia seen after an interruption of the supraoptico-neurohypophysial tract, or after lesions in the ventral hypothalamus has in most cases been shown to be secondary to a preceding polyuria (Richter, 1935; Fisher, Magoun & Hetherington, 1938; Fisher, Ingram & Ranson, 1938).

Various theories have been formulated to explain the cause and the origin of the sensation of thirst. The observation that fluid deprivation causes an increased serum osmotic pressure in the dog led Mayer, in 1900, to suggest that thirst is in some way related to hypertonicity of the 'milieu intérieur'. About twenty years later Leschke (1918) reported that the intravenous injection of strongly hypertonic NaCl solutions, used as a treatment for pulmonary bleeding, immediately causes intense thirst in the patient. Arden (1934) observed that whereas ingestion of hypertonic NaCl or $NaHCO_3$ solutions gives rise to strong thirst, ingestion of the same volume of an equally hypertonic potassium salt solution does not have this effect. Similarly, Gilman (1937) found that elevation of the osmotic pressure of the blood, caused by intravenous injections of hypertonic solutions of NaCl, causes a much greater intake of water in the dog than an equivalent rise obtained by the injection of urea. Since Cannon's (1918) 'dry mouth' theory has been more or less disproved (Montgomery, 1931; Bellows & van Wagenen, 1939; Steggerda, 1939; Archdeacon, Presnell & Walton, 1949; and others) these and other observations have made it very likely that the main factor responsible for the elicitation of thirst is a relative dehydration, that is a deficit of water relative to certain extracellular electrolytes. It has, however, remained open to discussion as to how, and where in the body, a relative dehydration becomes manifest as an urge to drink. The sensation of thirst has thus been thought either to be of 'general origin' or to originate from special 'thirst receptors' localized somewhere in the body.

Since the classical studies of Verney (1947) it has been generally accepted that osmoreceptors, localized in the hypothalamus, control the conservation of water by the kidney by regulating the release of antidiuretic hormone from the neurohypo-

131

physis. Wolf (1950), on the basis of an osmometric analysis of thirst in man, has suggested that the sensation of thirst originates in the same or similar osmoreceptors as those which Verney had found to regulate the release of antidiuretic hormone from the neurohypophysis. Earlier than this, however, evidence had been given that the hypothalamus was in some way involved in the regulation not only of water excretion but also of water intake. Baily & Bremer (1921) had found that lesions in the hypothalamus of dogs sometimes produced polydipsia on the day of operation, although polyuria did not appear until the next day. Also a few clinical cases have been reported in which polydipsia did not seem to be the consequence of a preceding polyuria (Fulton & Baily, 1929; Kourilsky, 1950 and others). Some of Hess's (1932) experiments also implied that the urge to drink may originate from the hypothalamus. Thus Brügger (1943), reviewing these experiments in which electrical stimulation of the hypothalamus in cats had caused abnormal hunger, noted that in some instances the animals had shown a preference for milk as contrasted to meat which suggests that they might also have drunk water if it had been offered to them.

POLYDIPSIA ELICITED BY INTRAHYPOTHALAMIC INJECTIONS OF HYPERTONIC SALINE

That hypothalamic stimulation can cause polydipsia was ultimately shown in the goat (Andersson, 1952, 1953). Andersson (1951) had found that intracarotid injections of hypertonic saline could cause milk ejection in the lactating goat. This observation led to a study of the effect of intrahypothalamic injections of 0·1 to 0·2 ml. of 1·5 to 2 per cent. NaCl solutions on water intake and it was found that injections made medially into a fairly wide area in the hypothalamus, often caused drinking of large amounts of water. This polydipsia was followed by a polyuria which, however, did not commence until about two hours after the ingestion of water. Later, Andersson & McCann (1955a) obtained the same effect from injections of much smaller amounts of hypertonic saline (less than 0·01 ml. of a 2 or 3 per cent. NaCl solution) given in approximately the same region of the hypothalamus. The main disadvantage of these injections was that the effect could not be easily repeated. The same authors (1955a, b) therefore tried electrical stimulation using Hess's (1932, 1949) technique.

POLYDIPSIA INDUCED BY ELECTRICAL STIMULATION

In general the results of electrical stimulation showed that this was a convenient and effective way to study hypothalamic polydipsia in the goat: experimentally induced drinking could be repeated at will, and the area concerned in the response could be more closely localized than in the injection experiments. The area was found to extend from the dorsal into the ventral hypothalamus, to have its anterior pole approximately at the level of a transverse section through the anterior commissure and to reach posteriorly as far as to the tract of Vicq d'Azyr (Fig. 1: black and open circles). The latency period before the onset of drinking was short—in many cases only about 5 sec.—and the animals stopped drinking a few seconds after the end of stimulation. As a rule they drank continuously during the periods of stimulation and, by prolonged stimulation could be induced to drink volumes of water up to 40 per cent. of their body-weight within short periods of time, an overhydration which was seen to produce haemolysis, haemoglobinuria and other signs of water intoxication

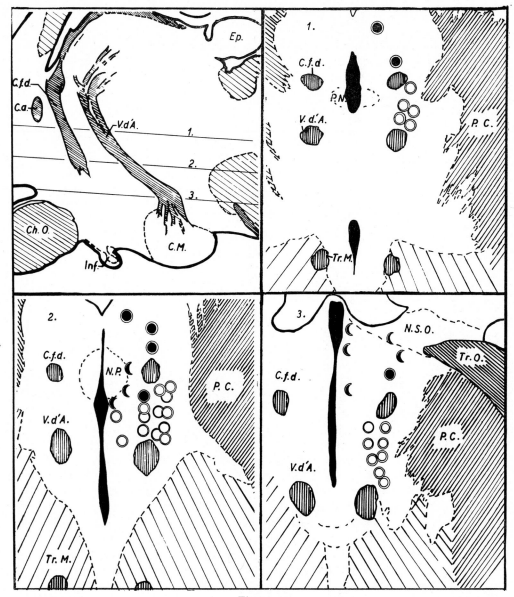

Figure 1

Points in the hypothalamus where electrical stimulation evoked drinking, inhibition of water diuresis and milk ejection.
Diagrams of a sagittal section, and, corresponding to the lines labelled 1, 2 and 3, three horizontal sections
(1, 2 and 3) through the hypothalamus of the goat.
Black circles: Points where electrical stimulation caused drinking, inhibition of water diuresis and milk ejection.
Open circles: Points where drinking was obtained in the absence of antidiuresis and milk ejection.
Black crescents: Points where stimulation produced inhibition of water diuresis and milk ejection, but no drinking.

C.a.:	Commissura anterior	*N.P.:*	Nucleus paraventricularis
C.f.d.:	Columna fornicis descendens	*N.S.O.:*	Nucleus supraopticus
C.M.:	Corpus mammillare	*P.C.:*	Pedunculus cerebri
Ch.O.:	Chiasma opticum	*Tr. M.:*	Tractus Meynert
Ep.:	Epiphysis	*V.d'A.:*	Tractus Vicq d'Azyr.
Inf.:	Infundibulum		

(From Andersson & McCann, 1955*b*.)

133

(Plate 1). When tested during such periods of stimulation the animals would accept a weak mixture of urine and water but would refuse to drink a more concentrated solution. Also, in other ways, the character of the polydipsia seen in these experiments gave the impression that the stimulus did cause a conscious urge to drink. Thus the animals went to the water by themselves even when it was placed in the opposite corner of the pen.

From these observations, taken together with the remarkable reproducibility of the polydipsic effect, the question arose whether the goats could get conditioned to the hypothalamic stimuli. Andersson & Larsson (1956) therefore made attempts to condition the polydipsic effect of electrical stimulation in the hypothalamus of the goat. In spite of up to 110 combinations of neutral and electrical stimuli, the neutral stimuli alone never caused the animals to drink—they did not even show any interest in the water offered. However, electrical stimulation of the 'drinking centre' combined with neutral stimuli never failed to evoke drinking of water after a very short latency period.

INHIBITION OF WATER DIURESIS AND MILK EJECTION AS RESULTS OF HYPOTHALAMIC STIMULATION

In most of the experiments done by Andersson & McCann (1955b) to 'map' the localization of the 'drinking area' of the hypothalamus, the effects of stimulation on water diuresis and on the flow of milk from cannulated teats were also measured. Stimulation in the anterior part of the 'drinking area' was found to cause inhibition of water diuresis of neurohypophysial type and ejection of milk simultaneously with polydipsia (Fig. 1: black circles). Stimulation in its posterior part did not seem to cause any release of hormone from the neurohypophysis (Fig. 1: open circles). Stimulation within or in regions adjacent to the paraventricular nuclei did not cause drinking of water, but did produce inhibition of water diuresis and ejection of milk (Fig. 1: horizonal section 2, black crescents). Similarly, stimulation within the supraoptic nuclei, or in the vicinity of the supraoptico-neurohypophysial tract, caused, as expected, inhibition of water diuresis (Harris, 1947) and milk ejection (Andersson, 1951; Cross & Harris, 1951), but failed to produce polydipsia (Fig. 1: horizontal section 3, black crescents). The inhibition of water diuresis seen in these experiments lasted from 45 to 60 min. During the period of inhibition there was a marked rise in the urinary concentration of Na^+, K^+ and Cl^- and in specific gravity; the total amounts of electrolytes excreted showed less consistent changes: Usually more Na^+ and Cl^- was excreted during the period of inhibition, but sometimes there was no obvious increase or even a small decrease. Increases in the excretion of potassium were even less consistent. There was no significant change in endogenous creatinine clearance during the period of inhibition.

Milk ejection, which was always combined with antidiuresis, began one to two minutes after the onset of stimulation, but since it was only visually determined by the increased flow of milk from the cannulated teats, no quantitative measure of the response could be obtained from the experiments.

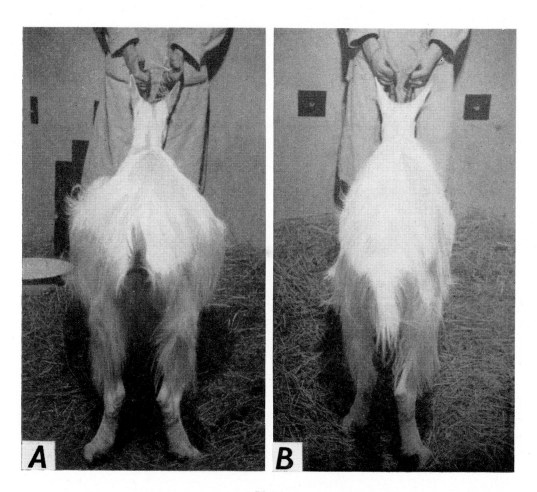

Plate I

The appearance of a goat immediately after it had drunk 15 l. of water following electrical stimulation of the 'drinking area' in the hypothalamus (*A*).
B shows the same goat the following morning when most of the water had been eliminated.

DISCUSSION

The experiments described above indicate that the hypothalamus plays an important role in the regulation of water intake, but they do not show whether the hypothalamic 'drinking area' is really essential for the development of an urge to drink. A number of clinical cases have been reported in whom injury to the basal portion of the brain was followed by increased plasma sodium and chloride concentrations. This finding has been interpreted by some workers as the result of damage of either a 'thirst centre' (Enström & Liebman, 1953; Elliot, 1955; Rothballer & Dugger, 1955), or a centre regulating the electrolyte metabolism (Welt, Seldin, Nelson, German & Peeters, 1952; Cooper, 1953). Further, Stevenson (1949) and Stevenson, Welt & Orloff (1950) have reported a decreased ratio of water to food intake, a decreased response to water loads, and moderately elevated plasma sodium concentrations in rats with hypothalamic obesity. These findings were interpreted as indicating the existence of a state of 'hypothalamic hypodypsia'. Still more striking are results briefly reported by Witt, Keller, Batsel & Lynch (1952), who found that the extension of the lesions of diabetes insipidus dogs dorsally and laterally, may result in temporary or even permanent adipsia. Their adipsic dogs ate and took tasty fluids like milk and broth but refused to drink water even when they became severely dehydrated. Similar experiments were later done by Andersson & McCann (1956): Having determined the localization of the 'drinking area' in the hypothalamus of the goat, they tried to inactivate as much as possible of the corresponding part of the brain in dogs by electrocoagulation, without destroying the supraoptic-neurohypophysial connexions. Such lesions caused permanent hypodipsia or adipsia lasting up to 14 days after the operation; the animals, in contrast to the absence of 'thirst', ate and drank milk and broth readily when offered. The degree of hypodipsia seemed to be roughly proportional to the extent of destruction of the same area of the hypothalamus, which on stimulation evokes drinking in the goat. However, no correlation was found in these experiments between the adipsia and the eventual presence of diabetes insipidus.

Thus strong evidence is now available that an essential thirst centre is located in the hypothalamus, since stimulation within a well-defined hypothalamic region produces drinking, whereas destructive lesions in the same region result in a marked decrease in water intake.

The thirst receptors seem to be localized in the portion of the hypothalamus outlined by the response to electrical stimulation but the physiological stimulus has not been determined. The osmotic stimuli discussed on p. 132 may have activated 'thirst receptors' in the hypothalamus but it cannot be ruled out that the polydipsia seen after intrahypothalamic injections of hypertonic saline was due to a non-specific effect. Further it is not clear from our results whether the regulation of water intake and that of water excretion involves distinct groups of receptors. If all the presumed osmoreceptors in the hypothalamus have a dual function in the regulation of both water intake and output, one would expect that their stimulation would induce both drinking and a release of antidiuretic hormone from the neurohypophysis. Both drinking and inhibition of water diuresis were indeed found after stimulation of the rostral portion of the 'drinking area'. Thus, if the osmoreceptors have a dual function, they

135

would be expected to lie in that region. In this case the caudal portion of the 'drinking area' from which antidiuresis could not be elicited might represent fibres passing from the receptors to higher centres, or may contain 'thirst receptors' of another kind. A second explanation would be that there are two groups of osmoreceptors in the hypothalamus, i.e. one group concerned with the conservation of water by the kidneys and the other with water intake. The two groups would then be localized in two areas which overlap in the region where both drinking and inhibition of water diuresis can be evoked by stimulation. Thirdly, since stimulations in or adjacent to, the paraventricular nuclei caused inhibition of water diuresis, the inhibition of water diuresis, which was obtained in the region where drinking could also be induced, may have been due to stimulation of fibres running from the paraventricular to the supraoptic nuclei and/or to the neurohypophysis. The results presented do not allow a decision between these and other explanations.

The fact that antidiuresis could be obtained when stimuli were applied within the paraventricular nuclei or in their vicinity, is at variance with Harris's (1947) findings in the rabbit that such stimuli do not cause inhibition of water diuresis.

Milk ejection was always seen combined with inhibition of water diuresis. This is consistent with the hypothesis (Abel & Nagayama, 1920) that only one hormone is released from the neurohypophysis, or that both antidiuretic and oxytocic hormones are released together. The observation (Andersson, 1951), that intracarotid injections of hypertonic saline can cause milk ejection in the goat, and the more thorough studies of Abrahams & Pickford (1954), showing that a variety of stimuli (such as emotion, intracarotid or intravenous injection of hypertonic saline solutions or of acetylcholine) inhibit water diuresis by liberation of antidiuretic hormone and also cause increased uterine activity in the dog, may also be interpreted as supporting the unitary hypothesis. However, although milk ejection could easily be demonstrated by observing milk flow in the goat, no conclusions could be drawn as to the amount of oxytocic activity responsible for this effect.

Milk ejection, caused by electrical stimulation in the paraventricular region, has also been described by Cross (1955) in the rabbit, but only after adrenalectomy. Cross (1953) showed in the same species that adrenaline blocked the response of the mammary gland to oxytocin by a peripheral action. He found that stimulation near the paraventricular nuclei also activates the sympathetico-adrenal system, and that this in turn inhibits the response of the mammary gland to oxytocin. It may be that stimulation of the paraventricular nuclei in the larger brain of the goat does not activate the sympathetico-adrenal system sufficiently to cause peripheral blocking of the mammary response.

SUMMARY

Injections of hypertonic sodium chloride solutions into, and electrical stimulation within a fairly wide region of the hypothalamus, were found to induce polydipsia in the goat. Electrical stimulation of the anterior portion of this 'drinking area', caused inhibition of water diuresis of the neurohypophysial type, and also milk-ejection, simultaneously with the drinking of water. Antidiuresis and milk ejection were not observed when the posterior part of the 'drinking area' was stimulated.

Electrical stimulation of the paraventricular nuclei or adjacent sites caused inhibition of water diuresis and milk-ejection, but no drinking of water.

The significance of these results is discussed.

REFERENCES

ABEL, J. J. & NAGAYAMA, T. X. (1920). On the presence of histamine in extracts of the posterior lobe of the pituitary gland and on preliminary experiments with the pressor constituent. *J. Pharmacol.* **15,** 347–99.

ABRAHAMS, V. C. & PICKFORD, M. (1954). Simultaneous observations on the rate of urine flow and spontaneous uterine movements in the dog, and their relationship to posterior lobe activity. *J. Physiol. (Lond.)* **126,** 329–46.

ANDERSSON, B. (1951). Some observations on the neuro-hormonal regulation of milk ejection. *Acta physiol. scand.* **23,** 1–7.

ANDERSSON, B. (1952). Polydipsia caused by intrahypothalamic injections of hypertonic NaCl solutions. *Experientia* **8,** 157.

ANDERSSON, B. (1953). The effect of injections of hypertonic NaCl solutions into different parts of the hypothalamus of goats. *Acta physiol. scand.* **28,** 188–201.

ANDERSSON, B. & MCCANN, S. M. (1955*a*). A further study of polydipsia evoked by hypothalamic stimulation in the goat. *Acta physiol. scand.* **33,** 333–46.

ANDERSSON, B. & MCCANN, S. M. (1955*b*). Drinking, antidiuresis and milk ejection from electrical stimulation within the hypothalamus of the goat. *Acta physiol. scand.* **35,** 191–201.

ANDERSSON, B. & MCCANN, S. M. (1956). The effect of hypothalamic lesions on the water intake of the dog. *Acta physiol. scand.* **35,** 312–20.

ANDERSSON, B. & LARSSON, S. (1956). An attempt to condition hypothalamic polydipsia. *Acta physiol. scand.* In the press.

ARCHDEACON, J. W., PRESNELL, M. W. & WALTON, C. J. (1949). Effects of atropine on food ingestion and water drinking in dogs. *Amer. J. Physiol.* **157,** 149–52.

ARDEN, F. (1934). Experimental observations on thirst and on potassium overdosage. *Aust. J. exp. Biol. med. Sci.* **12,** 121–2.

BAILY, P. & BREMER, F. (1921). Experimental diabetes insipidus. *Arch. intern. Med.* **28,** 773–803.

BELLOWS, R. T. & VAN WAGENEN, W. P. (1939). Effect of resection of olfactory, gustatory and trigeminal nerves on water drinking in dogs without and with diabetes insipidus. *Amer. J. Physiol.* **126,** 13–19.

BRÜGGER, M. (1943). Fresstrieb als hypothalamisches Symptom. *Helv. physiol. pharmacol. acta.* **1,** 183–98.

CANNON, W. B. (1918). The physiological basis of thirst. *Proc. roy. Soc. B* **90,** 283–301.

COOPER, I. S. (1953). Disorders of electrolyte metabolism in diseases of the central nervous system *Neurology* **3,** 119–25.

CROSS, B. A. & HARRIS, G. W. (1951). The neurohypophysis and 'let-down' of milk. *J. Physiol. (Lond.)*. **113,** 35P.

CROSS, B. A. (1953). Sympathetico-adrenal inhibition of the neurohypophyseal milk-ejection mechanism. *J. Endocr.* **9,** 7–18.

CROSS, B. A. (1955). The hypothalamus and the mechanism of sympathetico-adrenal inhibition of milk ejection. *J. Endocr.* **12,** 15–28.

ELLIOT, A. (1955). Hyperchloremia, azotemia and pulmonary edema of cerebral origin. *Acta. med. scand.* **150,** 467–76.

ENGSTRÖM, W. W. & LIEBMAN, A. (1953). Chronic hyperosmolarity of body fluids with central lesion causing diabetes insipidus and anterior pituitary insufficiency. *Amer. J. Med.* **15,** 180–6.

FISHER, C., MAGOUN, H. W. & HETHERINGTON, A. (1938). Effect of water deprivation on fluid exchange of cats with diabetes insipidus. *Amer. J. Physiol.* **121,** 112–22.

FISHER, C., INGRAM, W. R. & RANSON, S. W. (1938). *Diabetes insipidus and the neuro-hormonal control of water balance.* Ann Arbor: Edwards.

FULTON, J. F. & BAILEY, P. (1929). Tumours in the region of the third ventricle; their diagnosis and relation to pathological sleep. *J. nerv. ment. Dis.* **69**, 1–32; 145–64; 261–77.

GILMAN, A. (1937). The relation between blood osmotic pressure, fluid distribution and voluntary water intake. *Amer. J. Physiol.* **120**, 323–8.

HARRIS, G. W. (1947). The innervation and actions of the neurohypophysis; an investigation using the method of remote-control stimulation. *Philos. Trans.* B **232**, 385–441.

HESS, W. R. (1932). *Beiträge zur Physiologie des Hirnstammes I.* Leipzig: George Thieme.

HESS, W. R. (1949). *Das Zwischenhirn.* Basel: Schwabe.

KOURILSKY, R. (1950). Diabetes insipidus. *Proc. roy. Soc. Med.* **43**, 842–43.

LESCHKE, E. (1918). Über die Durstempfindung. *Arch. Psychiat. Nervenkr.* **59**, 773–81.

MAYER, A. (1900). Variations de la tension osmotique du sang chez les animaux privés de liquides. *C. R. Soc. Biol. (Paris)* **52**, 153–5.

MONTGOMERY, M. F. (1931). The role of the salivary glands in the thirst mechanism. *Amer. J. Physiol.* **96**, 221–7.

RICHTER, C. P. (1935). The primacy of polyuria in diabetes insipidus. *Amer. J. Physiol.* **112**, 481–7.

ROTHBALLER, A. B. & DUGGER, G. S. (1955). Hypothalamic tumor. *Neurology* **5**, 160–77.

STEGGERDA, F. R. (1939). The relation of dry mouth to thirst in the human. *Amer. J. Physiol.* **126**, 635P.

STEVENSON, J. A. F. (1949). Effects of hypothalamic lesions on water and energy metabolism in the rat. *Recent Progr. Hormone Res.* **4**, 363–94.

STEVENSON, J. A. F., WELT, L. G. & ORLOFF, J. (1950). Abnormalities of water and electrolyte metabolism in rats with hypothalamic lesions. *Amer. J. Physiol.* **161**, 35–9.

WELT, L. G., SELDIN, D. W., NELSON, W. P., GERMAN, W. J. & PEETERS, J. P. (1952). Role of central nervous system in metabolism of electrolytes and water. *Arch. intern. Med.* **90**, 355–78.

VERNEY, E. B. (1947). The antidiuretic hormone and the factors which determine its release. *Proc. roy. Soc.* B **135**, 25–106.

WITT, D. M., KELLER, A. D., BATSEL, H. L. & LYNCH, J. R. (1952). Absence of thirst and resultant syndrome associated with anterior hypothalamectomy in the dog. *Amer. J. Physiol.* **171**, 780P.

WOLF, A. V. (1950). Osmometric analysis of thirst in man and dog. *Amer. J. Physiol.* **161**, 75–86.

Discussion

Chairman : G. W. Harris

Folley. Dr. Andersson spoke of adipsia and referred to dogs which would not drink water. He also said that these dogs drank milk and since milk contains some 87 per cent. water is it correct to speak of these animals as being adipsic? I should also like to ask Dr. Andersson if he used the horns of the goats to support his electrodes.

Andersson. It is not necessary to use goats with horns. We find, however, that the horns protect the electrodes.

The dogs referred to by Dr. Folley were hyperphagic, that is they ate ravenously, and we interpreted the intake of milk as eating rather than drinking. We reduced some dogs to a severe state of dehydration but they would still not take water although they would take milk.

Harris, G. W. Could Dr. Andersson relate the region he stimulated to produce polydipsia with that reported by the Yale group (Delgardo & Anand: *Amer. J. Physiol.*, **172**, 162, 1953) which resulted in change of feeding habits. If I remember correctly they stimulated a little more laterally.

Andersson. Yes, a little more laterally and more posteriorly. It is possible to see the combination of both effects in that there are points which give simultaneous drinking and eating responses. However, drinking and eating responses can be obtained individually at other points, showing that the areas concerned are at least partly separated.

Sawyer. I want to report an interesting phenomenon noticed originally in my laboratory some years ago by Gordon Gilbert, who has since pursued this work in the Department of Anatomy at New York University. He found that centrally located lesions in the region of the posterior commissure in the rat, that is in an area quite distinct from that described by Andersson in the goat, cause complete adipsia. Lesions which overlapped the sub-commissural organ, whatever that may be, cause the rats to cease drinking water and, if allowed, to dehydrate themselves to death. They would, however, take milk if offered and this could provide the necessary fluid. On withdrawal of the milk, however, they would again refuse water.

Harris, G. W. This is a most interesting observation. I believe the sub-commissural organ has a neurosecretory function. Perhaps Professor Bargmann would comment on this.

Bargmann. There is a considerable amount of Gomori positive substance in this area but it is not necessarily the same as that found in the neurohypophysis. I have no information whether its secretion or release is evoked by various stimuli.

Cross. I should like to record my admiration of the excellent stimulation experiments of Dr. Andersson. He has extended the use of the Hess technique to unanaesthetized sheep and goats and has obtained new information about special aspects of ruminant physiology, in addition to contributing to our knowledge of the physiology of the neurohypophysis.

With regard to the induction of drinking by hypothalamic stimulation, I would like to ask Dr. Andersson if he feels confident that the goats really feel thirsty or whether the response might result from activation of motor mechanisms. In his film it appeared that the latency of the drinking response grew less with repetition of the stimuli until it became so short as to make it seem unlikely that the animal had time to experience thirst subjectively before starting to drink again.

Dr. Andersson's experiments appear to be the first demonstration that stimulation of the paraventricular nuclei may cause release of antidiuretic hormone. It seems clear, moreover, from his results, that such stimulation also releases oxytocin as shown by milk ejection. Some of my own experiments agree with the latter finding. Exploratory stimulation of the hypothalamus in a series of rabbits has so far yielded twelve animals in which histological reconstruction of the stimulation points indicates that localized stimulation of the paraventricular nucleus induces release of oxytocin, as shown by either ejection of milk or by the contractile response of the oestrogenized uterus *in situ*.

It might throw some light on the problem of what is released from the neurohypophysis, and on the role of the paraventricular and supraoptic nuclei in determining this, if simultaneous recordings were made of antidiuretic and milk ejection (or uterine) responses following localized stimulation of these nuclei, and the effects compared with injections of vasopressin and oxytocin.

Andersson. It is of course impossible, with certainty, to interpret whether the goats experience a sensation of thirst. However, we think it likely since in most cases they actively search for water.

There is a facilitation of response on repetition seen as a decrease in the latency period. It has been suggested to us that this may be a conditioned reflex by which the animal learns to respond to the light signal coincident with switching on the electrical stimulus. We have investigated this experimentally and have found that the animals do not become conditioned in this way.

Dale. There is insufficient time, I take it, for the mouth to be dry.

Andersson. That is so, and one can prolong the drinking even though the mouth is being bathed with water.

Dale. There is no effect on the salivary secretion?

Andersson. I do not think that could show so quickly.

Dale. No.

de Wardener. It might be possible to investigate the difference between milk and water by applying cocaine to the tongue and nose.

Jewell. It seems likely that these dogs were attracted to milk as a food and not as a 'drink' since the dogs which Dr. Andersson and I overhydrated, would show a distinct aversion to water but would accept milk.

Garrod. Dr. Andersson's elegant experiments have shown that polydipsia can be obtained by stimulating the appropriate hypothalamic centres. Is there any evidence that similar effects may result from *lesions* to the hypothalamus in goats or any other species. This is an important problem in clinical medicine; Kourilsky (*Rev. neurol.* **74,** 264, 1942) has described a case of primary polydipsia in which there was a hypothalamic lesion without a coincident neurohypophysial defect.

Andersson. I think this was an almost isolated observation of a chronic condition. It was a cyst pressing on the hypothalamus, otherwise there are only a few observations of an acute nature.

Noble. Dr. Andersson's experiments evidently show that in some circumstances one can lead an animal to water and make him drink! Do you have any information as to whether the anterior pituitary is essential for the maintenance of drinking following stimulation as seen in the goats in your film? Has the hypophysectomized goat been studied?

Cowie. I have hypophysectomized a few goats and the animal attendants have reported a great increase in water consumption for a few days after the operation. So far, however, no measurements of water intake have been made.

Conditions under which posterior pituitary hormones increase sodium and potassium excretion by the kidney

by

F. P. BROOKS *and* M. PICKFORD

Department of Physiology, University of Edinburgh

A NUMBER of workers have noticed that, whatever the stimulus they applied to the posterior pituitary, the gland liberated simultaneously both the oxytocic and vasopressor factors (Harris, 1955). The methods of stimulation and the species of animal used have varied, so have the proportional amounts of the two substances, but in every instance more oxytocin than vasopressin appears to be released. Oxytocin is of further interest in that it has been assigned a role only in one sex in mammals, a role which may never be played, or at best only intermittently. A number of attempts have been made to determine whether oxytocin has a more general activity than that on the uterus and mammae, for instance, in the control of kidney function. In their investigations most workers have used oxytocin in doses comparable with the anti-diuretic dose of vasopressin and have obtained negative results. However, Dicker & Heller (1946) reported that when given subcutaneously to rats in doses of 3 mU./100 g. of rat glomerular filtration rate (GFR) and renal plasma flow (RPF) were increased and Cl reabsorption diminished. Taking recent work into account, it seemed desirable to re-examine the effect of vasopressin and oxytocin on the kidney using larger doses of oxytocin than previously, and also, since the two factors are always liberated together, to test whether when given simultaneously they show mutual enhancement or interference. The observations to be described, then, had as their object a fresh study of the effect of vasopressin and oxytocin on the volume of urine excreted, on its Na and K content, and on the clearance rates of diodone and creatinine, and also the discovery, if possible, of the natural conditions in which the two substances are released to produce any effect noted.

METHODS

The observations were made on conscious dogs both during water diuresis and at resting rates of urine flow. Vasopressin and oxytocin were given either as single intravenous injections or as intravenous infusions at a rate of 6–7 ml. solution/hr. A number of experiments were done using Pitocin and Pitressin (Parke, Davis and Co.) and a number using highly purified vasopressin (both the arginine and lysine varieties, though almost entirely the former) and highly purified oxytocin. The purified substances were generously supplied by Dr. du Vigneaud. The doses of oxytocin used were chosen on the basis of information obtained by Abrahams & Pickford (1954) who found that the intracarotid injection into a 12-kg. dog of a small volume of hypertonic NaCl solution induced antidiuresis equivalent to that following the intravenous injection of 3 mU. Pitressin and, at the same time, an increase in spontaneous uterine activity equivalent to that following the injection of 80–100 mU. Pitocin, i.e., apparently 25–30 times as much oxytocin as vasopressin was released as a result of an osmotic stimulus. In the following experiments, then, vasopressin was used in antidiuretic doses, namely, for a single intravenous injection 0·2 to 0·4 mU./kg. body-weight, and for infusion at the rate of 0·01–0·02 mU./kg./min., oxytocin was given in doses of 2·5 to 15 mU./kg. body-weight for single injections, or infused intravenously at the rate of 0·1 to 0·2 mU./kg./min. Clearances of creatinine and diodone were measured by the method of Pickford & Ritchie (1945) or by the technique of a priming injection followed by a maintaining infusion. Again the volume infused was at the rate of 6 to 7 ml./hr. Na and K analyses were made by means of an EEL flame photometer. The dead space of the urine collecting system was reduced as much as possible, and in a number of instances the external part of the uretheral catheter was emptied at the end of each urine collection period by blowing air through it from a T-piece inserted at the site of emergence of the catheter from the vagina. As far as possible, in all graphs, correction has been made for dead space of the urinary system.

RESULTS

The earliest experiments compared the effects of single injections of Pitocin and Pitressin. On some occasions it was found that Pitocin greatly increased Na excretion during water diuresis, whereas Pitressin did not have this effect (Fig. 1), (Brooks & Pickford, 1956). When the purified oxytocin became available it was seen that this substance never increased Na excretion during water diuresis (Fig. 2). It became necessary, then, to determine whether synergism between Pitocin and its vasopressor contaminant was responsible for the positive effect seen, or whether either Pitocin or Pitressin contained some other active factor. Both preparations, therefore, were tested after treatment with thioglycollic acid, NaOH, ascorbic acid, and trypsin. All these agents destroyed any activity previously present and did not unmask one hitherto concealed. Thus, the enhanced excretion of Na sometimes seen during water diuresis after an intravenous injection of Pitocin was difficult to explain, unless some samples of Pitocin contain a greater than usual amount of vasopressin, and there is a synergism of the two active substances.

A careful study of the effect of single injections of vasopressin and oxytocin (Fig. 2) on Na excretion during water diuresis suggests that although these substances do not strikingly increase the excretion of Na or K they do prevent the steady fall in output/ min. which is the rule in simple water diuresis (Fig. 5). On the other hand, when oxytocin is injected at resting rates of urine excretion it has a marked effect on Na excretion and a definite one on K excretion (Fig. 3). In similar circumstances vasopressin only slightly increased the rate of Na excretion but did, in the instance shown in the graph, clearly increase the excretion of K. The positive action on K excretion was not always seen. The difference in the effects of oxytocin and vasopressin does not depend on the dose given. As others have shown, small doses of oxytocin have

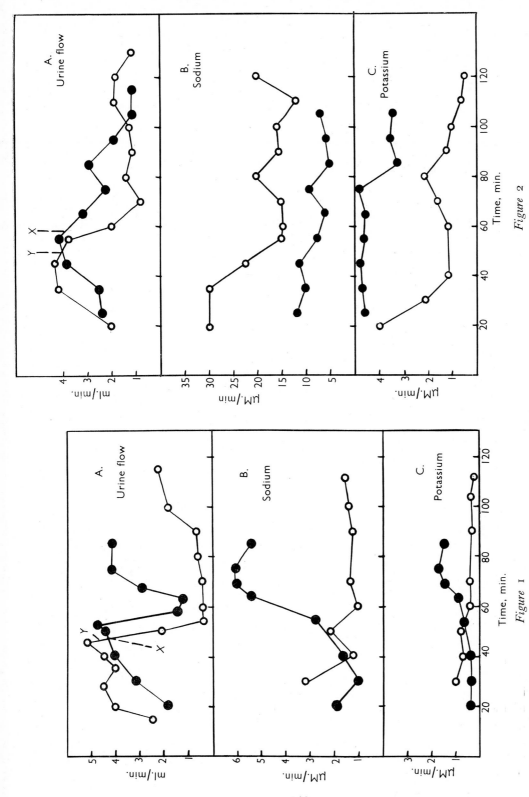

Figure 2

The effect of oxytocin and vasopressin on urine flow and Na and K excretion during water diuresis. (Thisbe, 15 kg.) 300 ml. water by mouth at zero time. Curves ●, intravenous injection of 60 mU. oxytocin at X. Curves ○——○, intravenous injection of 4 mU. vasopressin at Y.

Figure 1

The effect of Pitocin and Pitressin on urine flow and Na and K excretion during water diuresis. (Thisbe, 15 kg.) 300 ml. water by mouth at zero time. Curves ●——●, intravenous injection of 100 mU. Pitocin at X. Curves ○——○, intravenous injection of 4 mU. Pitressin at Y.

143

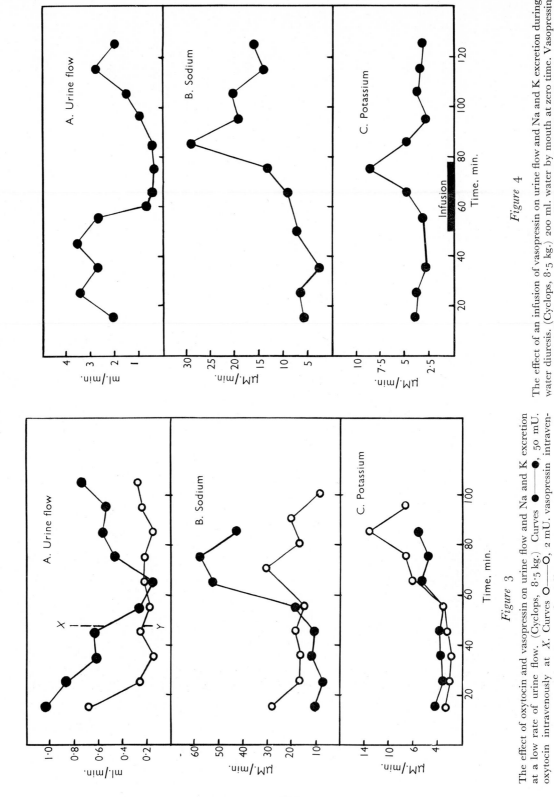

Figure 3

The effect of oxytocin and vasopressin on urine flow and Na and K excretion at a low rate of urine flow. (Cyclops, 8·5 kg.) Curves ●——●, 50 mU. oxytocin intravenously at X. Curves ○——○, 2 mU. vasopressin intravenously at Y.

Figure 4

The effect of an infusion of vasopressin on urine flow and Na and K excretion during water diuresis. (Cyclops, 8·5 kg.) 200 ml. water by mouth at zero time. Vasopressin infused at the rate of 0·1 mU./min. during period indicated.

144

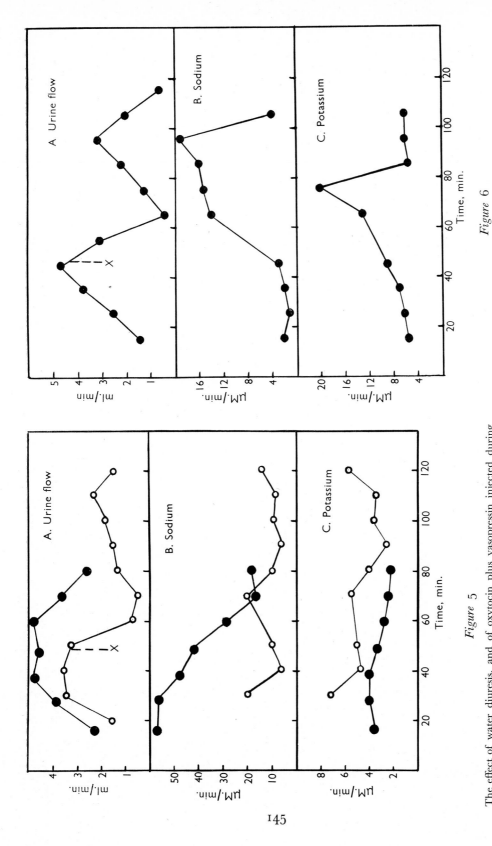

Figure 6

The effect of oxytocin plus Pitressin on rate of urine flow and on Na and K excretion during water diuresis. (Jess, 21 kg.) 350 ml. water by mouth at zero time. 150 mU. oxytocin plus 3 mU. Pitressin injected intravenously at *X*.

Figure 5

The effect of water diuresis, and of oxytocin plus vasopressin injected during diuresis, on rate of urine flow and Na and K excretion. (Cyclops, 8·5 kg.) 200 ml. water by mouth at zero time. Curves ———●, control water diuresis. Curves ○———○, 50 mU. oxytocin plus 1·6 mU. vasopressin injected intravenously at *X*.

145

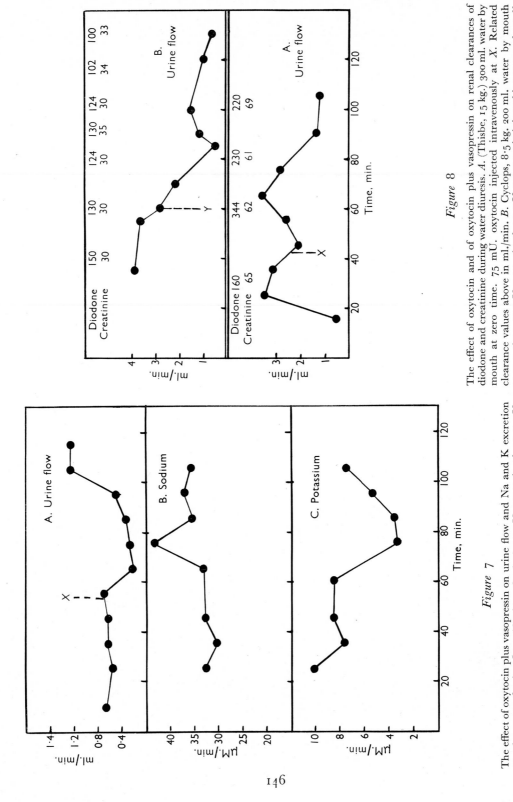

Figure 8

The effect of oxytocin and of oxytocin plus vasopressin on renal clearances of diodone and creatinine during water diuresis. *A.* (Thisbe, 15 kg.) 300 ml. water by mouth at zero time. 75 mU. oxytocin injected intravenously at *X*. Related clearance values above in ml./min. *B.* Cyclops, 8·5 kg. 200 ml. water by mouth at zero time. 25 mU. oxytocin plus 2 mU. vasopressin injected intravenously at *Y*. Related clearance values above in ml./min.

Figure 7

The effect of oxytocin plus vasopressin on urine flow and Na and K excretion at a low rate of urine flow. (Cyclops, 8·5 kg.) 50 mU. oxytocin plus 2·5 mU. vasopressin injected intravenously at *X*.

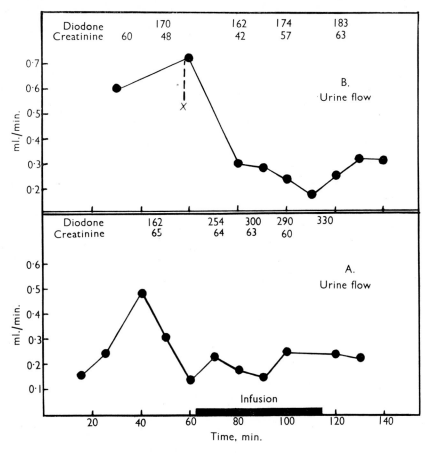

Figure 9

The effect of Pitocin and of Pitocin plus vasopressin on clearances of diodone and creatinine at a low rate of urine flow. *A.* (Thisbe, 15 kg.) Pitocin infused intravenously
during time indicated at rate of 2 mU./min. Related clearance values above in ml./min.
B. (Jess, 21 kg.) 75 mU. Pitocin plus 2 mU. vasopressin injected intravenously at *X*.
Related clearance values above in ml./min.

no discoverable action on renal activity. 40 or 20 mU. vasopressin only transitorily,
i.e. for one or at most two urine samples, increased the excretion of both Na and K.
This action of vasopressin could not be differentiated from the immediate effect of
strongly antidiuretic doses of adrenaline or 5-hydroxytryptamine. There is, then, a
clear difference between the action of single injections of vasopressin or oxytocin on
Na excretion, and between the effects of oxytocin at fast and slow rates of urine
flow. However, when vasopressin was infused during water diuresis the results
differed from those of a single injection. As can be seen in Fig. 4, it did then clearly
increase the excretion of both Na and K. These results are in agreement with those of
Anslow and Wesson (1955). It seems that vasopressin needs more time to produce
its effect on Na than does oxytocin.

The next step was to see whether oxytocin and vasopressin given simultaneously

147

had an action different from that of either given alone. The effect of the two given together in a single injection during water diuresis varied, at times the increased electrolyte excretion was minimal, but the normal fall in rate of excretion was prevented (Fig. 5), at other times there was an increase in rate of excretion of Na and K never seen during diuresis following the injection of either oxytocin or vasopressin alone (Fig. 6). At a low rate of urine flow the two factors injected together maintained a high level of Na excretion not seen in their absence nor following vasopressin alone (Fig. 7), but not as great as that following oxytocin alone.

Measurements of the clearances of diodone and creatinine brought out another difference between the actions of oxytocin and vasopressin and also showed the existence of an antagonism. Previous workers have found that the vasopressor fraction of posterior pituitary extracts given in antidiuretic doses does not alter either RPF or GFR (Maxwell & Breed, quoted by Smith, 1951; Sellwood & Verney, 1955). In Figs. 8a and 9a is shown the invariable effect of oxytocin on renal clearances in dogs, regardless of whether it was injected during water diuresis or at low rates of urine flow. The clearance of creatinine was unaffected, whilst that of diodone was increased by 75–100 per cent., whether the oxytocin was given as a single intravenous injection or as an infusion. At fairly high rates of urine flow the errors in clearance calculation due to renal dead space are small compared with those during low rates of urine flow. Nevertheless, the magnitude of the increase in diodone clearance is such that it cannot be discounted by any possible error due to dead space. Further, the increase begins too early to be easily explained by a process of cell storage of diodone. In the example given and in other instances too, there was always about the same proportionate increase in diodone clearance. Here, then, was a second difference between the effects of oxytocin and vasopressin on the kidney. The antagonism between them was seen when the two substances were injected simultaneously. During water diuresis 2 mU vasopressin entirely suppressed the increased diodone clearance which would be expected to follow the intravenous injection of 25 mU. oxytocin alone (Fig. 8b). Fig. 9b shows that at a low rate of urine flow 2 mU. vasopressin cancelled the expected action of 75 mU. Pitocin on diodone clearance. It follows from this then, that the observed fact that during antidiuresis of pituitary origin the clearances remain normal, does not controvert the possibility that oxytocin is at the same time released in amounts equivalent to 75–100 mU. This means that the liberation of such large amounts of oxytocin may well be a fact, and not merely apparent.

This analytic aspect of the problem obviously still needs more work, but it was of interest to pass to the next stage and see if stimuli presumed to activate the posterior pituitary induced urinary effects which could be explained by the information so far obtained. The stimulus chosen was an osmotic one, viz. the injection of hypertonic sucrose solution in the 0·89 M concentration used successfully by Verney (1947). The intravenous route of administration was used because, until the present time no dog with a carotid loop has been available. The intravenous route is not wholly satisfactory since to induce antidiuresis moderately large volumes of sucrose solution have to be injected and may well have some peripheral action in addition to that on the hypothalamus. The observations must be repeated using small volumes of sucrose solution injected into the carotid artery. Figure 10 shows the effect of injecting

148

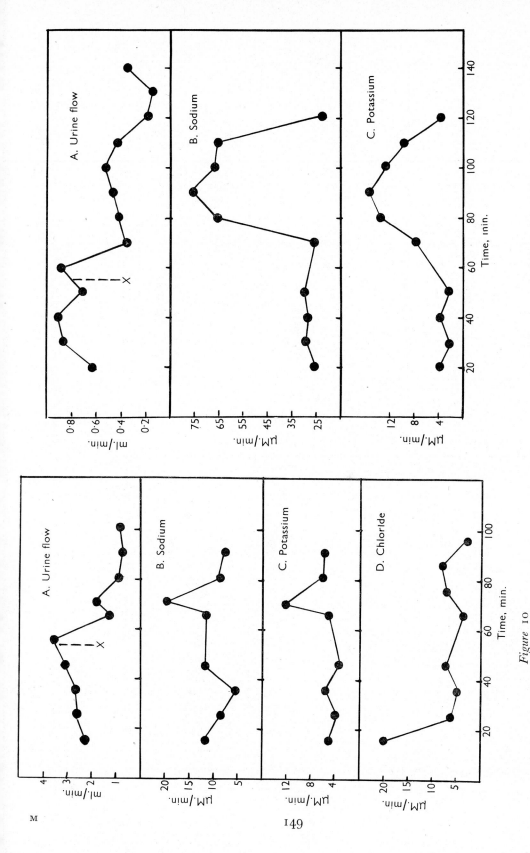

Figure II

The effect of 0·89 M sucrose solution on urine flow and Na and K excretion at a low rate of urine flow. (Thisbe. 15 kg.) 10 ml. sucrose solution injected intravenously at X.

Figure 10

The effect of 0·89 M sucrose solution on urine flow and Na, K and Cl excretion during water diuresis. (Cyclops, 8·5 kg.) 200 ml. water by mouth at zero time. 10 ml. sucrose solution injected intravenously at X.

M

149

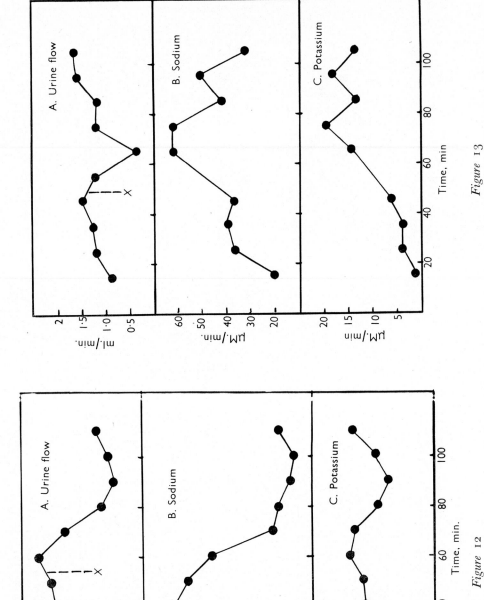

Figure 13

The effect of Pitocin on urine flow and Na and K excretion at a low rate of urine flow in a dog with diabetes insipidus. (Meg. 20 kg.) 150 mU. Pitocin injected intravenously at X.

Figure 12

Effect of Pitocin on urine flow, and Na and K excretion during water diuresis in a dog with diabetes insipidus. (Meg, 20 kg.) 300 ml. water by mouth at zero time. 100 mU. Pitocin injected intravenously at X.

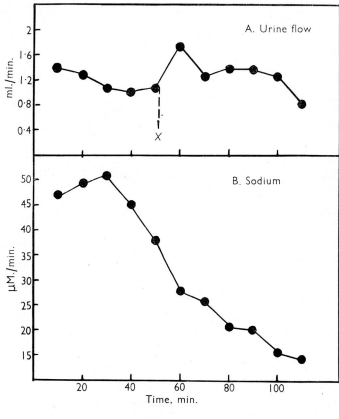

Figure 14

The effect of 0·89 M sucrose solution on urine flow and Na and K excretion
in a dog with diabetes insipidus. (Meg, 20 kg.) 20 ml. sucrose solution
injected intravenously at *X*. The amount of K excreted was constant
and too small to be worth recording.

hypertonic sucrose solution during the course of a water diuresis. There was a passing
increase in Na and K excretion following the injection. Figure 10 also shows that Cl
excretion was unaffected. Figure 11 shows an example of what occurred at low rates
of urine flow. Not in all instances was the increased excretion of Na and K as marked
as in this particular case, but it was always definite. The events following the intravenous injection of hypertonic sucrose solution, then, are not unlike those which
may be seen following the simultaneous injection of oxytocin and vasopressin (Figs.
5 and 7).

There is yet another indication that one or both posterior lobe hormones are important in the excretion of Na. In a dog with diabetes insipidus following section of
the supraoptico-hypophysial tracts the injection of Pitocin at high or low rates of
urine flow induced normal effects, thus, during water diuresis no increase in Na
excretion followed the injection (Fig. 12), but at resting rate of urine flow both Na
and K excretion increased (Fig. 13). However, the intravenous injection of hypertonic

sucrose solution, which, had the dog been normal would have increased Na excretion, was wholly without this effect (Fig. 14).

The above results do not give an answer to the question whether the action of oxytocin in the kidney is a physiological one. Also, these observations tell us little of the mode of action of the hormones on Na excretion, nor why K is sometimes definitely affected in the same sense as Na and at other times not at all or in an opposite direction. But the observations on clearances do give one piece of positive information, that an increase in Na excretion following oxytocin administration is not directly related to a change in plasma flow as measured by diodone clearance. The negative response to hypertonic sucrose solution of the dog with diabetes insipidus adds to the evidence that posterior lobe hormones must play some part in control of electrolyte excretion. There is no evidence that oxytocin is ever liberated almost alone in amounts sufficient to increase Na excretion, on the contrary, such evidence as has been obtained in these experiments suggests that the hormones act in concert, oxytocin being perhaps the more rapidly acting as far as Na excretion is concerned, and vasopressin far the more powerful for water retention. If oxytocin and vasopressin combine together to rid the body of Na and at the same time retain water, this activity would be useful at certain stages of dehydration.

Until more is known about the proportional amounts of oxytocin and vasopressin released by a single species in response to different types of stimuli further discussion can be no more than speculation.

SUMMARY

1. Observations were made on dogs of the effect of the oxytocic and vasopressor factors of the posterior pituitary on the rate of urine flow, on the excretion of sodium and potassium and on renal clearances of diodone and creatinine both during water diuresis and at low rates of urine flow. Vasopressin was used in antidiuretic doses and oxytocin in concentrations 20 to 30 times greater.

2. Highly purified oxytocin given as a single intravenous injection or as an intravenous infusion during water diuresis had little or no effect on the excretion of Na or K. If administered when the rate of urine flow was low oxytocin greatly increased Na excretion, and sometimes also that of K.

3. Highly purified vasopressin given as a single intravenous injection during water diuresis or when the rate of urine flow was low, did not strikingly increase the excretion rate of Na. Occasionally the excretion rate of K was increased. Given as an intravenous infusion during water diuresis vasopressin increased the excretion rate of both Na and K.

4. If the purified substances were injected together during diuresis or when the rate of urine flow was low the result was a sustained and moderate, or sometimes a marked, increase in excretion rates of both Na and K.

5. Measurements of diodone and creatinine clearances showed that at high or low rates of urine flow the administration of oxytocin was followed by a period when the diodone clearance increased by 75–100 per cent., though creatinine clearance was unaffected. When oxytocin and vasopressin were administered simultaneously there was no subsequent change in either diodone or creatinine clearance.

6. The intravenous injection of 0·89 M sucrose solution during water diuresis or

when the rate of urine flow was low had effects on Na and K excretion not unlike those due to the administration of mixtures of oxytocin and vasopressin.

7. A dog with diabetes insipidus responded normally to intravenous injections of oxytocin, but showed no increase in Na excretion following intravenously administered 0·89 M sucrose solution, either at high or low rates of urine flow.

We wish to express our deep gratitude to Dr. du Vigneaud for gifts of highly purified oxytocin and vasopressin.

REFERENCES

ABRAHAMS, V. C. & PICKFORD, M. (1954). Simultaneous observations on the rate of urine flow and spontaneous uterine movements in the dog, and their relationship to posterior lobe activity. *J. Physiol. (Lond.)* **126,** 329–46.

ANSLOW, Jr., W. P. & WESSON, Jr., L. G. (1955). Some effects of pressor-antidiuretic and oxytocic fractions of posterior pituitary extract on sodium, chloride, potassium and ammonium excretion in the dog. *Amer. J. Physiol.* **182,** 561–6.

BROOKS, F. P. & PICKFORD, M. (1956). The influence of posterior lobe hormones on the excretion of Na and K in the conscious dog. *J. Physiol. (Lond.)* **131,** 33–4P.

DICKER, S. E. & HELLER, H. (1946). The renal action of posterior pituitary extract and its fractions as analysed by clearance experiments on rats. *J. Physiol. (Lond.)* **104,** 353–60.

HARRIS, G. W. (1955). *Neural Control of the Pituitary Gland.* London: Edward Arnold (Publishers) Ltd.

PICKFORD, M. & RITCHIE, A. E. (1945). Experiments on the hypothalamic-pituitary control of water excretion in the dog. *J. Physiol. (Lond.)* **104,** 105–28.

SELLWOOD, R. V. & VERNEY, E. B. (1955). The effect of water and of isotonic saline administration on the renal plasma and glomerular filtrate flows in the dog, with incidental observations of the effects on these flows of compression of the carotid and renal arteries. *Philos. Trans.* B **57,** 361–96.

SMITH, H. W. (1951). *The Kidney,* p. 432. New York: Oxford University Press.

VERNEY, E. B. (1947). The antidiuretic hormone and the factors which determine its release. *Proc. roy. Soc.* B **135,** 27–106.

Discussion

Chairman: G. W. Harris

Sawyer. I think it is an extraordinarily interesting suggestion that oxytocin may have a physiological role in the regulation of renal function. Demunbrun et al. (Demunbrun, Keller, Levkoff & Purser, *Amer. J. Physiol.* **179,** 429, 1954) reported that large doses of oxytocin restored depressed renal functions in dogs with surgically-induced diabetes insipidus. They have not reported, however, on the use of synthetic oxytocin. This is important if we are to rule out the possibility that the effects they observed were due to contamination with anterior lobe substances since their dogs showed some evidence of mild adenohypophysial insufficiency.

Your hypertonic sucrose injections gave increased sodium excretion at low urine flow. Are you sure this is not the result of an osmotic diuresis? It would be interesting to see if the equivalent experiment could be done with equi-osmotic concentrations of urea to promote osmotic diuresis without stimulating liberation of antidiuretic hormone.

Pickford. I think the results in the diabetic dog with a normal functioning kidney, showing that it did not respond to sucrose, answered the last point of Dr. Sawyer.

Sawyer. What was the urine flow rate?

Pickford. Not higher than 1·5 ml./min. I think it was about 1·0 ml. per min. The experiments of Keller *et al.* are very interesting but they did use big doses and they did perform a terribly mutilating operation to produce diabetes and I don't see how they could avoid impairing anterior lobe function. They admit that there were changes in the reproductive system and that the dogs were blinded. Both these things suggest disturbance of anterior lobe function.

de Wardener. Is there an effect of oxytocin on cardiac output?

Pickford. I know of no evidence of this. I have seen no change in blood pressure after the intravenous injection of Pitocin in large doses into anaesthetized animals. This, of course, gives no information on cardiac output.

Chalmers. I would like to report two observations on patients with diabetes insipidus in which we found that the resting clearances of inulin and p-aminohippurate were not far below normal. One patient, a man aged 50, had an inulin clearance of 90 ml./min. and a p-aminohippurate clearance of 450; in the other, a boy of 20, the clearances were 115 and 455 respectively. We infused Pitocin at the rate of 1 mU. per min. for an hour—we perhaps should have used higher doses in view of Dr. Pickford's observations—and in the case with the higher initial clearances there was no change whatever, during or after the infusion. In the other case, during the infusion there was at first no change, but later this patient showed a febrile reaction in which the PAH clearance rose from 450 to 1,300 without change in the inulin clearance.

Croxatto. We made observations on rats using a special preparation of Pitocin (prepared by Parke, Davis and Co.) which contained only a small amount of vasopressin (less than 3 per cent.). In both normally hydrated rats and in hyper-hydrated rats it elicited a diuretic response with a striking increase in sodium excretion. In another series of experiments, oxytocin was injected after having been exposed to the action of various proteolytic enzymes. The diuretic and natriuretic effects, as well as the uterotonic effect were destroyed by chymotrypsin but not by trypsin. The doses of oxytocin given were 25 mU. and 50 mU. per rat.

Pickford. I think it important to interpret changes in sodium excretion after oxytocin in terms of what we believe to be physiological doses.

Garrod. With regard to the striking difference in the amounts of vasopressin and oxytocin which Dr. Pickford said were released, I would ask her on what evidence this was based.

Pickford. That was based on the simultaneous observation of spontaneous uterine activity and urine flow during water diuresis, in the same animal, after the intra-carotid injection of 1·2 to 1·4 ml. of hypertonic saline. Matching the responses with oxytocin and vasopressin (Pitocin and Pitressin) required about 80 mU. Pitocin and 3 mU. Pitressin.

Fitzpatrick. There is just a possibility that this discrepancy may be even larger, in that your observations do not take into account the possible antagonism between vasopressin and oxytocin on myometrial response. I have observed that a preliminary dose of vasopressin inhibits the response of the uterus to a subsequent dose of oxytocin in the bovine and in man. Other authors have reported similar findings (Weinstein & Friedman, *Amer. J. Obstet. Gynec.* **29**, 93, 1935).

Harris, G. W. There are some observations which show that vasopressin inhibits the response of the rabbit's uterus to administration of oxytocin (Harris, *J. Physiol.* **107**, 436, 1948 and *Neural Control of the Pituitary Gland*, London, Edward Arnold). I believe the evidence indicates that this is an action on the blood vessels of the uterus rather than directly on the muscle cells.

Dale. There is a point of general physiological importance here. How far are we to interpret the intra-arterial injection of small doses of markedly hypertonic saline as giving a physiological stimulus? If they do, we must conclude that the effect is not to produce, as might teleologically be expected, a preferential liberation of antidiuretic hormone but to produce, at the same time, 20 or 30 times as much of the oxytocic hormone.

Pickford. I do not think one can call an intra-arterial injection of sodium chloride physiological. On the other hand, this work raises the possibility that oxytocin itself has a physiological action on the kidney.

Dale. You cannot, however, be sure, I think, that you are really reproducing the normal, more gradual effect of a mild dehydration, such as we may get between meals, or between drinks.

Pickford. If oxytocin does facilitate sodium excretion it could, in mild dehydration, tend to delay the onset of thirst.

Heller. In diabetes insipidus there are, so far as I know, no very pronounced changes in the electrolyte metabolism. In adrenal insufficiency on the other hand, the disturbances are profound. If the neurohypophysial hormones are of physiological importance one would expect some alterations in diabetes insipidus.

Pickford. One possibility is that oxytocin is concerned with rapid changes and not slow changes.

Dale. So far as evidence goes, the antidiuretic effect, that is to say the production of urine in the normal volume and concentration, is the one function attributable to the neurohypophysis which is regularly in action, and necessarily physiological. Without it, we become insipid diabetics. If the effect of arterial hypertonic injections is really a proper representation of what is happening physiologically, we have to accept, I suppose, the fact that the neurohypophysis is putting out 20 to 30 times as much oxytocin as vasopressin. And since, by definition, the balance in units between oxytocin and vasopressin in the gland remains something like 1 : 1, that must mean that the manufacture of oxytocin is going on 20 to 30 times as rapidly as that of vasopressin. That would be an extraordinary and a profoundly important physiological conclusion.

Pickford. That is so, but as yet we do not know whether these effects are physiological or merely pharmacological.

de Wardener. When you say 20 to 30 times as much you refer to activity but is that any indication of the amount in milligrammes?

Dale. That must mean almost the same thing, because, according to Professor van Dyke, pure oxytocin contains about 500 mU./mg. and pure vasopressin about 600 mU./mg.

de Wardener. There is a further point. The concentration of the urine is greater after dehydration than after the administration of vasopressin. I wonder if this difference is due to oxytocin.

Pickford. One of the things we intend to do is to dehydrate ourselves and then try the effect of vasopressin, and then of vasopressin plus oxytocin, and see whether we can increase our urine concentrations up to the levels we get in dehydration. Also Vogt (*Brit. J. Pharmacol.* **8**, 193, 1953) has shown there is very little oxytocin in the hypothalamus of the dog and it all appears on the way down to the posterior lobe. We thought of removing the posterior lobe and trying to rid the dog of all oxytocin and still have some vasopressin about.

Cole. I wonder if anyone has a measure of the rate at which administered oxytocin disappears from the circulation. Heller and his co-workers (Heller & Urban, *J. Physiol.* **85**, 502, 1935; Ginsburg & Heller, *J. Endocr.* **9**, 283, 1953) have shown that injected vasopressin is removed very rapidly, and if the rate of removal of oxytocin is considerably slower it might help to account for the apparent high ratio of oxytocin/vasopressin in cases where the liberation of these hormones from the pituitary is inhibited.

Heller. That is an aspect in which we are interested but which we have not yet been able to investigate, since the methods of estimating oxytocin in blood have not been adequate. Bisset and Walker have recently improved the situation in this respect and they can perhaps help us.

Walker. By our method (*J. Physiol.* **126**, 588, 1954) it is possible to measure oxytocin when added to blood, and also, we believe, the level of endogenous oxytocin; but we have not yet tried estimating oxytocin in blood after administration of the commercial extract to the intact animal.

Bernstein. Has Dr. Pickford considered whether any of her results could be explained as diurnal? Further, has Dr. Pickford any observations concerning the effect of variations in sodium intake?

Pickford. Diurnal variation is eliminated since all procedures were done at the same time of day on each occasion. We are currently investigating the variation of sodium intake in this respect but we have too few observations as yet to draw conclusions.

van Dyke. Was there any difference between the excretion of sodium and of chloride?

Pickford. The chloride excretion was always qualitatively similar to that of sodium although perhaps not always of the same magnitude.

The location of antidiuretic action in the mammalian kidney

H. WIRZ

Physiologisches Institut der Universität Basel

IT seems to be a well-established fact that in the mammalian kidney the antidiuretic hormone acts chiefly by increasing the rate of water reabsorption, so that the osmotic pressure of the urine is raised above that of the plasma. With appropriate doses of the hormone full antidiuresis is obtained in most species without significantly altering filtration rate. Some modifications of solute reabsorption may ensue, but the increased urine concentration is due in the first place to the greatly diminished urine volume.

Oddly enough, in the absence of antidiuretic hormone the kidney is not producing what would seem to be the easiest thing to produce. An isotonic urine, in a normal kidney, is the result of a moderate antidiuretic action. With no antidiuretic hormone circulating in the body, as in water diuresis, urinary osmotic pressure is reduced well below isotonicity. If therefore we want to approach the antidiuretic mechanism, for instance by micropuncture studies, we ought to start at the bottom of the problem, investigating the conditions of water diuresis first.

Unfortunately it is rather difficult to produce a good water diuresis in an anaesthetized and laparatomized animal. The choice of the anaesthetic is one of the important factors. Alcohol is one very good anaesthetic which in the rat does not interfere with water diuresis. However, it is not suited for the purpose for another reason: it very appreciably depresses the freezing point, yet on biological membranes it does not seem to exert an osmotic activity. So any fluid containing alcohol may be biologically hypotonic whereas the physical determination seems to reveal hypertonicity. Finally I got acceptable results with intravenous injections of Inactin, which is a thiobarbiturate manufactured by Promonta (Hamburg).

Even with a perfect anaesthetic the laparatomy and the preparation of the kidney for micropuncture are very likely to interfere with water diuresis. This difficulty has finally been overcome by applying the following technique (Wirz, 1955, 1956): The kidney of male rats is approached by a lumbar incision. The adipose tissue is carefully removed from its dorsal face. For the micropuncture the organ is supported by a little cup, which by means of a stalk is firmly attached to the heated animal board. The advantage of this method is that it avoids any handling of abdominal organs, and that it affords an efficient immobilization of the kidney by simple means. With this method osmotic U/P ratios of as little as 0·2 may be obtained.

The procedure otherwise is very similar to that described by Walker & Oliver (1941), except that in the present investigation the Leitz Ultropak microscope was used instead of an ordinary binocular instrument. Osmotic pressures of tubular fluid, ureteral urine and systemic plasma were determined by our microcryoscopic method (Hargitay, Kuhn & Wirz 1951), which is similar to that described by Ramsay (1949). This method has a number of advantages over that of Barger (1904) hitherto used by micropuncture specialists. Its accuracy is nearly as good as that of the Beckmann method on a macro scale. The cryoscopy is performed in the same quartz capillary tube which previously had served for the micropuncture. Therefore any evaporation or condensation which might occur during a transfer from one tube to another is *a priori* excluded. Finally the amount of fluid required for cryoscopy is so minute that it can be drawn from any tubule at once. This avoids prolonged collecting periods, the blocking of the tubule by oil, and the hazard of contaminating the sample with fluid from higher up or lower down the nephron.

RESULTS

Proximal convoluted tubules

As to the location of the antidiuretic activity, it has been presumed by most investigators of recent times that the proximal convoluted tubules have nothing to do with it. Water reabsorption in this part of the nephron is regarded as a passive process secondary to an active reabsorption of solutes. Water seems to follow *pari passu* the actively reabsorbed glucose, sodium chloride, &c. leaving behind an essentially isotonic tubular fluid.

Experimental evidence so far has only been provided for the concentrating kidney by Walker, Bott, Oliver & McDowell (1941), but the same is also true for the diluting organ during water diuresis (Table I). The number of experiments is not very large,

TABLE I

Proximal tubular fluid/plasma ratios (TF/P) and ureteral urine/plasma ratios (U/P) of total molecular concentration. The site of puncture is given as per cent. of the length of the proximal convoluted tubule

TF/P	U/P	Site, (per cent.)
1·01	0·41	20
1·00	0·25	28
0·99	0·20	30
0·97	0·20	37
0·99	0·26	42

but the results are so clear cut—the osmotic tubular fluid/plasma ratio was close to unity in every single experiment, even at very low (ureteral) U/P ratios—that there is no need for extending these experiments further.

Distal convoluted tubules

By the use of the Ultropak system it has become possible to distinguish quite definitely distal from proximal convoluted tubules *in vivo*. The denomination of the

different parts of the nephron is still somewhat arbitrary. For convenience I understand by 'distal convoluted tubule' the segment which begins at the point where the
ascending limb of the loop of Henle touches the glomerulus of the same nephron,
and which ends at the nearest bifurcation of the collecting duct. This segment is
probably not identical with the part of the nephron referred to as 'distal system' by
most physiologists.

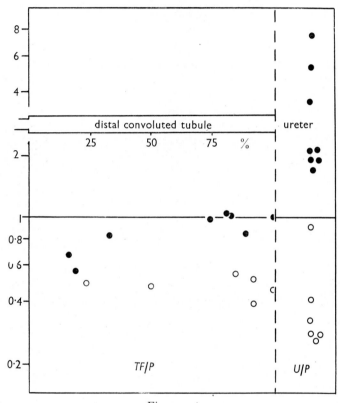

Figure 1

Distal tubular fluid/plasma ratios (*TF/P*) and ureteral urine/plasma ratios (*U/P*)
of total molecular concentration in the concentrating (●) and the diluting (O)
rat kidney. The site of micropuncture is given as per cent. of the length of the
distal convoluted tubule. (From Wirz, 1956.)

The results are shown in Fig. 1. The open circles relate to experiments with
animals in water diuresis and hypotonic urines, the black dots to antidiuretic
experiments with osmotic *U/P* ratios well above 1·0.

The most striking fact is that in the concentrating kidney distal convoluted tubule
fluid not only is not hypertonic but even very definitely hypotonic, particularly in
the beginning of this segment. The results of Walker *et al.* (1941) are thus fully confirmed. Owing to the small number of successful distal punctures these authors were
rather cautious as to the significance of their results. In the light of the new facts those
early findings are highly significant and so is the statement that 'it would appear that

the site of chloride reabsorption must be proximal to that of water'. Water re-absorption however seems to catch up with the reabsorption of solutes at the end of the distal convolution. In most cases the tubular fluid is strictly isotonic throughout the last third of this segment. In one case isotonicity was not quite reached, but the tubular fluid/plasma ratio was never greater than 1.02. Thus there is no sign of an active process of water reabsorption up to the beginning of the collecting ducts.

In the diluting kidney on the other hand the hypotonicity of tubular fluid is maintained (perhaps even enhanced) throughout the length of the distal convoluted tubule. At the end of the segment the hypotonicity in most cases is not quite as pronounced as in ureteral urine. It is questionable however whether this points to a further solute reabsorption in the beginning of the collecting ducts. Alternatively, since ureteral urine is the composite product of some 30,000 nephrons, this finding may be due to a somewhat different diluting capacity of different renal units.

In short it may be stated that the diluting process occurs before and possibly along the distal convolution. It is completed, or nearly so, at the beginning of the collecting ducts. The concentrating process on the other hand must in some way include the collecting duct system.

DISCUSSION

Apart from the possibility of water secretion in the distal segment which would have to occur even in antidiuresis, and for which I do not see any reason, the hypotonicity of the tubular fluid at the beginning of the distal convolution shows that there must take place between the end of the proximal and the beginning of the distal convolution a copious active reabsorption of one or more solutes without or with less than an equivalent amount of water. For lack of other evidence we may tentatively assume that this isolated solute reabsorption is located in the ascending limb of the loop of Henle.

As to the substance or substances whose reabsorption causes the hypotonicity of distal tubule fluid I agree with H. W. Smith (1951) and with Wesson & Anslow (1952) that the only solutes available for reabsorption in sufficient amount are sodium, conceivably the active part, and chloride as a concomitant anion. These experiments may be taken as a factual demonstration—and to some extent location—of what these authors call T_{Na}^d. Along the segment concerned with distal sodium reabsorption poor water permeability must exist in both the diuretic and the antidiuretic state. But only in water diuresis does this impermeability obtain throughout the entire distal convolution. By the action of the antidiuretic hormone the distal convoluted tubules apparently become permeable to water allowing the tubular content to become isotonic with the surrounding interstitial fluid. There is no sign however of an *active* water reabsorption in the distal convoluted tubules. Even in severe antidiuresis, at (ureteral) U/P ratios as high as 7 the cortical tubules show an isotonic content at best.

In the absence of antidiuretic hormone on the other hand, the epitheliae walls must be virtually impermeable to water not only in that part of the loop and the distal convolution where hypotonicity is produced but also in the collecting ducts, where the hypotonicity is maintained. Thus only is it explainable that the urine leaves the kidney in the same hypotonic state which it already attained in the distal convolution.

Those who are familiar with the matter will have noticed that the explanation I have given to the new findings is almost identical with that of H. W. Smith (1951) and of Wesson & Anslow (1952). From their clearance studies these authors have concluded that there must exist in the mammalian kidney three separate sites and three different mechanisms of water reabsorption. This hypothesis has now been corroborated in its essentials; a few modifications and specifications may be added on the strength of the new experimental facts. The first process of water reabsorption ($T^p_{H_2O}$ of these authors), amounting to approximately seven-eighths of the filtered water, occurs in the proximal convoluted tubules. It is visualized as an obligatory but passive process consequent to the proximal reabsorption of about seven-eighths of the filtered solutes, leaving the tubular content essentially iso-osmotic throughout the length of the proximal convolution. This has now been demonstrated to be true not only for the concentrating but also for the diluting kidney—at least as far as the proximal convolution is accessible from the renal surface. No sign of even slight hypotonicity has been encountered in the present investigation. It seems that osmotic equilibrium is maintained all along the proximal convoluted tubules.

Secondly we have to assume a facultative water reabsorption ($T^d_{H_2O}$) in what Smith calls the 'distal system'. This part of the reabsorptive process is facilitated by the antidiuretic hormone. It comprises the water osmotically liberated by distal sodium reabsorption (T^d_{Na}), and, if present, leads to an isotonic distal tubule fluid. Hence it is probably a passive process too. The present experiments demonstrate that $T^d_{H_2O}$ must be located in the convoluted part of the distal tubules. This site is not quite identical with that of distal sodium reabsorption. T^d_{Na} apparently takes place already in the loop of Henle.

Finally there must exist a site of hyperosmotic water reabsorption ($T^c_{H_2O}$) 'necessarily lower down in the nephron', which abstracts water to concentrate the isotonic tubule fluid above the osmotic pressure of the plasma. This hyperosmotic reabsorption must take place even beyond the nephron, in the collecting ducts, as no hypertonicity has ever been demonstrated to occur before the cortical branchings of the collecting ducts.

There is however still at least one important point of controversy between New York and Basel left as a basis for discussion. The ultimate process promoting $T^c_{H_2O}$ is considered by H. W. Smith and his group to be located in the epithelium of the collecting ducts, whereas we think that the collecting ducts play but a passive part, and that the leading system is the hair-pin counter-current system provided by the loops of Henle.

If water was removed from the collecting ducts by an active process located in the collecting duct epithelia, the interstitial fluid and the blood in the vasa recta of the papilla would have to become hypotonic with respect to systemic blood. This hypotonicity might admittedly be very slight, if the blood supply to the papilla was large as compared to urine flow. But such a process could never induce the papillary blood to become hypertonic which, according to micropuncture studies on the papilla of the golden hamster it is (Wirz 1953). Since these experiments are well known to some of you, I can report them briefly. The golden hamster has a long papilla protruding into the ureter where it can be exposed *in vivo*. It has been demonstrated that blood drawn by micropuncture from papillary blood vessels has practically the same osmotic pressure as the urine which is formed simultaneously. The experiments include osmotic U/P ratios between 1·0 and 2. It has been concluded from these experiments that in the concentrating kidney the whole of the papilla becomes hypertonic including the contents of the collecting ducts and the extracellular fluid.

Earlier experiments (Wirz, Hargitay & Kuhn 1951), using the method of direct cryoscopy of kidney slices had led to the conclusion that the contents of both limbs of the loops of Henle also were hypertonic in the papilla of concentrating kidneys. From these results the course of osmotic pressure along the nephron and collecting duct was outlined as in Fig. 2. The objection has been made that the results of direct

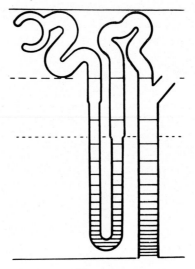

Figure 2

Variation of osmotic pressure in a single nephron and collecting duct as computed from direct cryoscopy of the rat kidney. (From Wirz *et al.*, 1951.)

cryoscopy might be partly influenced by diffusion *post mortem*. Apparently these experiments failed to disclose the slight hypotonicity at the beginning of the distal convoluted tubules of concentrating kidneys which was demonstrated by micropuncture studies. But even if the cryoscopic readings showed nothing but an average freezing-point depression in any single slice, they would be conclusive at least in one respect: Freezing points as low as $-4\cdot3°$ C. have been recorded in the papillae of antidiuretic rats. It is very improbable that so high an average osmotic pressure could be the result of a mixture of the hypertonic content of the collecting ducts and of the isotonic contents of loops, blood-vessels and interstices.

A different line of approach was followed by Ullrich, Drenckhahn & Jarausch (1955), who investigated the osmotic behaviour of slices taken from various depths of fresh dog kidneys. By extrapolation they computed the osmotic pressure of a saline solution with which the slices would be in osmotic equilibrium. In concentrating kidneys they found a steady increase of osmotic pressure from the cortico-medullary boundary towards the tip of the papilla. These results are significant in two respects. Firstly, as it is the cells that will shrink or swell, they demonstrate that the intracellular compartment too is involved in the osmotic stratification of the renal medulla. Secondly the last slices in all experiments on concentrating kidneys show, within the limit of methodical errors, the same osmotic pressure as the urine which was formed immediately before the animal was killed. Thus the epithelial cells of the collecting ducts seem to be in perfect osmotic equilibrium with the urine within.

The same authors found the sodium concentration of such slices too to increase with the depth of the renal medulla. Final concentrations of up to 425 mEq. sodium per litre of tissue water were found, about four times the sodium concentration of the urine. This suggests the existence of high ionic concentration gradients between the different compartments, combined with an absence of high total molecular concentration gradients.

The results of these workers recall the earlier experiments of Ljungberg (1947) who demonstrated an increase of chloride concentration in the medulla of rabbit kidney. Here again the average chloride concentration of slices from the deeper parts of the medulla was well above that of both the urine and systemic plasma or whole blood. According to Ljungberg's interpretation these findings indicated an active chloride reabsorption from the collecting ducts. He assumed that the chloride concentration of the extracellular fluid was the same in the renal medulla as in other parts of the body. An alternative view was offered by H. W. Smith (1951): namely that a high intracellular concentration of chloride might be involved in the reabsorption of water to form a hypertonic urine. He suggested that water might diffuse into such an intracellular system by osmotic pressure. Assuming an interstitial fluid of normal osmotic composition this interpretation would leave the question open, how the water, once in the epithelial cells, would be disposed of.

THE HAIRPIN COUNTER-CURRENT SYSTEM

There is only one explanation which covers all the known facts and moreover gives a satisfactory reason for the existence of the loops of Henle in the mammalian kidney. This theory is based on the combination of a flow along a tube that doubles back upon itself (hairpin counter-current), and an active process setting up a (small) osmotic pressure difference between the two limbs of this tube, the content of the descending limb being (slightly) hypertonic. The concentrating effect of this system starts being multiplied as soon as the (slightly) hypertonic content of the descending limb is carried by bulk flow around the bend into the ascending limb. The lower ends of both limbs now being equally hypertonic, the osmotic pressure difference between the two limbs is momentarily abolished. If the active osmotic process continues, a new osmotic pressure difference is set up, the content of the lower part of the descending limb now being twice as hypertonic as in the first step. This fluid is again transported into the ascending limb, again abolishing the osmotic pressure differences between the two limbs, and so on. . . . Finally a steady state arises, the fluid entering the system at the upper end of the descending limb being more and more concentrated towards the hairpin bend and rediluted on its way back up the ascending limb. Osmotic pressures many times higher than the initiating single effect may be produced.

The theory was developed both mathematically and experimentally with the help of a working model by Hargitay & Kuhn (1951). The primary difference in osmotic pressure in the model was brought about by a head of hydrostatic pressure applied to the descending limb, both limbs sharing a common membrane of semipermeable material. The significance of this model has often been misjudged. It was not meant to demonstrate by it that the renal concentrating mechanism might be operating by means of physical forces alone. The hydrostatic pressure was chosen by Hargitay & Kuhn as a simple and well-defined driving force to produce a small osmotic pressure difference across a semipermeable membrane. The model was to show that this small osmotic 'single effect' may be multiplied if applied to a counter-current system, resulting in final osmotic pressures several times higher than the single effect alone.

It is not likely that in the kidney the driving force is a hydrostatic pressure difference as in the model. The osmotic pressure difference between the descending and the ascending limb of the loop of Henle is probably brought about by an active cellular transport mechanism, either driving water from the descending limb across the interstices into the ascending limb, or by a process moving one or more solutes in the opposite direction—or a combination of both.

In any case the result of the counter-current mechanism would be a milieu of increasing hypertonicity towards the tip of the renal papilla. Besides the loops of Henle two other systems are passing through the same milieu. The vascular system is anatomically arranged as a number of hair-pin tubes extending more or less deeply into the medulla. All the blood irrigating the medulla enters and leaves the medulla at the cortico-medullary boundary, i.e. in an essentially isotonic region. In between it may adapt itself to the osmotic pressure of the surroundings by a passive uptake (on its way down) and release (on its way up) of osmotically active solutes. Hence the finding of hypertonic blood by micropuncture of the papilla of the golden hamster.

The second system passing through the medulla is that of the collecting ducts. Here too a passive adaptation to the hypertonic milieu is assumed, not by an uptake of solutes but by a passive transfer of water according to the osmotic pressures. Unlike the vasa recta the collecting ducts do not turn back to the cortex, and this urine concentration is final.

The precise nature of the process initiating the counter-current concentrating mechanism must be left open to further investigation. The present results however may help by giving a *tentative* description of the antidiuretic mechanism in the mammalian kidney.

The distal sodium reabsorption (T^d_{Na}) might serve a double purpose. Firstly the removal of a large part of what sodium is left over by the proximal system, and secondly the facultative initiation of the counter-current concentrating mechanism. If an active sodium transport was at work all along the ascending limb of the loop—and the present results seem to point in this direction—the extracellular fluid of the medulla would, as a first step, become slightly hypertonic. This alone would not suffice to get the concentrating mechanism going. For this the crucial point is the entering at the hairpin bend of a (slightly) hypertonic solution into the ascending limb. In other words, the contents of the descending limb would have to be granted osmotic equilibration with their (slightly) hypertonic surroundings.

164

One might assume that in the absence of antidiuretic hormone the descending limb is impermeable to both water and solutes. Its content would then stay isotonic as it was at the end of the proximal convolution. In this case renal function would proceed as if there was no counter-current system, distal sodium reabsorption combined with a watertight distal convolution and collecting duct, leading to large volumes of hypotonic urine.

The osmotic equilibration of the descending limbs with their surroundings might be facilitated by the antidiuretic hormone by opening pores to allow a passive transfer

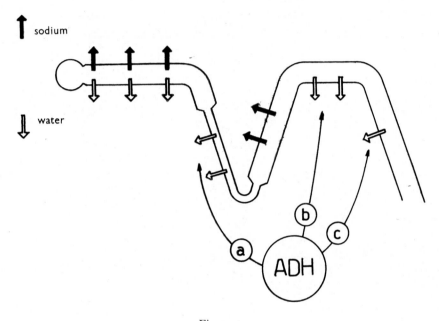

Figure 3

The action of the antidiuretic hormone is suggested as facilitating a passive transfer of water at three different sites in the nephron and collecting duct (for details, see text).

of water (Fig. 3, *a*) or sodium (chloride) or both. If the pores were opened for water, we would have to assume yet another site of facultative water reabsorption in the descending limb of the loop. This water would combine with the sodium (chloride) turned out by the ascending limb and be carried away by the medullary blood. If the pores were opened wide enough to allow an inward movement of sodium (chloride), we would have to assume a recirculation of part of this salt through the loop.

This hypothesis has the advantage that no other function would have to be attributed to the antidiuretic hormone than that of opening the pores to allow a passive transfer of water (and possibly some solutes). It was first shown by Sawyer (1951) that in the frog skin the action of postpituitary extracts consists 'in lowering the barrier to osmotic entrance of water' rather than in promoting any transport activity. Also Koefoed-Johnsen & Ussing (1952) concluded from tracer experiments on the isolated toad skin that the action of neurohypophysial hormones could be explained entirely by an increase in pore size in some layer of the skin. Although the active principle influencing the water uptake by the anuran skin is possibly not identical with the (mammalian) antidiuretic hormone, it seems to be an attractive hypothesis that the same purpose—the conservation of body water—is achieved by the neurohypophysis in mammals and amphibians by influencing very different tissues but in essentially the same manner.

In the mammalian kidney the sites of such action would be *a*, (see Fig. 3) the descending limb of the loop, allowing the tubular fluid to reach equilibrium with the hypertonic extracellular fluid and thus inducing the counter-current concentrating mechanism; *b*, the distal convoluted tubules, allowing water reabsorption to catch up with distal sodium reabsorption; and finally *c*, the collecting ducts, where a passive transfer of water to the hypertonic surroundings would concentrate the urine above isotonicity.

REFERENCES

BARGER, G. (1904). A microscopical method of determining molecular weights. *J. Chem. Soc.* **85,** 286.

HARGITAY, B. & KUHN, W. (1951). Das Multiplikationsprinzip als Grundlage der Harnkonzentrierung in der Niere. *Z. Elektrochem.* **55,** 539–58.

HARGITAY, B., KUHN, W. & WIRZ, H. (1951). Eine mikrokryoskopische Methode für sehr kleine Lösungsmengen. *Experientia (Basel)* **7,** 276–8.

KOEFOED-JOHNSEN, V. & USSING, H. H. (1952). The contributions of diffusion and flow to the passage of D_2O through living membranes. Effect of neurohypophyseal hormone on isolated anuran skin. *Acta physiol. Scand.* **28,** 60–76.

LJUNGBERG, E. (1947). On the reabsorption of chlorides in the kidney of the rabbit. *Acta med. Scand.* Suppl., 186.

RAMSAY, J. A. (1949). A new method of freezing-point determination for small quantities. *J. exp. Biol.* **26,** 57–64.

SAWYER, W. H. (1951). Effect of posterior pituitary extract on permeability of frog skin to water. *Amer. J. Physiol.* **164,** 44–8.

SMITH, H. W. (1951). *The kidney. Structure and function in health and disease.* New York: Oxford University Press.

ULLRICH, K. J., DRENCKHAHN, F. O. & JARAUSCH, K. H. (1955). Untersuchungen zum Problem der Harnkonzentrierung und -verdünnung. *Pflügers Arch. ges. Physiol.* **261,** 62–77.

WALKER, A. M., BOTT, B. A., OLIVER, J. & McDOWELL, M. C. (1941). The collection and analysis of fluid from single nephrons of the mammalian kidney. *Amer. J. Physiol.* **134,** 580–95.

WALKER, A. M. & OLIVER, J. (1941). Methods for the collection of fluid from single glomeruli and tubules of the mammalian kidney. *Amer. J. Physiol.* **134,** 562–79.

WESSON, L. G. & ANSLOW, W. P. (1952). Effect of osmotic and mercurial diuresis on simultaneous water diuresis. *Amer. J. Physiol.* **170,** 255–69.

WIRZ, H. (1953). Der osmotische Druck des Blutes in der Nierenpapille. *Helv. physiol. pharmacol. Acta* **11,** 20–9.

WIRZ, H. (1955). Druckmessung in Kapillaren und Tubuli der Niere durch Mikropunktion. *Helv. physiol. pharmacol. Acta* **13,** 42–9.

WIRZ, H. (1956). Der osmotische Druck in den corticalen Tubuli der Rattenniere. *Helv. physiol. pharmacol. Acta* **14,** 353–62.

WIRZ, H., HARGITAY, B. & KUHN, W. (1951). Lokalisation des Konzentrierungsprozesses in der Niere durch direkte Kryoskopie. *Helv. physiol. pharmacol. Acta* **9,** 196–207.

Discussion

Chairman : H. Heller

Heller. I should like to congratulate Dr. Wirz on his elegant work. I think I am right in saying that the only other workers who have succeeded in doing micropunctures in the mammalian kidney were Walker and his group and you of course have been able to get a great deal more information about the distal tubule.

de Wardener. I want first to add my own congratulations to Dr. Wirz. The observation that has delighted me most is your finding that when the urine in the ureter is hypertonic, that in the distal tubule is hypotonic. As you said, Walker and his co-workers also obtained similar results on three occasions but I think I am right in saying that in these experiments the fluid in the distal tubule was not as hypotonic as in your own. My pleasure in this finding is that it fits so admirably with the results of some of our own experiments.

McCance (*J. Physiol. (Lond.)* **104,** 196, 1945) first showed, and this has been confirmed on many occasions, that in a dehydrated man or animal the administration of a substance which has then to be excreted in the urine causes not only a rise in solute output but a simultaneous increase in urine flow and a fall in urine concentration towards that of plasma. It has been suggested that these changes are due to an increased flow of iso-osmotic tubular fluid into that site in the tubule where concentration takes place, so that the concentration of the urine is now approaching that of plasma. There is the assumption in this explanation that such an osmotic diuresis initiated at any level of hypertonicity, however minor, should be accompanied by a fall in urine osmolarity towards plasma.

Dr. del Greco and I however, have recently demonstrated that this assumption is not warranted and that, in fact, if an osmotic diuresis is initiated in man, when the urine osmolarity is only slightly above that of plasma, there is a fall in urine osmolarity below that of plasma, the urine becoming hypotonic. (del Greco & de Wardener, *Clin. Sci.* **14,** 715, 1955). To explain this phenomenon it seemed reasonable to suggest that when the urine is hypertonic there is somewhere in the tubule a site where the tubule fluid is hypotonic—a hypothesis first put forward by Shannon (*J. exp. med.* **76,** 371, 1942). It appeared therefore that the concentration of the urine not only depends on the level of circulating antidiuretic hormone and its action on the collecting tubules, but also on the rate at which hypotonic fluid is being delivered to this site.

If this was correct it followed that it should be possible to make a hypotonic urine hypertonic by reducing the solute output. This we have found is a correct deduction (del Greco & de Wardener, *J. Physiol. (Lond.)* **131,** 307, 1956). We performed the experiment in animals made resistant to the effect of Pitressin by large and rapid expansions of the extracellular volume (Wesson, Anslow, Raisz, Bolomey & Ladd, *Amer. J. Physiol.* **162,** 677, 1950), and which were therefore passing hypotonic urine. Changes in solute output were produced by aortic occlusion by means of an indwelling aortic inflatable rubber balloon. Upon inflating the balloon the solute output fell and the urine became hypertonic; upon deflating the balloon the urine again became hypotonic within 1–3 min. Dr. Sawyer tells me that Dr. Berliner has recently completed almost identical experiments and has obtained very similar results.

I think these observations fit very nicely with the findings of Dr. Wirz that, somewhere in the tubule, the urine is at all times hypotonic.

Heller. There is a question which I might ask Dr. Wirz and Dr. Sawyer at the same time: what in your present schemes is the significance of the thin loop of Henle? Homer Smith has suggested that it might be an equilibrating region—where iso-osmoticity is obtained. Do you agree with this concept?

Wirz. Homer Smith suggested that proximal tubule fluid might, at times at least, be hypotonic. This does not seem to follow from the experiments of Walker *et al.* They however have worked exclusively on concentrating kidneys, and many of their experiments were done during osmotic diuresis. In my series I have never seen a hypotonic proximal tubule fluid even at low ureteral urine osmotic pressures, and without the use of osmotic diuretics. I therefore do not see any need for further equilibration in the thin limb.

Sawyer. There are two data I want to get clear about in connexion with several criticisms which have been levelled against your work. You do not think that in your sections there could be post-mortem diffusion of water because your freezing-point depressions were so high. Is that right?

Wirz. I don't see how a freezing-point depression of more than 4° C. could be attributed to a mixture of an isotonic fluid and one which in this case would have to be much more hypertonic. A freezing-point depression of 4° C. nearly corresponds to the osmotic ceiling of the rat.

Sawyer. Would you also consider the possibility that the high osmotic pressure could be due to the hydrolysis of intracellular substances such as ATP which are described by Conway (Conway, Geoghegan & McCormack, *J. Physiol.* (*Lond.*) **130,** 427, 1955) as occurring in renal tissue even at 0° C.?

Wirz. In cortical tissue slices we always found freezing-point depressions close to 0·56° C. which you would expect from isotonic fluids. Furthermore this objection would certainly not apply to the findings—by other workers—of high sodium and chloride levels.

Sawyer. You have determined the osmotic pressure of blood taken from renal vessels in the living animal. Is the blood flowing when you draw these samples?

Wirz. Yes.

Pickford. There is one question I would like to ask about the blood vessels. Do you ever see any change in the size of the blood vessels during the effect of antidiuretic hormone? Can you judge the size of the blood vessels which run parallel to Henle's loop? I think it has been suggested that constriction or dilation of these vessels is one of the factors involved.

Wirz. This is one thing I have not managed to do but which ought to be investigated. Golden hamsters are very awkward. You can only do these experiments with animals of about 50 grammes, and golden hamsters grow so quickly. I have obtained a species of desert rat, *Meriones shawi*, which has a papilla similar to that of the golden hamster. But what I have been doing up to now is breeding them.

Sawyer. We have another species of desert rat, the Mongolian gerbil, *Meriones unguiculatus*, which also has a long thin papilla and presumably long collecting ducts. This species is capable of living without weight loss on a diet of dry oatmeal without water. The closely related African gerbil *Gerbillus gerbillus* has recently been reported by Burns (*Endocrinology* **58**, 243, 1956) to be capable of surviving on dry grain, as can the kangaroo rat (*Dipodomys*) and the jerboa. A number of desert rodents such as *Dipodomys, Meriones, Gerbillus, Jerboa* and *Perognathus* also have long renal papillae as Sperber (*Zool. Bidr. Uppsala* **22,** 1944) has pointed out. The gerbil breeds very easily. However, the man who is breeding them commercially in the U.S. will only let us have males.

The antidiuretic action of neurohypophysial hormones in Amphibia

by

WILBUR H. SAWYER

Department of Physiology, New York University College of Medicine and the Mount Desert Island Biological Laboratory

THE importance of the neurohypophysis in the regulation of the water metabolism of mammals is well known. However, an increasing body of evidence reveals that the neurohypophysial hormones are also concerned with water balance in the Amphibia. These hormones act not only on the skin but also on the kidney and urinary bladder. I intend to speak principally about neurohypophysial action on the kidney, and will argue that the antidiuretic response in this organ resembles that in amphibian skin with respect to the fundamental mechanism of action. Because the skin is readily accessible to direct study the action of neurohypophysial hormones on this organ has been the subject of numerous studies which have afforded us considerable insight into the mechanisms involved.

Neurohypophysial hormones markedly increase the rate of water uptake through the skin of the frog and toad. Here water uptake appears to be a passive process, activated by the osmotic gradient between the body fluids and the external medium (Sawyer, 1951a). The skin, however, does not behave like a simple homogeneous semipermeable membrane. The net influx of water is several times that predicted from the measurement of total flux if it is assumed that the entire area of the skin is available to diffusion and that influx and outflux are directly proportional to water concentration on the respective sides of the skin (Hevesy, Hofer & Krogh, 1935; Capraro & Bernini, 1952). Koefoed-Johnsen & Ussing (1953) point out that it is unnecessary to invoke active water transport to explain this discrepancy if, instead, the skin is conceived as a system in which osmotic flow occurs through minute pores. Neurohypophysial hormones increase the net flux of water without proportionately increasing the total flux (Capraro & Bernini, 1952). This is most readily explained by assuming that the hormones dilate the pores.

Professor Ussing, at the Colston Research Society Symposium two years ago, adduced substantial evidence in support of his 'pore theory' from an examination of the permeability of toad skin to isotopically labelled thiourea (Ussing, 1954). The thiourea molecule is considerably larger than water and normally penetrates toad skin at a slow rate. Neurohypophysial hormone increases the rate of flux in both directions, the increase in flux of thiourea being much greater than the increase in the flux of water. This is best explained by assuming that the neurohypophysial hormone dilates pores that are normally barely large enough to admit water, but too small to admit thiourea. The influx of thiourea is more rapid than the outflux, even when the concentration is the same on both sides, but this phenomenon, in Ussing's view, merely reflects the fact that thiourea is swept through the pores in the stream of the osmotic inflow of water.

The pore theory has been supported by Garby & Linderholm (1954) on the basis of the effects of aminophylline on the relative rates of flux of urea and electrolytes through frog skin.

The pore theory suggests a possible interpretation of how neurohypophysial principles may act on other semipermeable membranes. No data previously available indicate whether it is applicable to the kidney, but the evidence presented here points in that direction.

The older view in mammalian physiology held that the neurohypophysial anti-diuretic hormone acts on the mechanism responsible for the elaboration of hypertonic urine. On this basis we once believed that the change in the permeability of frog skin could not share a common mechanism with the response of the mammalian nephron (Sawyer, 1951a). But we now have reason to revise this opinion radically. On recent evidence Professor Homer Smith (1956) has argued that the antidiuretic hormone may not be necessary for the activation of the concentrating mechanism, an interpretation which agrees with the observation that hypertonic urine can be produced in the apparent absence of this hormone (Shannon, 1942; Levkoff, Demunbrun & Keller, 1954; Berliner & Davidson, 1956).

Turning to the amphibian kidney, where the urine is never hypertonic to the blood, neurohypophysial extracts are known to increase the tubular reabsorption of water (Pasqualini, 1938; Sawyer, 1955; Jancsó, 1955a, 1955b; Sawyer, 1956). Here we have an opportunity to examine neurohypophysial action on the nephron in the absence of a mechanism for elaborating a hypertonic urine.

Two large amphibians, the North American bullfrog, *Rana catesbiana*, and the South American toad, *Bufo marinus*, have provided material for these studies. The basic technique consisted of cannulating both ureters through a ventral abdominal incision with fine polyethylene tubing. The tubing was brought out through the cloaca, the abdomen closed, and the animal allowed to recover from anaesthesia. The next day ureteral urine was collected continuously from the unanaesthetized animal. Ureteral cannulation has the advantages of eliminating most of the dead space and any errors due to reabsorption through the bladder.

This preparation allows one to make multiple consecutive determinations of exogenous creatinine or inulin clearances. These clearances, when determined simultaneously in our preparations, are essentially identical and are assumed to be valid measurements of filtration rate (Forster, 1938; Sawyer & Sawyer, 1952; Sawyer, unpublished). The osmotic concentrations of plasma and urine were deter-mined by freezing-point (Wesson, 1952) or vapour-pressure (Sawyer, 1954) depres-sion. These data enable us to calculate the osmotic and free-water clearances, respectively (Smith, 1956). The osmotic clearance ($C_{osm} = U_{osm}V/P_{osm}$) is defined as that portion of the total urine flow required to contain the urinary solutes in an isosmotic solution. The free-water clearance ($C_{H_2O} = V - C_{osm}$) is the water excreted in excess of that which is obligated osmotically. This is the water that dilutes urine below the isosmotic state.

Neurohypophysial extract administered in large doses to the bullfrog causes a marked decrease in free-water clearance, even when this is factored by the filtration rate to eliminate variable changes in this function. (Fig. 1). This reduction in free-water clearance leads to antidiuresis, and to an increase in the osmotic concentration of the urine, this concentration approaching that of the plasma. Tubular antidiuresis is irregularly accompanied by a decrease in filtration rate (Fig. 2) which we have previously described as the glomerular antidiuretic response (Sawyer, 1951*b*; Sawyer & Sawyer, 1952). We believe that the glomerular action is attributable to specific constriction of the afferent glomerular arterioles by the neurohypophysial hormones.

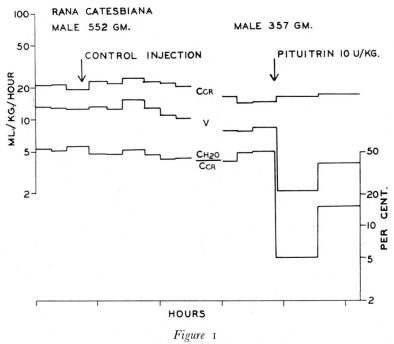

Figure 1

Antidiuretic response of the bullfrog to mammalian neurohypophysial extract. The control injection was dilute acetic acid of the same volume and pH as the Pituitrin solution. In this example the extract did not depress the filtration rate (Ccr). The reduction in urine flow (V) was due to the depression of the relative free-water clearance (C_{H_2O}/Ccr.).

The responses of the toad to neurohypophysial extract are similar to those of the bullfrog. The change in filtration rate is variable, as in the frog, and the antidiuresis is attributable primarily to reduction in free-water clearance (Sawyer, 1956).

Similar changes in urinary concentration and filtration rate have been described in the bullfrog (Schmidt-Nielsen & Forster, 1954) and toad (Sawyer, 1956) in response to dehydration, but the data are insufficient to implicate the neurohypophysis. We have, however, demonstrated depletion of hormone in the frog neurohypophysis during dehydration (Levinsky & Sawyer, 1953), an observation which has been recently confirmed by Jancsó (1955*a*, 1955*b*), and we infer that dehydration evokes release of neurohypophysial hormone in the frog.

Moreover, there is clearly enough hormone present in the amphibian neurohypophysis to produce antidiuresis. An injection of bullfrog pituitary extract corresponding to 1/100 of a gland produces marked antidiuresis in this animal (Fig. 3). This

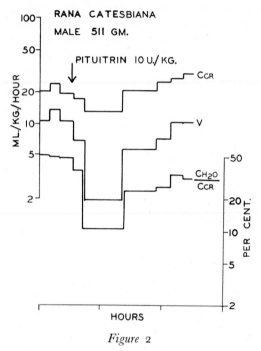

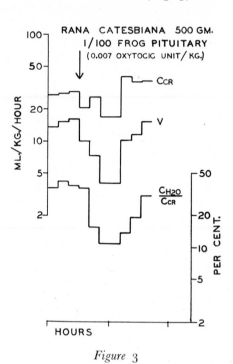

Figure 2

Antidiuretic response of the bullfrog to mammalian neurohypophysial extract. In this instance the extract caused a decrease in filtration rate. The reduction in free-water clearance, however, accounts for the greater part of the antidiuresis.

Figure 3

Antidiuretic response of the bullfrog to the injection of frog neurohypophysial extract equivalent to 1/100 of a gland. This amount of extract corresponded to a dose of 0·007 oxytocic u./kg.

extract, when assayed on the rat uterus, contained only 0·4 oxytocic units per gland. The effective antidiuretic dose in the frog was, therefore, only 0·007 rat oxytocic units/kg. It takes five to ten oxytocic units/kg. of mammalian extract to produce a comparable antidiuretic effect. A similar difference in the effectiveness of amphibian and mammalian extracts with respect to the frog water-balance response has been demonstrated by Heller (1941).

Similarly, a dose of toad pituitary extract corresponding to 1/100 of a gland produced as great an antidiuresis in the toad as one unit of mammalian extract (Sawyer, 1956).

This discrepancy implies class specificity among the active neurohypophysial principles. There is a difference with respect to one amino-acid between vasopressin from the ox and hog (Popenoe, Lawler & du Vigneaud, 1952), and, as Heller (1955) has implied, a greater difference between mammalian and amphibian neurohypophysial principles would not be surprising. The fact that oxytocin is more effective than is vasopressin in producing water balance (Heller, 1930) and antidiuretic

(Sawyer, 1951*b*; Sawyer & Sawyer, 1952) responses in the frog suggests that oxytocin resembles the frog neurohypophysial hormone more closely than does vasopressin (Sawyer, 1955).

That a physiologically active contaminant of the neurohypophysial extract does not account for the difference in antidiuretic activity of these extracts in the bullfrog seems to be excluded by the fact that synthetic oxytocin (supplied by Dr. Vincent du Vigneaud) per oxytocic unit is just as active as whole mammalian extract in producing an antidiuresis (Fig. 4).

Precarious as it may be to do so, we may venture to diagram the possible action of neurohypophysial hormone on tubular water reabsorption in the Amphibia (Fig. 5).

If we agree that urinary water is wholly derived from the glomerular filtrate,* it follows that osmotically free water in the urine is formed by the reabsorption of solute (chiefly NaCl) from this filtrate, leaving water behind for excretion in the urine. This requires a tubular segment capable of active solute reabsorption, but relatively impermeable to water. In the Amphibia the renal tubule must be almost impermeable to water throughout its length during water diuresis since the excretion of osmotically free water may amount to 50 per cent. of the filtered water.

We need only suppose that neurohypophysial hormones increase the permeability of the tubule to water to explain the observed changes in free-water clearance. Jancsó (1955*a*, 1955*b*) has confirmed the increase in total water reabsorption by the frog renal tubule under the influence of neurohypophysial hormones, and derived evidence on the anatomical location of the reabsorptive process by observations on the excretion of trypan blue and non-reabsorbable polyvinyl polymers. During antidiuresis, these substances are deposited as casts in channels occurring only in a specialized segment of the terminal distal tubule, immediately before it joins the collecting duct, and, to a lesser extent, in the collecting ducts themselves.

We have noted that the skin of the frog and toad shows variable permeability to water. Neurohypophysial extracts and synthetic oxytocin (Sawyer, unpublished) increase this permeability, probably by increasing the size of pores (Ussing, 1954). We have recently found that neurohypophysial extracts (Schisgall & Sawyer, 1956) and synthetic oxytocin (Sawyer, unpublished) also increase water reabsorption from the frog urinary bladder, an organ ordinarily not included in discussions of water balance. There is evidence, however, that water in the amphibian bladder can be reabsorbed (Steen, 1929; Ewer, 1952*a*, Schisgall & Sawyer, 1956).

The probability that the responses of the renal tubules, skin, and bladder involve a common mechanism is brought out by a comparison of the effects of neurohypophysial hormones on these organs in frogs and toads (Table 1). In all three instances permeability to water is increased by dehydration, and amphibian extracts are more effective than mammalian extracts. In the frog the response is greater with oxytocin, while in the toad the response is greater with vasopressin. All these phenomena may depend on the dilatation of pores, though there is no evidence for the pore theory except in the case of the skin.

---

* In view of the fact that the frog tubule can secrete urea and other solutes we cannot deny that some water may enter the urine accompanying such solutes (Schisgall, Buxer & Sawyer, 1956). It is also apparent that water flux will occur in both directions between tubular urine and the interstitial fluid if the tubule is at all permeable to water. In this argument we are, however, concerned only with net flux.

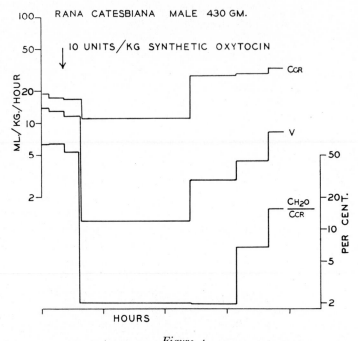

Figure 4

Antidiuretic response of the bullfrog to the injection of synthetic oxytocin.

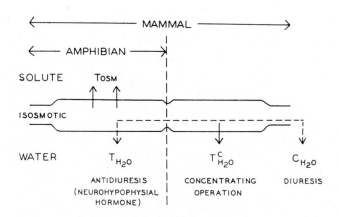

Figure 5

Schematic representation of the relationship of solute reabsorption (T_{osm}) to the formation of free water (C_{H_2O}) in mammal and amphibian, in diuresis and antidiuresis. Neurohypophysial hormone is indicated as acting to allow the passive reabsorption (T_{H_2O}) of water freed osmotically by solute reabsorption. The portion of the diagram labelled 'amphibian' is supposed to include the entire nephron. The portion labelled 'mammal' is intended to represent only the nephron distal to the thin segment.

176

TABLE I

Properties of the change in water permeability of skin, bladder and renal tubule of frogs and toads

	Animal	Increase in water permeability		
		Skin	Bladder	Renal tubule
Occurs in dehydration	Frog	+(1)*	+(2, 3)	+(4)
	Toad	+(5)	+(6)	+(7)
Amphibian pituitary extract more active than mammalian	Frog	+(8, 9, 10)	+(9)	+(11, 12)
	Toad	+(13)		+(7)
Oxytocin more active than vasopressin	Frog	+(10, 14, 15)	+(9)	+(10, 16)†
Vasopressin more active than oxytocin	Toad	+(17, 18, 19)	+(5)	+(18, 19, 20)†
Synthetic oxytocin active	Frog	+(9)	+(9)	+(11)

* Species and references as indicated by numbers in parentheses:

(1) *Rana pipiens.* Levinsky and Sawyer, 1953.
(2) 'Frog.' Probably *R. pipiens.* Steen, 1929.
(3) *R. catesbiana.* Schisgall & Sawyer, 1956.
(4) *R. clamitans.* Schmidt-Nielsen & Forster, 1954.
(5) *Bufo regularis.* Ewer, 1952*b*.
(6) *B. regularis.* Ewer, 1952*a*.
(7) *B. marinus.* Sawyer, 1956.
(8) *R. temporaria.* Heller, 1941.
(9) *R. pipiens.* Sawyer, unpublished.
(10) *R. temporaria.* Jørgensen, 1950.

(11) *R. catesbiana.* Sawyer, this paper.
(12) *R. esculenta.* Jancsó, 1955*a*, 1955*b*.
(13) *B. bufo.* Jørgensen, 1950.
(14) *R. esculenta.* Heller, 1930.
(15) *R. pipiens.* Sawyer, Travis & Levinsky, 1950.
(16) *R. catesbiana.* Sawyer & Sawyer, 1952.
(17) *B. arenarum.* Novelli, 1932.
(18) *B. regularis.* Ewer, 1951.
(19) *B. carens.* Ewer, 1952*b*.
(20) *B. marinus.* Sawyer & Sawyer, 1952.

† Total antidiuretic effect measured, not tubular effect alone.

The interpretation given here for the function of neurohypophysial hormones in the Amphibia brings this function into line with the present interpretation of the action of the antidiuretic hormone in the mammalian nephron (Fig. 5). It is supposed by most investigators that in the mammal about 80 per cent. of the filtered solute is reabsorbed by the proximal tubule, the free water formed by proximal solute reabsorption diffusing back into the blood either here or through the thin segment (Smith, 1951) so that the urine delivered to the distal segment‡ is again isotonic with the blood though reduced in volume by four-fifths. Free water becomes available for excretion in the distal tubule where most of the remaining sodium is actively reabsorbed (Wesson & Anslow, 1952; Smith, 1952). During water diuresis this free water diffuses so slowly through the relatively impermeable epithelium of the distal tubule that it escapes reabsorption. Up to this point the mammalian distal tubule bears a close resemblance to the amphibian tubule.

In the mammal, however, during antidiuresis the urine may be concentrated to an osmotic pressure above that of the plasma, an operation which involves, directly

‡ The terms 'distal segment' as used here indicates a functional portion of the nephron between the thin segment and the concentrating mechanism, as defined below, but cannot be identified as yet with any specific anatomical portion of the distal tubule or connecting tubule in the Amphibia or mammals.

or indirectly, the active reabsorption of water in contradistinction to the passive diffusion with which we have been concerned up to this point. Reasons have been given for believing that this concentrating operation ($T^c_{H_2O}$) is physiologically and anatomically distinct from the mechanism of water diuresis (Wesson & Anslow, 1952; Smith, 1951, 1952, 1956). This concentrating operation may or may not be continuous, but it removes water from the urine subject to two limitations: it is limited by a maximal rate (ml./min.) when the volume of urine delivered to it is large, while, at lower volumes, it is limited to a maximal osmotic U/P ratio. Berliner & Davidson (1956) have recently reported that during acute reduction of filtration rate in one kidney in hydrated dogs otherwise showing maximal water diuresis, the urine may be concentrated to an osmotic level above that of the plasma, implying that the concentrating operation proceeds independently of the presence of the antidiuretic hormone.

In this view the degree of urinary concentration in the mammal is determined, therefore, largely by the volume of water delivered to this concentrating mechanism. We do not know how this concentrating mechanism acts, but reasons have been given for believing that this concentrating mechanism is located in the collecting ducts (Smith, 1956). If it is supposed that the antidiuretic hormone increases the permeability of the distal segment to water, then during antidiuresis the volume of water delivered to the concentrating mechanism is reduced and the urine is correspondingly more concentrated by the operation of the latter. As matters stand, diuresis and antidiuresis can then be explained in the mammal simply in terms of an increase in permeability of the distal segment to water under the influence of the antidiuretic hormone. This increase in permeability, since it involves reabsorption of water only up to the isosmotic state, could be interpreted in terms of a change in pore size, as the evidence indicates to be the case in the skin, and as we have inferred to be the case in the frog bladder and the amphibian nephron.

REFERENCES

BERLINER, R. W. & DAVIDSON, D. G. (1956). Paper in preparation.

CAPRARO, V. & BERNINI, G. (1952). Mechanism of action of extracts of the posthypophysis on water transport through the skin of the frog (*Rana esculenta*). *Nature*, (*Lond.*) **169**, 454.

EWER, R. F. (1951). The effect of Pitressin and Pitocin on water balance in *Bufo regularis* Reuss. *J. exp. Biol.* **28**, 374–84.

EWER, R. F. (1952a). The effect of Pituitrin on fluid distribution in *Bufo regularis* Reuss. *J. exp. Biol.* **29**, 173-7.

EWER, R. F. (1952b). The effects of posterior pituitary extracts on water balance in *Bufo carens* and *Xenopus laevis*, together with some general considerations of anuran water economy. *J. exp. Biol.* **29**, 429-39.

FORSTER, R. P. (1938). The use of inulin and creatinine as glomerular filtrate measuring substances in the frog. *J. cell. comp. Physiol.* **12**, 213–22.

GARBY, L. & LINDERHOLM, H. (1954). The permeability of frog skin to urea with special reference to the effect of aminophylline. *Acta physiol. scand.* **32**, 263–70.

HELLER, H. (1930). Über die Wirkung der getrennten Hypophysenhinterlappenhormone auf die Wasseraufnahme beim Frosch. *Arch. exp. Path. Pharmak.* **157**, 323-9.

HELLER, H. (1941). Differentiation of an (amphibian) water balance principle from the antidiuretic principle of the posterior pituitary gland. *J. Physiol.* (*Lond.*), **100**, 124–41.

HELLER, H. (1955). The hormonal control of water and salt-electrolyte metabolism with special reference to higher vertebrates. *Mem. Soc. Endocrinol.* **5**, 25–37.

HEVESY, G. V., HOFER, E. & KROGH, A. (1935). The permeability of the skin of frogs to water as determined by D_2O and H_2O. *Skand. Arch. Physiol.* **72,** 199–214.

JANCSÓ, N. (1955*a*). Storage of proteins and vinylpolymers in histiocytes and in the renal epithelium. *Acta Med. Acad. Sci. Hungaricae.* **7,** 173–210.

JANCSÓ, N. (1955*b*). *Speicherung. Stoffanreicherung im Retikuloendothel und in der Niere.* Budapest: Adadémiai Kiadó.

JØRGENSEN, C. B. (1950). The amphibian water economy, with special regard to the effect of neuro-hypophyseal extracts. *Acta physiol. scand.* **22,** Suppl. 78.

KOEFOED-JOHNSEN, V. & USSING, H. H. (1953). The contributions of diffusion and flow to the passage of D_2O through living membranes. *Acta physiol. scand.* **28,** 60–76.

LEVINSKY, N. G. & SAWYER, W. H. (1953). Significance of the neurohypophysis in regulation of fluid balance in the frog. *Proc. Soc. exp. Biol.* (*N.Y.*) **82,** 272–4.

LEVKOFF, A. H., DEMUNBRUN, T. W. & KELLER, A. D. (1954). Disparity between fluid intake and renal concentrating deficit in dogs with diabetes insipidus. Polydipsia, independent of the renal concentrating deficit. *Amer. J. Physiol.* **176,** 25–32.

NOVELLI, A. (1932) Lobulo posterior de la hipofisis e imbibicion de los batracios. *Rev. Soc. argent. Biol.* **8,** 631–7.

PASQUALINI, R. Q. (1938). Estudios sobre el metabolismo hídrico en el *Bufo arenarum* Hensel. V. Acción de los extractos hipofisarios. *Rev. Soc. argent. Biol.* **14,** 260–74.

POPENOE, E. A., LAWLER, H. C. & DU VIGNEAUD, V. (1952). Partial purification and amino-acid content of vasopressin from hog posterior pituitary glands. *J. Amer. Chem. Soc.* **74,** 3713.

SAWYER, W. H. (1951*a*). Effect of posterior pituitary extract on the permeability of frog skin to water. *Amer. J. Physiol.* **164,** 44–8.

SAWYER, W. H. (1951*b*). Effect of posterior pituitary extract on urine formation and glomerular circulation in the frog. *Amer. J. Physiol.* **164,** 457–66.

SAWYER, W. H. (1954). Determination of osmolarity in small samples with a modified Baldes-Hill technique utilizing thermistors instead of thermocouples. *Fed. Proc.* **13,** 127.

SAWYER, W. H. (1955). The hormonal control of water and salt-electrolyte metabolism with special reference to the Amphibia. *Mem. Soc. Endocrinol.* **5,** 44–59.

SAWYER, W. H. (1956). Increased renal reabsorption of water in the toad, *Bufo marinus*, in response to dehydration and toad neurohypophysial extract. *Bull. Mt. Desert I. Biol. Lab.* **5.** In press.

SAWYER, W. H. & SAWYER, M. K. (1952). Adaptive responses to neurohypophyseal fractions in vertebrates. *Physiol. Zoöl.* **25,** 84–98.

SAWYER, W. H., TRAVIS, D. F. & LEVINSKY, N. G. (1950). Identity and specificity of frog water-balance principle of posterior pituitary extract. *Amer. J. Physiol.* **163,** 364–9.

SCHISGALL, R. M., BUXER, J. & SAWYER, W. H. (1956). The excretion of urea by the perfused kidney of the bullfrog, *Rana catesbiana. Bull. Mt. Desert I. Biol. Lab.* **5.** In press.

SCHISGALL, R. M. & SAWYER, W. H. (1956). Increased reabsorption of water from the urinary bladder of the bullfrog, *Rana catesbiana*, in response to dehydration and neurohypophysial extracts. *Bull. Mt. Desert I. Biol. Lab.* **5.** In press.

SCHMIDT-NIELSEN, B. & FORSTER, R. P. (1954). The effect of dehydration and low temperature on renal function in the bullfrog. *J. cell. comp. Physiol.* **44,** 233–46.

SHANNON, J. A. (1942). The control of the renal excretion of water. I. The effects of variations in the state of hydration on water excretion in dogs with diabetes insipidus. *J. exp. Med.* **76,** 371–99.

SMITH, H. W. (1951). *The Kidney. Structure and Function in Health and Disease.* New York: Oxford University Press.

SMITH, H. W. (1952). Renal excretion of sodium and water. *Fed. Proc.* **11,** 701–5.

SMITH, H. W. (1956). *Principles of Renal Physiology.* New York: Oxford University Press.

STEEN, W. B. (1929). On the permeability of the frog's bladder to water. *Anat. Rec.* **43,** 215–20.

USSING, H. H. (1954). Membrane structure as revealed by permeability studies. In *Recent Developments in Cell Physiology. Proceedings of the Seventh Colston Research Society Symposium.* Ed. Kitching, J. A. New York: Academic Press.

WESSON, L. G., Jr. (1952). Electrolyte excretion studies in the dog. In *Methods in Medical Research,* **5,** 175–91. Chicago: Year Book Publishers.

WESSON, L. G., Jr. & ANSLOW, W. P., Jr. (1952). Effect of osmotic and mercurial diuresis on simultaneous water diuresis. *Amer. J. Physiol.* **170,** 255–69.

Discussion

Chairman : H. Heller

Wirz. There is a slight difference in definition between Homer Smith's terminology and that which I have used. Smith calls everything after the ending of the thin limb, distal. What I have punctured is the convoluted part of the distal tubule. If we allow for the differences in definition then Dr. Sawyer and I are in much greater agreement than might appear.

Sawyer. I entirely agree. I meant to point that out myself. Although there is hypotonic urine in the distal convolutions, it does not rule out the possibility that it is isotonic at the end of the thin limb.

Dale. I am still a little puzzled. Not having followed the modern developments in renal physiology, I find it a little difficult to relate these ideas to my conception of the structure of the nephron. When you say 'distal limb' what do you mean? What is the loop of Henle doing? I got the impression that Dr. Wirz and Dr. Sawyer were using the word 'distal' in different senses.

Wirz. Next to the glomerulus we have what is commonly referred to as proximal convoluted tubule. It consists of a convoluted part and a pars recta which passes down beneath the cortico-medullary boundary. In the outer zone of the medulla is the beginning of the thin limb, which may be 'long' or 'short'. The thin limb gives way to the thick, ascending limb of the loop of Henle. This segment touches the glomerulus of the same nephron, and what I call the distal convolution starts at this point. The end of the distal convolution is defined by the branching of the collecting duct. This is a somewhat arbitrary definition, but it is very convenient as the two end points of my distal convolution are easily recognized in post-mortem microdissections. All my 'distal' micropunctures are located between these points. Homer Smith would include the thick ascending limb of the loop in what he calls the distal system.

Sawyer. We use the term distal system to mean anything past the thin limb.

Dale. Where does the concentrating start?

Wirz. I have found, by micropuncture, the urine in the proximal part of the distal convolutions to be hypotonic in both diuretic and antidiuretic states. In the distal parts of the distal convolutions the urine is hypotonic in the diuretic state and isotonic in the concentrating kidneys. So some of the diluting process must occur somewhere in the ascending limb, and the concentrating process somewhere lower down in the collecting duct.

Bargmann. Would it be possible that this segment is rather long? Maybe the 'Hauptstück' with brush border reaches the bend.

Wirz. There are wide species differences among mammals. In rats and hamsters there are mostly what I think the anatomists call 'long loops', in which the bend is made up entirely of thin limb tissue. In man the incidence of 'long loops' is only about one in eight.

Sawyer. In following what Dr. Wirz has said may I mention a fact which is frequently mentioned as evidence against his theory, that is the low incidence of long thin loops in man, and the lack of any correlation between the number of long loops and concentrating ability in kidneys from mammals in general. His theory does not require, however, that every nephron has a long loop. If only one out of four or six had a long thin loop the hypothetical counter-current system would still account for the final concentration of urine in the collecting ducts, since the volume of urine that must be concentrated is, in the antidiuretic state, greatly decreased during passage through the distal convolutions.

Wirz. I think that the 'short' loops may nevertheless be called 'loops'.

Sawyer. Yes.

de Wardener. When the urine is hypertonic in the collecting ducts, it is in equilibrium with the thin loops, that is why the urine in the collecting ducts is hypertonic. Is that right?

Wirz. There cannot be much difference.

de Wardener. And when the urine in the collecting ducts is hypotonic you suggest that the fluid is iso-osmotic. Is that right?

Wirz. My assumption is that in the absence of the antidiuretic hormone the descending limb is virtually impermeable to water. Then kidney function would proceed as if there was no counter-current system. The multiplying action of the counter-current depends on the entering of a (slightly) hypertonic solution into the ascending limb.

de Wardener. My difficulty is that you suggest that there is equilibrium between the thin loop and the collecting tubules only when the kidney is passing hypertonic urine, but this is prevented when the urine is hypotonic.

Wirz. This is why I have to assume that the antidiuretic hormone influences the water permeability in the collecting ducts as well (see the last figure of my paper).

Sawyer. I do not feel that it is necessary to postulate that the hormone alters the permeability of the thin limb or the collecting duct to water. If enough water is available the reabsorption of water by the final concentrating mechanism ($T^c_{H_2O}$) is continuous, under all conditions in which it can be measured (refer to my Fig. 5). It is limited by a maximal urine osmotic pressure or by a maximum rate of water reabsorption. We have previously assumed that this is an active transport of water, and like other active tubular transports, it has a maximum rate ($T^c_{mH_2O}$).

I do not see that it is inconsistent with your theory if we assume that $T^c_{H_2O}$ is going on continuously to the extent of, say 5 per cent. of the filtration rate when at least that much free water is delivered to it from the distal tubule. We don't have to postulate any changes in $T^c_{H_2O}$ in diuresis and antidiuresis. If, in diuresis, perhaps 15 per cent. of the filtered water is presented at this level and $T^c_{H_2O}$ reabsorbs 5 per cent. that still leaves 10 per cent. for excretion. That is a fairly high rate of urine flow. In the presence of antidiuretic hormone however, the volume of urine delivered from the distal tubule is reduced and $T^c_{H_2O}$ acts to concentrate this smaller volume to an osmotic pressure above that of plasma. Our theory presented here is somewhat simpler than yours in that it requires only one site of action for the antidiuretic hormone, namely the distal tubule.

Wirz. I do not see any serious objection to this. I assume an impermeable collecting duct in the absence of antidiuretic hormone because in my experiments ureteral urine is, if anything, more dilute than distal tubular fluid. Thus I have some difficulty in visualizing the passage of water in an absolutely fixed amount not dependent upon a concentration gradient.

Sawyer. I was assuming here that $T^c_{H_2O}$ proceeds continuously with or without anti-diuretic hormone. There are Berliner's experiments in which he was able to produce a hypertonic urine in a dog in maximal water diuresis. If he reduced the filtration rate of one kidney to the correct level, he could get a definitely concentrated urine even though the urine secreted by the other kidney was maximally dilute. This seems to be due to the fact that he has reduced the volume of fluid delivered to the con-centrating mechanism ($T^c_{H_2O}$) so that this mechanism, whatever it may be, is taking out enough water to make the urine hypertonic. Shannon, of course, saw the same thing in the diabetes insipidus dog when the GFR was low, but the criticism can always be levelled that the absence of antidiuretic hormone was not complete.

Cole. I would like to ask Professor Wirz a question about the 'multiplication principle' he has described.

In the paper by Hargitay & Kuhn (*Z. Elektrochem.* **55,** 539, 1951), there is a diagram suggesting that water goes from the collecting duct into the ascending limb of Henle's loop; in Professor Wirz's diagram he suggests that it goes into the descend-ing limb. So far as the system is concerned is this of any importance or is the water taken up from the collecting duct primarily removed by the blood vessels.

Wirz. I think in the first paper of Hargitay & Kuhn in which they describe their artificial model they had just limbs and no interstitial spaces. At that time we thought too little of the effect of the blood circulation and only after we found in the golden hamster that the concentration of the blood goes up as high as the concentra-tion of the urine, we became aware of the fact that the blood is an integral part of the whole concentrating mechanism. Now I think that is not the ascending or the de-scending limb but mostly the blood which carries the water away.

Neurohypophysial hormones and the mammary gland

by

A. T. COWIE *and* S. J. FOLLEY

National Institute for Research in Dairying, Shinfield, Reading

THE phenomenon of lactation can be considered as comprising two main phases: first, the phase of milk secretion in which the milk is synthesized in the alveolar cells and passed from the cytoplasm of the cells into the alveolar lumen, and secondly, the phase of milk removal in which there is a passive component—passive withdrawal—and an active component—milk ejection (for terminology, see Cowie, Folley, Cross, Harris, Jacobsohn & Richardson, 1951). These two phases were recognized many years ago by Gaines (1915) who remarked that 'milk secretion, in the sense of the formation of the milk constituents is one thing, the ejection of the milk from the gland after it is formed is quite another thing.' Unfortunately this distinction was overlooked by many investigators in the field of lactational physiology. Much confusion thereby arose and the necessity for distinguishing these two phases was stressed by one of us, Folley (1947*b*) and again by Cowie *et al.* (1951). We now propose to consider the roles which hormones of the neurohypophysis may play in these two phases.

MILK REMOVAL

It is convenient to start with a consideration of the second phase since more is at present known of the role of the neurohypophysis in this phase. In the lactating mammary gland the greater portion of the milk secreted by the alveolar cells remains within the alveolar lumen and fine ducts, a smaller portion passing into the large ducts and cisterns (or sinuses). This smaller portion can be *immediately* removed by the action of suckling or milking or by cannulation. The physiological contractile mechanisms of the gland play no part in the removal of this fraction of the milk, and the process may be described as one of *passive withdrawal*. The larger portion of the milk in the alveoli and fine ducts must be actively ejected from these positions, by the intervention of the special contractile tissue of the mammary gland, into the large ducts and cisterns before it becomes available to and can be withdrawn by the suckling young or the hand milker. This process of *milk ejection* is believed to be brought about by the reflex contraction of the myoepithelium (see Plate 1) which forms a network over the stromal surface of the alveoli (Richardson, 1949; Linzell, 1952). In agricultural circles the milk-ejection process is commonly termed the 'let-down' of milk. The misleading and inappropriate nature of this term was first stressed by one of us some years ago (Folley, 1947*b*) and later the term 'milk ejection' was recommended by a group of workers in this field (Cowie, *et al.*, 1951; and Cowie, Folley &

183

Richardson, 1954). The term 'milk ejection' was first used by Gaines in his classical paper in 1915 and we still consider it to be the best yet brought forward or invented for use in scientific literature to describe this process.

MILK-EJECTION REFLEX

Neuro-hormonal arc

The reflex contraction of the myoepithelial cells is normally brought about by the stimulus of suckling or milking. Like other reflexes, this milk-ejection reflex can be conditioned. In the milking shed, the cow readily becomes conditioned to a variety of auditory, tactile and visual stimuli associated with the act of milking, such

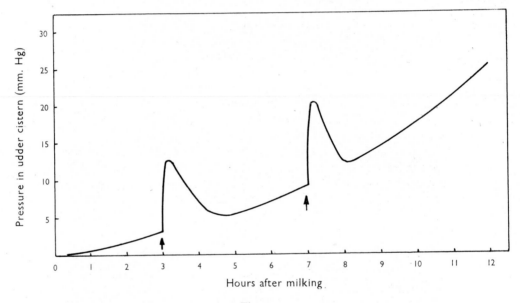

Figure 1

Milk pressure curve (cow) between one milking and the next showing the reaction to the milking stimulus, on milk however being withdrawn. Arrows indicate application of stimulus. (Redrawn from *Tgetgel*, 1926.)

as the rattle of milk buckets, washing of the udder and appearance of the milking machines. It can also be conditioned experimentally to the ringing of a bell (Gračev, 1952). Waller (1938), in his book, has described similar examples of conditioning in lactating women. The milk-ejection reflex manifests itself by a sudden rise in the milk pressure in the mammary gland. This rise in pressure is well illustrated in Fig. 1 taken from a paper by Tgetgel (1926) which shows the curve of increase of milk pressure in the mammary cistern of a cow between one milking and the next. Two successive applications of the milking stimulus, at times marked by the arrows, produced a sudden increase in the pressure of the milk within the cistern which soon subsided even though no milk was withdrawn. The milk-ejection reflex is thus the means by which the active but unconscious participation of the lactating mother comes into play so that the full yield of milk can be obtained by the suckling young

184

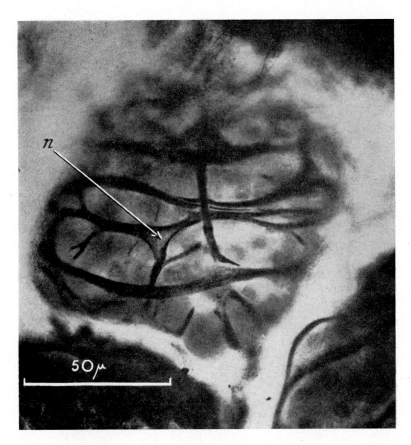

Plate I

Section of part of the surface of a contracted alveolus from the mammary gland of the goat showing a myoepithelial cell with nucleus (*n*) and branching processes. (From Richardson, 1949.)

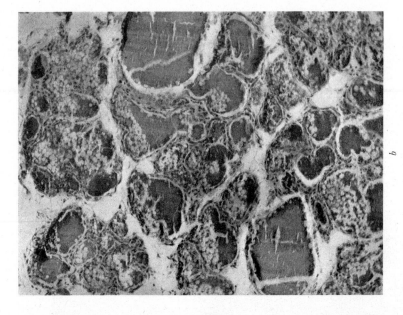

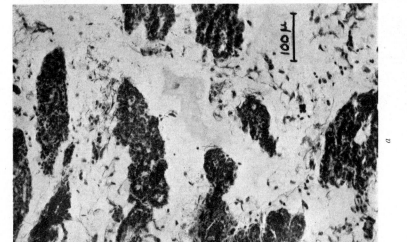

Plate II

Abdominal mammary glands of rats from which the pups were removed at the 4th day of lactation, the mother thereafter receiving intraperitoneally injections of (*a*) 1·0 ml. saline thrice daily for 9 days, and (*b*) 1·0 I.U. oxytocin in 1·0 ml. saline thrice daily for 9 days.

or by the milker. Even after normal milk ejection, however, the gland cannot be completely milked out and there is always a small quantity of milk left in the gland. This residual milk can only be obtained if oxytocin be injected.

The milk-ejection reflex was once believed to consist of a purely neural arc, but, as we shall see, there is now much evidence for the view that the arc is a neuro-hormonal one, the efferent component of which is a hormone, in all probability oxytocin, released from the neurohypophysis into the blood-stream. On reaching the mammary gland this hormone is believed to evoke the contraction of the myoepithelium.

It is over forty years since Ott & Scott (1911) and Schäfer (1913) observed that the milk-ejection reflex could be mimicked by the injection of extracts of the posterior lobe of the pituitary. Gaines (1915) carried out a series of experiments on the milk-ejection reflex and he showed *inter alia* that anaesthesia abolished the reflex in the nursing bitch and that this inhibition could be overcome by the injection of posterior pituitary extract (Fig. 2). Despite his clear-cut results, which today would be inter-

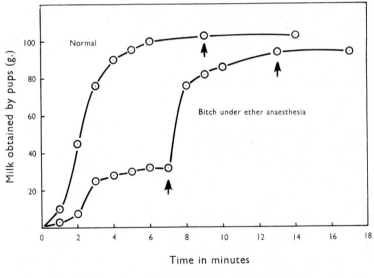

Figure 2

Milk flow curves from a bitch, under normal conditions and under ether anaes-thesia. Arrows indicate injection of posterior pituitary extract. (Redrawn from Gaines, 1915.)

preted as strongly suggesting a physiological role for the neurohypophysis in milk ejection, Gaines regarded the milk-ejection reflex as a neural arc, and the action of posterior pituitary extract as only of pharmacological interest. It was not until fifteen years later that Turner & Slaughter (1930) suggested that the milk-ejection reflex might act through the posterior-pituitary gland. It was another eleven years before this possibility was further explored, and its practical significance realized. Ely & Petersen (1941) showed that milk ejection could occur in response to the normal milking stimulus in the half of the bovine udder in which the two nerves, believed to carry all the efferent fibres to the gland, had been cut. Evidence was also obtained that both the reflex and the action of injected oxytocin could be inhibited by the injection of adrenaline thus providing an explanation for the well-known observation that fear or pain may inhibit the normal milk-ejection reflex. It was further shown that blood collected from cows after stimulation produced ejection of milk when perfused through the isolated cow udder (Petersen & Ludwick, 1942). Petersen and his colleagues concluded that the milk-ejection reflex embodied a neurohormonal arc and that the reflex could be initiated by the suckling or milking stimulus or by stimuli arising from the sight or sound of events which the cow had come to associate with the beginning of milking. It was further postulated that once oxytocin was liberated into the blood-stream, it was quickly inactivated and hence rapid milking was desirable to obtain proper emptying of the gland. This work of Petersen aroused wide interest because of its physiological and practical importance. Despite the attractiveness of his postulates, however, the experimental evidence on which they were based was scanty and our colleague Mrs. M. H. I. Macaulay (1951), reviewing the literature some ten years later, concluded that there was 'insufficient evidence to do any more than suggest that the neural lobe participates in milk ejection'. In the last five years however, more evidence has accumulated to confirm the role of the neurohypophysis in milk ejection, and we shall now briefly consider this evidence.

Hormone content of neural lobe

Attempts to demonstrate alterations in the hormone content of the neural lobe following the suckling or milking stimulus have led to no clear conclusions. Mrs. M. H. I. Dodd (formerly Mrs. Macaulay), in our laboratory, compared the oxytocic and pressor hormone contents of the neural lobe of goats killed before milking with those of the neural lobe of goats killed immediately after milking (Table 1) but observed no significant depletion of either hormone (see Folley, 1952a). Subsequent experiments both in our laboratory and by Denamur & Martinet (1953) suggested that the quantity of oxytocin necessary for evoking milk ejection in the goat was only 10 per cent., or perhaps much less, of the total hormone content of the gland and it is therefore hardly surprising that no significant depletion was observed since the small quantity of oxytocin released may have been well within the limits of error of the assay procedure. Similar experiments in the cow by Whittlestone, Bassett and Turner (1952) likewise failed to show any appreciable depletion. In some smaller species, however, (the dog, cat, guinea-pig and rat) a pronounced decrease in oxytocic activity of the pituitary has been observed during lactation by Dicker & Tyler (1953). This observation has been confirmed in the case of the dog by van Dyke, Adamsons and Engel (1955), and in the rat by Professor Fromageot, as he has reported to us in his paper to this symposium. It is possible that the differences may represent species variation in the amount of oxytocin necessary to produce milk ejection or in its replacement rate following liberation.

Neurosecretory material

Histochemical studies on the variations in amount of the neurosecretory material present in the hypothalamus and neurohypophysis during lactation have likewise

TABLE I

Amounts of oxytocin and vasopressin in posterior pituitaries of goats
(Unpublished work of Margaret H. I. Dodd, cited by Folley, 1952a.)

No. of goat	Sex	Age	Vasopressin I.U./mg. dry tissue	Oxytocin I.U./mg. dry tissue
Non-lactating goats				
393	♀	6 months	0·7–0·8	0·8
385	♀	8 ,,	1·8	1·8
342	♂	2½ years	0·5	0·6
Lactating goats, unmilked for 24 hr. before autopsy				
316	♀	2 years	0·6	0·8
326	♀	2 ,,	0·6	0·6
338	♀	2 ,,	0·8	∼0·7
100	♀	6½ ,,	0·8	0·8
Lactating goats, killed immediately after milking out				
79	♀	8 years	0·7	0·65
127	♀	6 ,,	∼0·6	∼1·0
165	♀	5 ,,	0·8	0·8–1·0
291	♀	3 ,,	0·6	0·8
232	♀	4 ,,	0·8	0·8–1·0
222	♀	4 ,,	0·6	1·0
226	♀	4 ,,	0·28 (?)	0·7

given results which are at present difficult to evaluate. Stutinsky (1953) reported that twenty-four hours after parturition in the rat there was a dramatic loss of neurosecretory material from the neurohypophysis which did not occur if suckling was prevented. Malandra (1955) also reported a reduction of neurosecretory material in the neurohypophysis of the rat during early lactation. Other workers have observed a loss of neurosecretory material in early lactation in the guinea-pig (Collin & Racadot, 1953) and in the mouse (Brightman, 1955). On the other hand, Drager & Rennels (1955) could find no consistent alteration in the amount of neurosecretory material in the rat neurohypophysis associated with parturition or lactation. While studies on the effect of the milking or suckling stimulus on the amount of hormonal or neurosecretory material in the neurohypophysis have added no convincing evidence in support of the neurohypophysial participation in the milk-ejection reflex it is equally true that they provide no evidence against such a view.

Antidiuresis

Indications have been obtained by another procedure that the milk-ejection reflex involves activation of the neurohypophysis. The occurrence of an antidiuretic effect of the posterior pituitary type shortly after the application of the suckling or milking stimulus has been demonstrated in the water-loaded animal. Such results have been obtained in the rabbit by Cross, (1950), the cow by Peeters and Coussens, (1950), the woman by Kalliala and Karvonen, (1951) and the bitch by Kalliala, Karvonen and Leppänen, (1952).

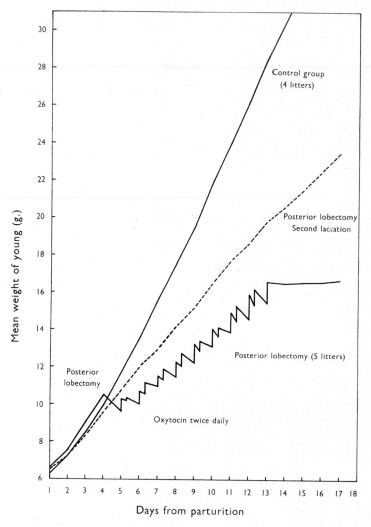

Figure 3

Growth curves of litters of (*a*) control rats (4), (*b*) rats (5) lobectomized on fourth day after parturition and receiving oxytocin (0·75 I.U.) intraperitoneally twice daily from day 5 to day 13, (*c*) same lobectomized rats in second lactation but receiving no oxytocin.

Hypothalamic stimulation and lesions

The most convincing evidence however, of the intervention of a hormone of the neurohypophysis in the milk-ejection reflex comes from experiments involving electrical stimulation of the hypothalamus and interruption of nerve tracts within the hypothalamus by electrolytic lesions. Cross & Harris (1950, 1951, 1952) showed that electrical stimulation of the supraoptico-hypophysial tract caused milk ejection in the anaesthetized rabbit. Rabbits, moreover, with lesions in this tract failed to exhibit milk ejection on electrical stimulation of the tract central to the lesion and the litters of these rabbits were unable to obtain significant quantities of milk on suckling unless the mother was injected with oxytocin. Andersson (1951*a*, *b*) evoked milk ejection in lactating ewes and goats by electrical stimulation of hypothalamic centres in or adjacent to the supraoptic nucleus. Andersson concluded that these responses were undoubtedly hormonally mediated because they could be elicited during sacral anaesthesia or in denervated udder-halves. He further showed that blood taken from a goat immediately after electrical stimulation evoked a prompt flow of milk from the cannulated teats of another lactating animal on intravenous injection, thus demonstrating that the stimulation had caused the discharge of a milk-ejection hormone into the blood stream.

Posterior lobectomy

Experiments on the effect of removal of the neural lobe on the milk-ejection reflex have given results which are at first sight confusing. Smith (1932) in a study on the effect of ablation of the posterior lobe on parturition in the rat observed that rats so treated could raise their young and he concluded that removal of the posterior lobe did not seriously affect lactation. Houssay (1935) also claimed that bitches lactated normally after removal of the posterior lobe. On the other hand, Harris & Jacobsohn (1952) in the course of studies on the transplantation of the pituitary in the rat observed that hypophysectomized rats possessing functional anterior-pituitary grafts could only rear their young if regularly injected with posterior-pituitary extract. In agreement with this are the observations of Cowie (quoted by Folley, 1952*a*) that when the posterior pituitary is removed from rats on the fourth day of lactation such rats are unable to raise their litters unless injected two or three times daily with oxytocin. An explanation of these contradictory findings on the effect of posterior lobectomy may be forthcoming from some recent experiments by Benson & Cowie (1956), who have confirmed that the milk-ejection reflex is abolished in the rat after posterior lobectomy, but that if such rats again become pregnant they then rear their second litter without requiring injections of oxytocin (Fig. 3). In the rat, at least, it would appear that on removal of the neural lobe other parts of the neurohypophysis —the neural stalk or the median eminence—can take over the function of the posterior lobe in the milk-ejection reflex. Benson & Cowie, by measuring the volume of the neurohypophysial tissue from serial sections, have demonstrated that after posterior lobectomy the neural stalk hypertrophies (Table II). This is in agreement with the findings of Stutinsky (1952) and Billenstien & Leveque (1955) who report that after hypophysectomy there is an hypertrophy and reorganization of the end of the stalk which gradually assumes the appearance of a small neural lobe. It is of interest to note that whereas there was at least a partial restoration of the milk-ejection reflex, the rats continued to show diabetes insipidus (Table III). Further experiments are in progress to decide how long after removal of the neural lobe it is before the milk-ejection reflex reappears. Since Smith (1932) lobectomized his rats some weeks before they became pregnant it is likely that the reflex was at least partly functional by the time suckling started.

TABLE II

Volume of residual hypophysial tissue in the rat after hypophysectomy and posterior lobectomy
(From Benson & Cowie, 1956.)

Treatments	Volume (mm.³) of		
	Anterior lobe	Intermediate lobe	Neurohypophysis
Control rats (7)	3·21 ±0·23	0·16 ±0·01	0·36 ±0·01 (stalk+median eminence= 0·10 ±0·01)
Posterior lobectomy, killed immediately after operation (6)	2·33 ±0·31	—	0·09 ±0·01
Hypophysectomy, killed immediately, or within 14 days of operation (13)	—	—	0·09 ±0·01
Posterior lobectomy, killed 4–5 months after operation (14)	2·46 ±0·22	(0·027, in one rat only)	0·15 ±0·01

It is apparent from what has been said that the evidence for the neuro-endocrine regulation of milk ejection by a pathway involving activation of the neurohypophysis is impressive in amount and in sum convincing.

TABLE III

Effect of posterior lobectomy on urine production in the rat
(From Benson & Cowie, 1956.)

Treatments	Mean urine volume (ml.) over 48-hr. period		
	After 1st lactation	After 2nd lactation	Before killing
Control rats (5)	27±2·5	22±2·2	20±2·0
Posterior lobectomy (17)	54±4·9	49±4·5	38±4·0

The nature of the milk-ejection hormone

It is now necessary to consider briefly the nature of the milk-ejection hormone. It has uniformly been found that while both the oxytocic and vasopressor fractions from the posterior lobe possess milk-ejection activity, the oxytocic fraction is much more active in this respect than the pressor fraction (for references see Folley, 1954). However, the activity of the pressor fraction is considerably more than can be accounted for on the basis of contamination with the oxytocic factor. The earlier experimental evidence relating to this question was discussed by Folley (1954) who concluded that in view of the uncertainties associated with the present assay procedures for oxytocin it seemed reasonable, on the basis of the available evidence, to believe that milk ejection and oxytocic activities are facets of the same biological activity characteristic of the oxytocic polypeptide, and that both activities are also possessed in some small degree by the vasopressor polypeptide. Studies on the highly purified or synthetic polypeptides of du Vigneaud have now confirmed this view (for references see review by van Dyke, Adamsons & Engel, 1955), and the discrepancies arising from different assay procedures are well illustrated by the recently published data of van Dyke, Adamsons and Engel (1955) which show that when purified *oxytocin* is assayed by three different procedures (rat-uterine, avian-depressor, and milk-ejection methods) the potency is the same in all cases, but when purified *vasopressin* is assayed by these methods, the potency as determined by the avian-depressor and milk-ejection methods is about three times that obtained by the rat-uterine method.

Inhibition of milk-ejection reflex

Of great scientific and practical interest are the experiments on the various physiological and psychological factors which may interfere with, or inhibit, the normal milk-ejection reflex. It has long been known to the farmer that fright or discomfort can inhibit the milk-ejection reflex in the cow (Ely & Petersen, 1941). Clinicians have made similar observations regarding the nursing mother (Newton & Newton, 1948). As previously stated the possibility that sympathetic activity might play a part in the phenomenon was suggested by Ely & Petersen (1941) who found that the injection of adrenaline interfered with milk ejection in the cow. They believed that the suppression was peripheral in nature and occurred in the udder. Inhibition of milk ejection by injection of adrenaline has been reported in the sow by Braude & Mitchell (1952), and in the rabbit by Cross (1953). The nature of this inhibitory process has been extensively studied by Cross (1953, 1955a) who showed that in the anaesthetized rabbit stimulation of the posterior hypothalamus inhibits milk ejection in a manner similar to that of physiological doses of exogenous adrenaline. He showed, moreover, that adrenalectomy abolishes the inhibitory effect of posterior-hypothalamic stimulation. Cross was of the opinion that constriction of the mammary blood vessels was the major factor involved in this peripheral block of the mammary response to circulating oxytocin and recent studies by Linzell (1955) on the action on the myoepithelium of topically applied drugs support this view. While the experiments of Cross clearly showed that central stimulation by causing sympathetico-adrenal activity could inhibit the milk-ejection response to oxytocin, Cross was careful to point out that it did not necessarily follow that this mechanism was the one normally in action in the conscious animal suckled under conditions of emotional disturbance. In a further series of experiments Cross (1955b) showed that the main factor in emotional inhibition of milk ejection in the conscious rabbit was a central block of release of oxytocin since the injection of oxytocin could restore normal milk removal during emotional disturbance. Only in a few cases was this unsuccessful, indicating a concomitant activation of the sympathetico-adrenal system. These experiments of Cross, moreover, provide further confirmation of the essential role of oxytocin in milk ejection. As Dr. Cross is here with us, he will no doubt wish to say something about his work and we will not therefore deal further with it.

MILK SECRETION

So far we have been considering only one phase of lactation, namely milk removal. The other phase, that of milk secretion, is a process known to be under the hormonal control of the anterior pituitary. We need not here go into the debatable question whether there is one lactogenic factor—prolactin or a complex of factors of which prolactin is only a component (for references, see reviews by Folley, 1952a, b), but we now wish to consider briefly whether there may not be an integration of the functioning of the two main phases of lactation by means of the hormone(s) of the posterior lobe.

It has been recognized for some years that the suckling or milking stimulus not only results in the reflex ejection of milk but also results in the reflex liberation of the lactogenic and galactopoietic factor or factors from the anterior lobe. It may be recalled that the rapid involution of the mammary gland following weaning of the young was once believed to be due to the effects—perhaps chemical, perhaps physical —of accumulation of milk within the alveoli. The observations of Selye (1934) first provided an indication that the removal of the suckling stimulus was a more important factor than the non-removal of the secretion in causing the onset of mammary involution after weaning. Selye showed, *inter alia*, that when the main milk ducts to the nipples of the lactating rat were ligated so that milk could not be removed from the glands, rapid involution of the gland, such as occurred in non-suckled animals, did not occur if suckling were continued. Selye and his collaborators suggested that the suckling stimulus initiated a nervous reflex which elicited the secretion of prolactin from the anterior pituitary which maintained the functional activity and structural integrity of the gland. These experiments of Selye have since been confirmed and extended by several investigators (for references see review by Folley, 1947b).

The question therefore arises as to what extent the arcs of these two reflexes elicited by the suckling or milking stimulus share common paths. Little appears to be known about the afferent neural paths, but it is not improbable that a common path is shared as far as the hypothalamus. Thereafter the route to the posterior lobe is likely to be *via* the hypothalamic nuclei and hypothalamo-hypophysial tracts. There is much less certainty, however, about the route followed by stimuli passing from the hypothalamus to the anterior lobe. Harris (1955) considers that there is convincing evidence in favour of the view that the link is a neurohormonal one, achieved by the liberation from nerve fibres from the hypothalamus of some humoral substance(s) or chemotransmitter into the primary plexus of the hypophysial portal system. It is believed that this substance is then carried in the portal circulation to the anterior lobe. Various suggestions have been made regarding the nature of the chemotransmitter substance. Some authorities however question its reality (Zuckerman, 1954). One view of particular interest to us here is that of Benoit & Assenmacher (1953) who suggest that the chemotransmitter for the release of gonadotrophins may be carried in the neurosecretory material associated with the hypothalamic nuclei and hypothalamo-hypophysial tract, thus implying an integration of anterior and posterior lobe functions. In this connexion there have been in the past few years several studies on the possible control of adrenocorticotrophin release by posterior-pituitary hormones (Fraja & Martini, 1952; Mirsky, Stein & Paulish, 1954; Barrnett, 1954; Scharrer & Scharrer, 1954; Shibusawa, Saito, Fukuda, Kawai & Yoshimura, 1955, and Martini & Morpurgo, 1955).

Neurohypophysis and control of secretion of lactogenic and galactopoietic hormones

The fact that the suckling stimulus, as we have seen, appears to play a central role in the two main phases of lactation—milk secretion and milk ejection, led us to speculate whether the reflex release of oxytocin might not provide a hormonal link between these two phases. This concept that the release of the lactogenic and galacto-poietic factors from the anterior lobe may be controlled by oxytocin is an intriguing one since it would provide a simple explanation of how the hormonal integration and co-ordination of mammary function is achieved. The oxytocin liberated as a result of the suckling or milking stimulus would thus not only cause contraction of the myoepithelium and ejection of milk from the alveoli, but would liberate the lactogenic and galactopoietic factor(s) from the anterior lobe which are necessary for the main-tenance of further secretion of milk by the alveolar cells.

In order to test the validity of this concept, Mr. Benson in our laboratory has been carrying out some preliminary experiments which have so far given encouraging results (Benson & Folley, 1956). One approach to this problem has been to investi-gate whether the rapid involution of the mammae which occurs after weaning can be prevented by frequent injections of oxytocin. It will be recalled that Williams (1945), investigating Selye's theory, has demonstrated that these involutionary changes could be retarded by the injection of prolactin just as they could by suckling and it should therefore be possible to get a similar retardation with oxytocin if oxytocin can release prolactin. In Mr. Benson's experiments the pups were removed from 44 lactating rats on the fourth day of lactation. Eight of these rats were kept as controls and received daily injections of 1 ml. saline intraperitoneally three times a day. The remainder were divided into three groups of 12 and given respectively, 0·25, 1·0 and 1·5 I.U. oxytocin intraperitoneally three times a day. Four of the animals in each of the oxytocin-treated groups were killed after 3, 6 and 9 days of treatment. Four controls were killed after 6 and 9 days of treatment. Histological sections of the left abdominal gland were prepared and classified subjectively accord-ing to the degree of glandular involution which had occurred and also by a quantita-tive procedure based on measuring the mean diameter of the alveoli. No differences were detected between the control glands 6 days after weaning and those receiving oxytocin for 3 and 6 days. Involution was markedly retarded, however, in the glands of the animals receiving oxytocin for 9 days in contrast to glands of the 9-day control animals. Sections of glands of the oxytocin-treated animals showed mammary alveoli distended with milk whereas in the control glands there were only scattered islands of small disintegrating alveoli which in many places had become reduced to clusters of epithelial cells (Plate II). In agreement with these subjective observations the mean alveolar diameter was significantly greater in the oxytocin-treated animals ($P <$ 0·01). While it does not necessarily follow from these experiments that oxytocin is the normal stimulus to the anterior pituitary causing the release of the galactopoietic factor(s) under physiological conditions, it is clear that this possible role of oxytocin requires further investigation. We consider it unlikely that these results are due to a direct effect of oxytocin on the mammary gland because Dr. T. R. Bradley in our laboratory has found that prolactin alone of a number of anterior- and posterior-pituitary principles tested, including oxytocin, had a localized lactogenic effect when injected intraductally into the mammae of suitably prepared rabbits. Experiments are being planned, however, to study the effects of oxytocin in rats hypophysectomized at the time of weaning.

If the above views on the role of oxytocin be correct, it is reasonable to believe that, under certain circumstances, the repeated injection of oxytocin into a lactating animal might result in an increase in milk production by virtue of the release of extra amounts of the galactopoietic factors from the anterior pituitary. In this connexion it is most necessary to distinguish clearly between apparent and true increases in milk yield. It has long been established that after a normal milk ejection there remains in the udder a quantity of residual milk which can be obtained if oxytocin be injected intravenously. This is not, of course, a galactopoietic effect since the extra milk so obtained will be compensated for by a reduced yield at the next milking unless oxytocin be again injected (for references, see review by Folley, 1947a). On the other hand there is evidence that when oxytocin is injected daily over periods of time, a true increase in yield is obtained. In 1944, Knodt & Petersen reported that the rate of decline of the milk yield in cows could be diminished if the residual milk was removed by injections of oxytocin after each milking. This effect has in the past been ascribed to the beneficial effects on the functions of the secretory cells of more efficient removal of milk from the alveoli, thus preventing the build-up of intra-alveolar pressure. Recent experiments by H. G. Turner (1955) and Elliott & Brumby (1955), however, cast some doubt on this explanation since these workers have shown independently that the increase in intra-alveolar pressure does not affect the rate of secretion until some twenty hours after milking. Since the cows in the experiment of Knodt & Petersen were milked at twelve-hour intervals, the galactopoietic effects they observed may well have been due to the exogenous oxytocin rather than to the beneficial effect on alveolar pressure of removal of the residual milk. Increases both in milk and butter-fat yield of cows following regular injections of oxytocin have been reported by Adams and Allen (1952), Sprain, Smith, Tyler & Fosgate (1954), and Donker, Koshi & Petersen (1954). It is also of interest to note that Donker, et al. (1954) considered that the increases in yield observed by them were sufficiently large to indicate that some factor, in addition to removal of residual milk, must be playing a stimulatory role, and that as early as 1944, Petersen tentatively suggested that oxytocin might stimulate the release of lactogenic factors from the anterior pituitary.

With reference to the above views on the release of the lactogenic and galactopoietic factors from the anterior lobe it is necessary to consider the nature of the vascular connexions between the two lobes. If there were a direct flow of blood from the posterior lobe to the anterior lobe then conditions would be ideal as the anterior lobe would then receive blood, highly charged with oxytocin, before any dilution of the hormone with blood from other parts of the body had occurred. Landsmeer (1951) has shown that such direct vascular connexions from posterior to anterior lobe are present in the rat. Daniel & Prichard (1956) have confirmed and extended Landsmeer's observations in the rat and are now investigating the vascular connexions between the pituitary lobes in the sheep (Daniel, private communication). With reference to the question of vascular connexions between the lobes of the pituitary, it may be noted that if the anterior lobe receives blood rich in oxytocin direct from the posterior lobe then in experimental studies it may well be necessary to inject apparently unphysiological quantities of oxytocin into the general circulation in order to achieve the physiological levels necessary for stimulation of the adenohypophysis.

In the past, as its name implies, the main physiological action attributed to oxytocin has been its effect in stimulating uterine contractions at parturition although Harris (1955) has recently pointed out that unequivocal proof of this role is still lacking. We can, however, now claim with some conviction that oxytocin has another important and even better established physiological function, namely its role in milk ejection. There is, moreover, as we have discussed, the further possibility that oxytocin may be responsible for the release of the anterior pituitary factors necessary for milk secretion. If this be so, then it becomes the all-important hormonal factor responsible for the integration and co-ordination of mammary function. This possibility is an attractive one. It has both the merit of simplicity and, as we have shown, is capable of explaining many observations, but further investigation is required before it can be accepted as fact.

REFERENCES

ADAMS, H. P. & ALLEN, N. N. (1952). The effect of removal of residual milk by the use of oxytocin upon the yield and fat content of subsequent milkings. *J. Dairy Sci.* **35**, 1121–4.

ANDERSSON, B. (1951a). Some observations on the neurohormonal regulation of milk-ejection. *Acta physiol. scand.* **23**, 1–7.

ANDERSSON, B. (1951b). The effect and localization of electrical stimulation of certain parts of the brain stem in sheep and goats. *Acta physiol. scand.* **23**, 8–23.

BARRNETT, R. J. (1954). Histochemical demonstration of disulfide groups in the neurohypophysis under normal and experimental conditions. *Endocrinology* **55**, 484–501.

BENOIT, J. & ASSENMACHER, I. (1953). Rapport entre la stimulation sexuelle préhypophysaire et la neurosécrétion chez l'oiseau. *Arch. Anat. micr.* **42**, 334–86.

BENSON, G. K. & COWIE, A. T. (1956). Lactation in the rat after hypophysial posterior lobectomy. *J. Endocr.* **14**, 54–65.

BENSON, G. K. & FOLLEY, S. J. (1956). Oxytocin as stimulator for the release of prolactin from the anterior pituitary. *Nature (Lond.)* **177**, 700.

BILLENSTIEN, D. C. & LEVEQUE, T. F. (1955). The reorganization of the neurohypophysial stalk following hypophysectomy in the rat. *Endocrinology* **56**, 704–17.

BRAUDE, R. & MITCHELL, K. G. (1952). Observations on the relationship between oxytocin and adrenaline in milk ejection in the sow. *J. Endocr.* **8**, 238–41.

BRIGHTMAN, M. W. (1955). Neurosecretion and milk-ejection in the mouse. *Anat. Rec.* **121**, 287.

COLLIN, R. & RACADOT, J. (1953). La chute du taux de la substance Gomori-positive neurohypophysaire dans le *post partum* chez le cobaye. *Ann. Endocr. (Paris)*, **14**, 546–9.

COWIE, A. T., FOLLEY, S. J., CROSS, B. A., HARRIS, G. W., JACOBSOHN, D. & RICHARDSON, K. C. (1951). Terminology for use in lactational physiology. *Nature (Lond.)* **168**, 421.

COWIE, A. T., FOLLEY, S. J. & RICHARDSON, K. C. (1954). Terminology in lactational physiology. *Lancet* **267**, 601–2.

P

CROSS, B. A. (1950) Suckling antidiuresis in rabbits. *Nature (Lond.)* **166,** 612.

CROSS, B. A. (1953). Sympathetico-adrenal inhibition of the neurohypophysial milk-ejection mechanism. *J. Endocr.* **9,** 7–18.

CROSS, B. A. (1955a). The hypothalamus and the mechanism of sympathetico-adrenal inhibition of milk ejection. *J. Endocr.* **12,** 15–28.

CROSS, B. A. (1955b). Neurohormonal mechanisms in emotional inhibition of milk ejection. *J. Endocr.* **12,** 29–37.

CROSS, B. A. & HARRIS, G. W. (1950). Milk ejection following electrical stimulation of the pituitary stalk in rabbits. *Nature (Lond.)* **166,** 994.

CROSS, B. A. & HARRIS, G. W. (1951). The neurohypophysis and 'let-down' of milk. *J. Physiol. (Lond.)* **113,** 35P.

CROSS, B. A. & HARRIS, G. W. (1952). The role of the neurohypophysis in the milk-ejection reflex. *J. Endocr.* **8,** 148–61.

DANIEL, P. M. & PRICHARD, M. M. L. (1956). Anterior pituitary necrosis infarction of the pars distalis produced experimentally in the rat. *Quart. J. exp. Physiol.* **41,** 215–29.

DENAMUR, R. & MARTINET, J. (1953). Sensibilité de la glande mammaire de la chèvre aux hormones posthypophysaires. *C.R. Soc. Biol. (Paris)* **147,** 1217–20.

DICKER, S. E. & TYLER, C. (1953). Vasopressor and oxytocic activities of the pituitary glands of rats, guinea-pigs and cats and of human foetuses. *J. Physiol. (Lond.)* **121,** 206–14.

DONKER, J. D., KOSHI, J. H. & PETERSEN, W. E. (1954). The influence of oxytocin-induced udder evacuation on milk and butterfat production in a complete lactation. *J. Dairy Sci.* **37,** 299–305.

DRAGER, G. A. & RENNELS, E. G. (1955). The independent behavior of Gomori-positive neurosecretion and the oxytocic hormone in the rat neurohypophysis. *Anat. Rec.* **121,** 287.

VAN DYKE, H. B., ADAMSONS, K., Jr. & ENGEL, S. L. (1955). Aspects of the biochemistry and physiology of the neurohypophyseal hormones. *Recent Progr. Hormone Res.* **11,** 1–35.

ELLIOTT, G. M. & BRUMBY, P. J. (1955). Rate of milk secretion with increasing interval between milking. *Nature (Lond.)* **176,** 350.

ELY, F. & PETERSEN, W. E. (1941). Factors involved in the ejection of milk. *J. Dairy Sci.* **24,** 211–23.

FOLLEY, S. J. (1947a). Endocrine control of the mammary gland. II. Lactation. *Brit. med. Bull.* **5,** 135–42.

FOLLEY, S. J. (1947b). The nervous system and lactation. *Brit. med. Bull.* **5,** 142–8.

FOLLEY, S. J. (1952a). Aspects of pituitary-mammary gland relationships. *Recent Progr. Hormone Res.* **7,** 107–33.

FOLLEY, S. J. (1952b). Lactation. In *Marshall's physiology of reproduction*, 2, chapter 20, ed. Parkes, A. S. London: Longmans Green.

FOLLEY, S. J. (1954). *Recherches récentes sur la physiologie et la biochimie de la sécrétion lactée.* Liège: Desoer; Paris: Masson.

FOLLEY, S. J. (1956). *The physiology and biochemistry of lactation.* Edinburgh, London: Oliver & Boyd.

FRAJA, A. & MARTINI, L. (1952). Studi sui rapporti tra ipofisi anteriore ed ipofisi posteriore. *Boll. Soc. ital. Biol. sper.* **28,** 407–10.

GAINES, W. L. (1915). A contribution to the physiology of lactation. *Amer. J. Physiol.* **38,** 285–312.

GRAČEV, I. I. (1952). Obrazovanie uslovnogo molokovydeliteljnogo refleksa na base mehaničeskogo razdraženija soska. *C.R. Acad. Sci. U.R.S.S.* **86,** 441–4.

HARRIS, G. W. (1955). *Neural control of the pituitary gland.* London: Arnold.

HARRIS, G. W. & JACOBSOHN, D. (1952). Functional grafts of the anterior pituitary gland. *Proc. roy. Soc. B* **139,** 263–76.

HOUSSAY, B. A. (1935). Action de l'hypophysectomie sur la grossesse et la sécrétion lactée, chez la chienne. *C.R. Soc. Biol. (Paris),* **120,** 496–7.

KALLIALA, H. & KARVONEN, M. J. (1951). Antidiuresis during suckling in lactating women. *Ann. Med. exp. Biol. Fenn.* **29,** 233–41.

KALLIALA, H., KARVONEN, M. J. & LAPPÄNEN, V. (1952). Release of antidiuretic hormone during nursing in the dog. *Ann. Med. exp. Biol. Fenn.* **30,** 96–107.

KNODT, C. B. & PETERSEN, W. E. (1944). The effect of complete evacuation of the mammary gland by Pitocin upon milk and fat production. *J. Dairy Sci.* **27,** 449–57.

LANDSMEER, J. M. F. (1951) Vessels of the rat's hypophysis. *Acta anat. (Basel)* **12,** 83–109.

LINZELL, J. L. (1952). The silver staining of myoepithelial cells, particularly in the mammary gland and their relation to the ejection of milk. *J. Anat. (Lond.)* **86,** 49–57.

LINZELL, J. L. (1955). Some observations on the contractile tissue of the mammary glands. *J. Physiol. (Lond.)* **130,** 257–67.

MACAULAY, M. H. I. (1951). Factors involved in the ejection of milk from the mammary gland. *Colloq. Int. C.N.R.S.,* XXXII, 1950, 145–56.

MALANDRA, B. (1955). Neurosecretion in pregnant and lactating rats. *Lancet* **269,** 296.

MARTINI, L. & MORPURGO, C. (1955). Neurohormonal control of the release of adrenocorticotrophic hormone. *Nature (Lond.)* **175,** 1127.

MIRSKY, I. A., STEIN, M. & PAULISH, G. (1954). The secretion of an antidiuretic substance into the circulation of adrenalectomized and hypophysectomized rats exposed to various stimuli. *Endocrinology* **55,** 28–39.

NEWTON, M. & NEWTON, N. R. (1948). The let-down reflex in human lactation. *J. Pediat.* **33,** 698–704.

OTT, I. & SCOTT, J. C. (1911). The action of infundibulin upon the mammary secretion. *Proc. Soc. exp. Biol. (N.Y.)* **8,** 48–9.

PEETERS, G. & COUSSENS, R. (1950). The influence of the milking act on the diuresis of the lactating cow. *Arch. int. Pharmacodyn.* **84,** 209–20.

PETERSEN, W. E. (1944). Lactation. *Physiol. Rev.* **24,** 340–71.

PETERSEN, W. E. & LUDWICK, T. M. (1942). The humoral nature of the factor causing the let-down of milk. *Fed. Proc.* **1,** 66.

RICHARDSON, K. C. (1949). Contractile tissues in the mammary gland, with special reference to myoepithelium in the goat. *Proc. roy. Soc.* B **136,** 30–45.

SCHÄFER, E. A. (1913). On the effects of pituitary and corpus luteum extracts on the mammary gland in the human subjects. *Quart. J. exp. Physiol.* **6,** 17–9.

SCHARRER, E. & SCHARRER, B. (1954). Hormones produced by neurosecretory cells. *Recent Progr. Hormone Res.* **10,** 183–232.

SELYE, H. (1934). On the nervous control of lactation. *Amer. J. Physiol.* **107,** 535–8.

SHIBUSAWA, K., SAITO, S., FUKUDA, M., KAWAI, T. & YOSHIMURA, F. (1955). On the role of the hypothalamic-neurohypophyseal neurosecretion in the liberation of the adenohypophyseal hormones. *Endocr. Japon.* **2,** 47–56.

SMITH, P. E. (1932). The non-essentiality of the posterior hypophysis in parturition. *Amer. J. Physiol.* **99,** 345–8.

SPRAIN, D. G., SMITH, V. R., TYLER, W. J. & FOSGATE, O. T. (1954). The effect on milk and fat production of injections of oxytocin at alternate 14-day periods during lactation. *J. Dairy Sci.* **37,** 195–201.

STUTINSKY, F. (1952). Sur la substance Gomori-positive du complexe hypothalamohypophysaire du rat. *C.R. Assoc. Anat.* **38,** 942–50.

STUTINSKY, F. (1953). La neurosécrétion au cours de la gestation et le *post-partum* chez la rate. *Ann. Endocr. (Paris)* **14,** 722–5.

TGETGEL, B. (1926). Untersuchungen über den Sekretionsdruck und über das Einschiessen der Milch im Euter des Rindes. *Schweiz. Arch. Tierheilk.* **68,** 335–48, 369–87.

TURNER, C. W. & SLAUGHTER, I. S. (1930). The physiological effect of pituitary extract (posterior lobe) on the lactating mammary gland. *J. Dairy Sci.* **13,** 8–24.

TURNER, H. G. (1955). Changes in capacity of the udder of the dairy cow during the course of lactation. *Austral. J. Agric. Sci.* **6,** 143–60.

WALLER, H. K. (1938). *Clinical studies in lactation.* London: Heinemann.

WHITTLESTONE, W. G., BASSETT, E. G. & TURNER, C. W. (1952). Factors influencing the amount of milk 'let-down' hormone in the posterior lobe of Jersey cattle. *J. Dairy Sci.* **35,** 889–93.

WILLIAMS, W. L. (1945). The effects of lactogenic hormone on post-parturient unsuckled mammary glands of the mouse. *Anat. Rec.* **93,** 171–83.

ZUCKERMAN, S. (1954). The secretions of the brain. Relation of hypothalamus to pituitary gland. *Lancet,* **266,** 739–43, 789–96.

Discussion

Chairman: Sir S. Zuckerman

Zuckerman. Dr. Folley will of course be aware that myoepithelial cells were first described other than in the mammary gland. Presumably the responses of the mammary myoepithelial cells to oxytocin, described by Folley and Cowie, are not associated with corresponding responses by similar cells in other secretory tissue, for instance, the salivary glands.

When speaking of the rate of growth of young after posterior lobectomy of the mother, Dr. Folley implied that certain changes had occurred in the stalk which re-created from what was left of the neurohypophysial tissue (median eminence and the other parts of the stalk) a new neural process, and in this connexion he referred to the work of Stutinsky and others. What does he really think happens to the remaining tissue? Is there any reason why neurosecretory substances should not be emerging from the central part of the stalk immediately after lobectomy? Or is he suggesting that after the operation there is some kind of differentiation of the central stump of the stalk which results in the re-establishment of the same kind of cellular structure which we find in the neural process?

Cowie. We have not been able to investigate this yet. We merely draw attention to the fact that after posterior lobectomy milk ejection in response to suckling does return and at the same time, there is an hypertrophy of the end of the stalk. There may not be any direct connexion between the two things.

Zuckerman. Is it conceivable that the failure of the young to grow after lobectomy of the mother, is related to the operation itself?

Cowie. Sham operations in which the hypophysis is exposed but not removed have no effect on the growth of the young. Further, in a few experiments, I accidentally removed only half the posterior lobe, and in these cases the growth curve was inhibited only for part of the first lactation.

G. W. Harris. We have observed the tuber cinereum, not after posterior hypophysectomy but after stalk section and after total hypophysectomy in rats, rabbits and ferrets. We have found that the stalk remnant and median eminence show thrombosis in the first twenty-four hours after operation. Together they appear as a small hard nodule, cherry-red in colour, which is in contrast to the white hypothalamus. This is presumably due to the blockage in blood-flow in the hypophysial portal vessels. At a later date the vessels seem to recanalize and the primary plexus of the portal vessels is reformed. Recent observations of Dr. B. T. Donovan and Dr. J. J. van der Werff ten Bosch (*Proceedings of Physiological Society*, 20–21 April 1956) show that after pituitary stalk section in the ferret the median eminence appears as a globular mass instead of as a flat plate when viewed in sagittal section. They have not yet made measurements of the tissue volume of the tuber cinereum in the ferret, but simple inspection of the slides gives the impression that the tuber cinereum has increased in mass. I wonder if these observations might explain the temporary inhibition of milk ejection described by Dr. Cowie and Dr. Folley.

Zuckerman. The histological appearance of the tuber cinereum of the ferret is different from that of the neural process. What I am concerned with is the belief—and Dr. Pickford knows more about this than I do—that the neural process itself does something, in the sense of a chemical transformation, to whatever hormone may be streaming down from the hypothalamus. The actual structure of the neural process is always different from the median eminence both before and after stalk section. Does differentiation in the morphological sense really occur in the central stump of the stalk, and transform it into a neural process capable of transforming the presumed hypothalamic secretion?

Pickford. The impairment of milk ejection really does parallel experimental diabetes insipidus, for if you do an incomplete section of the tract, or if you remove only the posterior lobe and part of the stalk, you then get polyuria for about 10–14 days, followed by recovery to a normal water output. Perhaps in the dog the time relationships may not be the same as in the rat, but the general idea is the same. Why this temporary change should occur we do not know, it may be a clot.

I wish to ask Dr. Folley if the second lactation enhances the apparent hypertrophy, or does this occur in the absence of a second pregnancy and lactation?

The effect of oxytocin on the release of prolactin is one thing Dr. Brooks and I must naturally take into account in relation to sodium excretion by the kidney. Does it mean that oxytocin is doing something to the anterior lobe and thus indirectly to the suprarenal cortex?

Cowie. With regard to the question of the possible effects of the second lactation, we have not examined serial sections from animals after the first pregnancy, but I believe Dr. Stutinsky has relevant observations.

Stutinsky. I was extremely interested by the findings of Dr. Folley and I was glad to hear of his results which confirm my work.

I should like to show a slide which shows a horizontal section of the hypothalamus from a rat neurohypophysectomized two months before. A part of the anterior lobe is present, there is no pars intermedia and the end of the stalk has enlarged. This enlarged end is reorganized and shows a normal neural lobe structure which reacted to hypertonic saline in a normal manner.

Another slide shows the structure of the neural lobe of a normal rat during labour. This lobe contains much neurosecretory substance. In the following slides you can see the depletion of this material which occurs twenty-four hours after parturition.

Zuckerman. Is it a constant finding that a neural process as such is redifferentiated after the definitive one is removed?

Stutinsky: In the rat, always.

Zuckerman. In at least two other species, the ferret and monkey, nothing like this happens. Once the neural process is destroyed it does not reform.

G. W. Harris. I am disturbed by one aspect of 'regeneration' of the neural process. There is a great deal of evidence that the cells of the supraoptic and paraventricular nuclei largely atrophy and disappear after sectioning the supraoptico-hypophysial tract. There are several people in this room, for example, who have published figures showing a greatly reduced number of cells in these nuclei after hypophysectomy. It is difficult to see, therefore, if the hormone is originating in these nuclei, how 'regeneration' at a lower level in the system, that is at the end of the stalk, could increase the discharge of neurohypophysial hormone. It would seem better to replace the term 'regeneration' by 'reorganization'. It certainly seems possible that the thrombosed region of the tuber cinereum and pituitary stalk, following stalk section or hypophysectomy, can become reorganized in the sense that the vessels are recanalized and the region once more takes over the function of discharging posterior pituitary hormones into the blood-stream.

Sloper. I wish to make a plea for the more accurate use of the word 'hypertrophy'; for from what Professor Harris has said about the hypophysectomized ferret and from my experiences with the hypophysectomized human, I suspect that the swellings noted by Dr. Cowie and Folley could have been due to infarction and oedema, processes which in themselves could impede for a time the release of hormone from neurosecretory fibres in the median eminence. Certainly in the human, both thirty-two hours and ten days after hypophysectomy, there were severe infarcts which ascended the pituitary stalk and spread well up into the median eminence. In the human, unlike the rat, the accumulation of neurosecretory material in this region does not persist and no regeneration of the type described by Stutinsky develops. In fact, I think we may have been attributing too much importance to this question of neurohypophysial regeneration, by which I mean the persistent accumulation of vascularized neurosecretory tissue in the median eminence. For in the human 100 and 240 days after hypophysectomy no such change occurs. On the other hand, some neurosecretory material can be found in the median eminence presumably derived largely from the caudal half of the paraventricular nucleus, where about half the normal number of large neurones survive, many of them containing neurosecretory material. Since these patients did not have overt diabetes insipidus, in spite of treatment with cortisone, it is probable that they retained a fair measure of neurohypophysial function. I believe therefore that we must attach importance not so much to the regeneration of a neurohypophysis, but rather to the persistence of some intact median eminence, and the survival of cells capable of neurosecretion.

Zuckerman. With reference to the duration of the effect, I can report that in a series of monkeys subjected to stalk section diabetes insipidus ensued and in some cases continued for a year or more.

Chester Jones. In the rats the effects of neurohypophysectomy vary considerably. The best results are obtained by removal of the posterior lobe, taking it as high up the stalk as possible, together with minimal disturbance of the anterior lobe. It is possible to produce 'permanent' diabetes insipidus in some rats with from four to five times the normal intake of water and with attenuation of the supraoptic and paraventricular nuclei; in such cases I have not seen 're-growth' of the neural lobe. Water intake may be used as functional criteria of the lesion produced. It may be legitimate to assume that in rats, showing no obvious antidiuretic hormonal effect, oxytocin secretion is also minimal.

Bargmann. May I add a detail about the connexion between the neurosecretory system and the adenohypophysis; they are connected by special vessels in the infundibular wall; vessels which are surrounded by thick and swollen fibres containing neurosecretory substance. This may be the site of liberation of hormone into the blood-vessels.

Martini. In connexion with Dr. Folley's observation, that oxytocic hormone seems to stimulate the release of lactogenic hormone, we (Martini & Morpurgo, *Nature, (Lond.)* **175,** 1127, 1955; Martini & de Poli, *J. Endocr.* **13,** 229, 1956) have shown, that both the antidiuretic and the oxytocic hormone may produce the release of corticotrophin and thyrotrophic hormone. These experiments appear to indicate that antidiuretic hormone and oxytocin may act as neurohormonal agents linking the hypothalamus to the adenohypophysis.

Folley. With regard to Dr. Pickford's remarks about the rats in the second lactation in which the milk-ejection reflex had returned, at least for the greater part, it should be noted that the rats still exhibited polyuria.

Cowie. I certainly agree with Dr. Chester Jones about the difficulty of neurohypophysectomy in the rat, and because of this we made careful measurements of the volume of neurohypophysial tissue present both immediately after lobectomy and several months later. We found a significant increase in volume. We did not measure water intake but immediately after the first lactation the lobectomized rats were excreting twice the volume of urine excreted by the controls. They were still excreting twice the volume after the second lactation.

On oxytocin and uterine function

by

R. J. FITZPATRICK

Department of Pharmacology, University of Bristol

SINCE it was first demonstrated fifty years ago by Dale that posterior pituitary extracts have the property of inducing contractions of uterine muscle, our understanding of this relationship has lagged behind corresponding advances linking the neurohypophysis with kidney and mammary function. To a large extent this may be attributed to the intermittent nature of myometrial activity, especially its brief activation at parturition and about the time of mating, which has rendered quantitative investigation difficult. These difficulties are enhanced by our lack of knowledge of the physiological criteria by which we should measure the functional activity of the uterus as an organ; this gives rise to obvious difficulties in interpreting, for instance, the normality or otherwise of parturition in animals, or in women, with lesions of the neurohypophysial system (Fisher, Magoun & Ranson, 1938; Harris, 1955; and others).

Newton (1937) focused attention on this problem when he stated that 'Mere contraction of the uterus is too primitive a process to be dignified by the name of parturition', and he presented evidence, subsequently extended by other workers (Bonnycastle & Ferguson, 1941; Adler, Bell & Knox, 1944; Schild, Fitzpatrick & Nixon, 1951), that activation of the myometrium at parturition follows a co-ordinated pattern for different parts of the uterus. This is discussed more fully below, in relation to the nature of uterine response to oxytocin, but before embarking on this it is appropriate to consider briefly the evidence suggesting that myometrial function is probably under neurohypophysial control.

Two main functions have been ascribed to oxytocin in relation to the control of uterine contractility:

   (*a*) In the non-pregnant female, at the time of mating, to propel seminal fluid in a rostral direction.

   (*b*) In the pregnant female, at term, to propel the foetus(es) in a caudal direction.

Release of oxytocin in relation to seminal transport

Rothschild (1953) has indicated on the basis of the purely physical study of spermatozoan movement, that such movement is essentially random in nature, and that spermatozoa deposited in the female reproductive tract cannot progress towards the fallopian tubes unless they are impelled by some external propulsive force, such as uterine contraction.

This is in keeping with the demonstration in many species that the ascent of spermatozoa in the female tract occurs too rapidly to be accounted for by the flagellate motility of the spermatozoa (in the rat—Hartman & Ball, 1930; Blandau, 1945; the dog—Evans, 1933; the rabbit—Krehbiel & Carstens, 1939; the guinea-pig—Florey & Walton, 1932; the cow—VanDemark & Moeller, 1951; the sheep Starke, 1949).

Not only is ascent too rapid to be accounted for by independent spermatozoan movement but, moreover, this phenomenon is seen with non-motile spermatozoa (VanDemark & Moeller, 1951). Rapid ascent of semen has been demonstrated in the absence of the male (Krehbiel & Carstens, 1939; VanDemark & Moeller, 1951) which eliminates copulation itself as an essential propulsive force; further it is seen with fluids other than semen (Krehbiel & Carstens, 1939; Rowson, 1955) indicating that the pharmacologically active substances known to be present in semen (von Euler, 1937) are non-essential.

It is reasonable to conclude that the explanation of this rapid transport lies predominantly, or entirely, with the female and this has led to the view that sperm propulsion after natural mating is effected by uterine contractions—possibly due to the release of oxytocin. Oxytocin has in fact been stated to increase the rate of ascent of spermatozoa and other fluids in the isolated perfused bovine uterus (Hays & VanDemark, 1952) and in the intact cow (Rowson, 1955).

An increase in contractile activity of the uterus, compatible with this hypothesis, has been demonstrated after natural mating, after tactile stimulation of the external genitalia and after mechanical stimulation of uterus or cervix, as indicated in Table 1. It is possible that uterine contraction after stimuli such as these may be explained in terms of local organ response or very simple nervous reflexes. However Ferguson's (1941) observations in rabbits suggest that this may be an over-simplification. This author found that stretching of the cervix results, after a short delay, in increased myometrial activity, similar to that seen after intravenous injection of oxytocin and that this phenomenon is abolished by spinal section (at T.7), or by electrolytic destruction of the pituitary stalk.

That this increased uterine activity at the time of mating may be due to the release of oxytocin is supported by the observation, in several species, of milk ejection accompanying mating (Hammond 1936; Harris & Pickles, 1953; Campbell & Petersen, 1953; VanDemark & Hays, 1953). Similarly manipulation of the vulva, the cervix or the uterus, in the goat (Andersson, 1951) and in the cow (Tgetgel, 1926; Piana & Curto, 1950; Usuelli, Piana & Curto, 1952; VanDemark & Hays, 1951a, 1953) also results in milk ejection.

The concept of a neurohormonal reflex would be strengthened by the demonstration of an increase in the concentration of oxytocin in the blood at the time of mating. No figures have as yet been published, although VanDemark & Hays (1953) claim to have detected, in the bovine, an increase in milk-ejecting activity of jugular blood at the time of mating. We (Fitzpatrick & Hughes, 1956) have recently made some preliminary investigations in cows under similar conditions.

External jugular blood was collected from cows into heparinized polythene vessels over a two- or a three-minute period during which the uterus and cervix were stimulated manually *per rectum*. The blood was extracted by a modification of the methods of Vogt (1953) and of Bisset & Walker (1954), and finally assayed according to Holton (1948) using the superfused rat uterus. Our results show that the oxytocic potency of the blood after our stimulation procedure ranged from 420 to 850 micro-units/ml. as compared with pre-stimulation values of 120 to 300 micro-units/ml. This oxytocic activity was not blocked by atropine (1×10^{-7}) or lysergic acid diethylamide (2×10^{-8}) but was eliminated by treatment with 0·01 M sodium thioglycollate (Ames, Moore & van Dyke, 1950).

TABLE I

Oxytocin-like responses

Species	Stimulus	Response	Author
Mare	Mating	Milk ejection	Hammond, 1936
Man	Mating	Milk ejection	Pickles, 1953
Man	Mating	Milk ejection	Harris & Pickles, 1953
Man	Mating	Milk ejection	Campbell & Petersen, 1953
Cow	Mating	Milk ejection	VanDemark & Hays, 1953
Cow	Mating	Milk ejection	Campbell & Petersen, 1953
Cow	Mating	Uterine motility	VanDemark & Hays, 1952, 1953
Bitch	Mating	Uterine motility	Evans, 1933
Goat	Manual: cervix	Milk ejection	Andersson, 1951
Cow	Manual: cervix	Milk ejection	VanDemark & Hays, 1951a
Cow	Manual: uterus	Milk ejection	Tgetgel, 1926
Cow	Manual: uterus	Milk ejection	Piana & Curto, 1950
Cow	Manual: uterus	Milk ejection	Usuelli *et al.*, 1952
Cow	Manual: uterus/cervix	Milk ejection	VanDemark & Hays, 1953
Cow	Manual: vulva/cervix	Uterine motility	VanDemark & Hays, 1951b, 1954
Rabbit	Stretching: cervix	Uterine motility	Ferguson, 1941
Rabbit	Manual: vulva	Uterine motility	Krehbiel & Carstens, 1939
Rabbit	Increased intrauterine pressure	Uterine motility	Reynolds, 1930
Cat	Increased intrauterine pressure	Uterine motility	Schubel & Gehlen, 1933

Release of oxytocin at parturition

That oxytocin may be liberated as an essential part of normal parturition is suggested by the remarkable superficial similarity between spontaneous labour and that induced with oxytocin. This view is also supported by the demonstration, in the post-parturient rabbit, that electrical stimulation of the neurohypophysis results in increased uterine activity, apparently due to release of a humoral agent; and further, that stretching the cervix of these animals evokes a neurohormonal reflex by which a stimulant substance is released from the posterior pituitary gland apparently in accordance with the requirements of labour. (Haterius & Ferguson, 1938; Ferguson, 1941.) The reports of Dicker & Tyler (1953) and Fromageot (this symposium) indicating that oxytocin is depleted from the neurohypophysis for some hours after labour, in rats and dogs, are in keeping with this hypothesis. That oxytocin is liberated into the circulation during labour in women is indicated by Gunther's (1948) observation of the expression of milk coincident with uterine contractions.

However, attempts to demonstrate the presence of oxytocin in body fluids at the time of parturition have not given convincing results. Increased oxytocic activity has been detected at this time, in urine (Cockrill, Miller & Kurzrok, 1934) and jugular blood (Bell & Morris, 1934; Bell & Robson, 1935) but the methods of extraction and assay were not specific and it would seem necessary for these experiments to be repeated using the more specific methods available now.

Experiments involving removal or lesions of the posterior pituitary and its hypothalamic relationships, have in some hands shown that the neurohypophysial system plays some part in parturition. Thus the work of Pencharz & Long (1933) in rodents, Smith (1946) in monkeys, and Ranson and his colleagues in cats and guinea-pigs (Fisher, Magoun & Ranson, 1938; Dey, Fisher & Ranson, 1941) showed that hypophysectomy or electrolytic destruction of the pituitary stalk, resulted in prolonged labour and in maternal and foetal deaths. These findings, moreover, are supported by observations of abnormally prolonged labour, in successive pregnancies, in a woman with permanent diabetes insipidus (Marañon, 1947).

These positive results, to my mind, carry greater weight than the corresponding negative reports (Allan & Wiles, 1932; Selye, Collip & Thomson, 1933a and b; Firor, 1933; Percharz & Lyons, 1934; McPhail, 1935; Dandy, 1940) which indicate, in several species, that stalk section or hypophysectomy fails to affect the course of subsequent parturition. It has been suggested that these negative results may be explained as incomplete extirpations (Fisher et al., 1938): in this context the indications of 'regeneration' made in the discussion of the preceding paper of this symposium may be relevant. On the other hand it has been reported that such lesions to the neurohypophysis may occasionally result in diabetes insipidus unaccompanied by detectable change in the course of parturition (Fisher et al., 1938; Dey et al., 1941; Dandy, 1940). Although these reports to some extent argue against the participation of the neurohypophysis in labour, they are by no means conclusive, since effective delivery, in the presence of diabetes insipidus, can be explained in terms of (a) compensation by extra-uterine components at parturition, or (b) by the survival of sufficient neurohypophysial tissue to promote labour, although insufficient to fully control water diuresis, or (c) by invoking the concept of independent secretion of oxytocin and vasopressin. The last possibility is particularly interesting in the light of the discussion to Dr. Pickford's paper at this symposium. Some such independence, in varying degrees, has been seen after natural stimulation or electrical interference (Harris, 1948; Peeters & Coussens, 1950; Cross, 1951, 1955; Kalliala, Karvonen & Leppänen, 1952; Abrahams & Pickford, 1954, and Olivecrona, 1954).

Oxytocinase

It is perhaps appropriate here to recall that several workers have demonstrated that the incubation of added oxytocin and vasopressin with the blood of pregnant women leads to inactivation of the hormones (von Fekete, 1930; Werle, Hevelke & Buthmann, 1941; Woodbury, Ahlquist, Abreu, Torpin & Watson, 1946; Page, 1946; Hawker, 1955). It is claimed that this inactivating power is also present at the time of parturition. If these findings apply to endogenous oxytocin *in vivo*, this would indicate that release of oxytocin from the neurohypophysis is not a factor in the process of birth, unless one invokes the suggestion of Usuelli et al. (1952) that the function of circulating 'oxytocinase' is merely to modify the duration of action of endogenous oxytocin, thus preventing uterine spasm.

Unfortunately the majority of workers have confined their attention to blood-serum which in the light of present knowledge of non-specific oxytocic activity of serum, detracts from the significance of their results. On this and on other points Tyler (1955) has recently criticized the quantitative aspects of previous work on 'oxytocinase' and has reinvestigated the problem with improved techniques. She has found that the 'oxytocinase' activity of human plasma *decreases* over the last few weeks of pregnancy although vasopressin inactivating potency is unchanged. Occasional persistence of plasma 'oxytocinase' activity until the end of pregnancy she found to be associated with abnormally long labour. A corresponding decrease in 'oxytocinase' activity of tissues at the very end of pregnancy has also been reported by Sawyer (1954) in the rat.

These more recent results change the significance of 'oxytocinase' in relation to parturition (Nixon & Smyth, 1956). Its function, if any, may be to facilitate the maintenance of pregnancy for the greater part of gestation, this protection being withdrawn at the appropriate time.

THE NATURE OF UTERINE RESPONSE TO OXYTOCIN

It is of interest to consider certain pharmacological aspects of the response of the uterus to oxytocin in relation to the requirements of parturition and seminal transport.

Sensitivity

We have been impressed by the exquisite sensitivity of the superfused uterus of the rat in oestrus, which responds to 25 micro-units oxytocin. This corresponds to a total dose of approximately 5×10^{-11} grams, or 10^{10} molecules of du Vigneaud's polypeptide. (Livermore & du Vigneaud, 1949; Pierce, Gordon & du Vigneaud, 1952; du Vigneaud, Ressler, Swan, Roberts, Katsoyannis & Gordon, 1953.) In Table II is indicated in grammes and in molecules the corresponding sensitivity of this preparation to adrenaline, nor-adrenaline, acetylcholine and 5-hydroxytryptamine. Only reports on high sensitivity to these substances have been included—in one case

TABLE II

Uterine sensitivity in vitro
(Oestrous rat uterus)

Drug	Minimum concentration g./ml.	Mole-cular weight	Molecules per ml.	Authors
Nor-adrenaline	$7 \cdot 5 \times 10^{-6}$	170	$3 \cdot 7 \times 10^{15}$	Gaddum *et al.*, 1949
Acetylcholine	1×10^{-8}	163	$3 \cdot 7 \times 10^{13}$	Fletcher, 1953
Adrenaline	1×10^{-7}	184	$3 \cdot 4 \times 10^{14}$	Gaddum *et al.*, 1949
Adrenaline	$1 \times 10^{-10}*$	184	$3 \cdot 4 \times 10^{11}$	Holzbauer & Vogt, 1954
5-hydroxytryptamine	2×10^{-9}	174	$7 \cdot 2 \times 10^{12}$	Garven, 1956
Oxytocin				
30 μU./ml.	$3 \cdot 8 \times 10^{-11}$	1005	$2 \cdot 3 \times 10^{10}$	Gaddum & Hameed, 1954
100 μU./ml.	$1 \cdot 25 \times 10^{-10}$	1005	$7 \cdot 7 \times 10^{10}$	Fitzpatrick, 1956

* This sensitivity was exceptional.

'exceptional' sensitivity (Holzbauer & Vogt, 1954)—but despite this, it is obvious from the Table that sensitivity to oxytocin is as great or greater than to any other substance, particularly when expressed in terms of molarity.

In vivo sensitivity to oxytocin, of a similar or even greater order to that seen *in vitro*, can be deduced from available figures for plasma volume and for the minimum effective dose given intravenously in man, as shown in Table III.

TABLE III

Uterine sensitivity to oxytocin in vivo

Species	State	Dose, i.v.	Calculated plasma Conc./ml.	Authors
Man	Pregnant 38 w.	100 mU.	30 μU.	Woodbury *et al.*, 1946
,,	Pregnant 39 w.	100 mU.	30 μU.	Nixon & Smyth, 1956
,,	Term	50 mU.	15 μU.	Theobald *et al.*, 1948
,,	Term	20 mU.	6 μU.	Cantarow, 1954
,,	Term	10 mU.	3 μU.	Nixon & Smyth, 1956
,,	Term	12 mU.	4 μU.	Theobald *et al.*, 1948
,,	Term	5 mU.	1·5 μU.	Ratzan & Schulman, 1955
Cow	Pregnant 38 w.	1000 mU.	40 μU.	Fitzpatrick, 1956
,,	Term	250 mU.	10 μU.	Fitzpatrick, 1956
,,	Oestrus	500 mU.	20 μU.	Fitzpatrick, 1956

This remarkable sensitivity, particularly at times of special interest such as parturition and oestrus, carries the implication that to produce physiological responses, only very small quantities of oxytocin need to be liberated into the circulation. The effective concentration of oxytocin in the blood, under these conditions may not be very much greater than that of vasopressin operative in the physiological control of water excretion.

The response of the cervix uteri to oxytocin

It is commonly accepted that the sensitivity of the myometrium to oxytocin varies with changes in sex hormone secretion in an apparently purposeful manner. Thus uterine reactivity to oxytocin is usually increased when under the influence of oestrogens and in many species depressed by progesterone (Knaus, 1934; Robson, 1947; Reynolds, 1949 and others). These generalizations have been accepted as applying to uterine muscle as a whole. Differences in response of different parts of the organ were not considered until the observations of Newton (1934, 1937) which focused attention on the differences in reactivity of the cornua and cervix.

There is now wide agreement in all species studied (Table IV) that the cervix uteri contains muscle fibres which can contract independently of those of the corpus or cornua. This applies to spontaneous contractions (Karlson, 1949; Adler *et al.*, 1944;

TABLE IV

Species in which independence of cervical contractions from corpus (or cornual)
contractions has been described

Species	Method	Author
Rabbit	*in vitro*	Bonnycastle & Ferguson, 1941
Rabbit	*in vivo*	Adler, Bell & Knox, 1944
Rabbit	*in vivo*	Schofield, 1949, 1952
Guinea-pig	*in vitro*	Newton, 1937
Guinea-pig	*in vivo*	Adler, Bell & Knox, 1944
Rat	*in vitro*	Newton, 1937
Cat	*in vivo*	Adler, Bell & Knox, 1944
Goat	*in vitro*	Newton, 1934
Cow	*in vivo*	Fitzpatrick, 1951
Sheep	*in vivo*	Fitzpatrick, 1951
Monkey	*in vivo*	Ivy, Hartmann & Koff, 1931
Man	*in vivo*	Karlson, 1949
Man	*in vivo*	Schild, 1951
Man	*in vivo*	Woodbury *et al.*, 1947
Man	*in vitro*	Danforth, 1954

Fitzpatrick, 1951), to those following nerve stimulation (Schofield, 1952) and to responses to drugs and hormones, including posterior pituitary hormones (Sauter, 1948; Newton, 1934; 1937; Bonnycastle & Ferguson, 1941; Adler *et al.*, 1944; Fitzpatrick, 1951; Schild *et al.*, 1951).

Newton's early *in vitro* work showed that the isolated cornual muscle from the pregnant goat (1934) and the guinea-pig (1937) contracted to low concentrations of oxytocin (400 micro-units/ml.) although under the same conditions cervical muscle from the same animal failed to respond to concentrations 100 times as great. In contrast adrenaline stimulated the cervix but not the cornu. This reciprocal pattern of response was also observed *in vitro* with cornual and cervical muscle of the parturient rabbit by Bonnycastle & Ferguson (1941). Such a pattern of response to oxytocin —absolute cornual dominance—is, of course, that appropriate to the process of parturition. However, this simple relationship between cervix and cornua was not found *in vivo* by Adler *et al.* (1944) in the rabbit, guinea-pig and cat. Oxytocin elicited contractions of both cornua and cervix and although quantitative differences were detected they were not pronounced.

Our own observations are an extension of these and were made chiefly in ruminants, and less extensively in pregnant women. Ruminants have anatomical advantages over laboratory animals (and man) in the facility and the fidelity with which simultaneous intracervical and intrauterine recordings can be made. This account is confined to results obtained in cows, although similar results were obtained in sheep and in a small number of observations in man. The recording method used was that described by Schild, *et al.* (1951) and employs small intracervical and intrauterine balloons, coupled by water transmission, via a double co-axial cannula, to linearly magnified mercury manometers writing frontally on kymographs.

In the bovine, posterior pituitary hormones elicit contraction of both cervix and corpus but the reactivity of the two structures varies independently. However, this lack of parallelism between responses of cervix and corpus does fall into an orderly pattern when considered in relation to the prevailing hormonal conditions of the animal.

Responses in pregnant animals. The magnitude of the response of the corpus to oxytocin increases slowly throughout most of the second half of pregnancy, and this accelerates dramatically just before parturition. No such augmentation is seen with the cervix however, the reactivity remaining constant or even diminishing.

Since we recorded intrauterine and intracervical pressures simultaneously and independently, it permits us to express the magnitude and direction of the intra-uterine pressure gradient at the height of drug action, as the algebraic difference in the pressures in the two cavities. This is illustrated in relation to duration of pregnancy in Fig. 1. For simplicity, only responses at one dose level are shown; similar variation

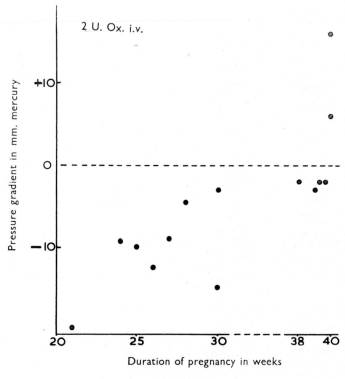

Figure 1

The gradient of pressure from corpus to cervix recorded after intravenous injection of a standard dose of 2 U. oxytocin, is shown in relation to duration of pregnancy. This gradient is given by the algebraic difference between the pressures recorded simultaneously from the two cavities.
Points above the dotted zero line (positive values) indicate a greater pressure in corpus than in cervix: points below the line (negative values) indicate the reverse.

was seen at all doses studied. At mid-pregnancy cervical response is dominant but this decreases in late pregnancy and, in animals studied less than thirty-six hours before delivery the pressure gradient changes in favour of the corpus. These changes are further indicated in Fig. 2 in which simultaneous cervical and corpus responses are compared in the form of log. dose—response curves for two experiments, one at mid-pregnancy and the other at term (40 weeks). Thus the response of the uterus as a whole is in favour of retention at mid-pregnancy and of expulsion immediately before parturition.

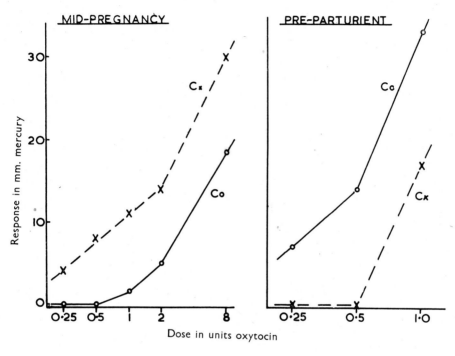

Figure 2

Simultaneously recorded responses of corpus (Co) and cervix (Cx) are plotted against dose of oxytocin (i.v.) at two stages of pregnancy.
At mid-pregnancy (22 weeks) the cervical responses are consistently greater than those of the corpus whilst in a cow 36 hours before delivery the corpus responses are the greater.

These findings of a change in pattern of response immediately before parturition are in keeping with some earlier results which previously have appeared contradictory. Robson (1933) and Russell (1943) each compared the *in vitro* reactivity to Pituitrin shown by strips of muscle obtained at Caesarian section from the fundus and the lower uterine segment in man. Russell found the lower uterine segment strips more reactive than the fundal, whereas Robson found the fundal muscle dominant. Russell's material however was obtained from women at term but not in labour, whereas Robson's were from women in active labour. The dissimilar results of these two workers may possibly be explained on the basis of a change in the pattern of response immediately before the physiological onset of labour, similar to that seen in the bovine over the last forty-eight hours of pregnancy.

Response in non-pregnant bovines. In the non-pregnant cow there is a marked variation in reactivity of the cervix to oxytocin: it is low at mid-cycle (luteal phase) and high during the oestrogen phase or after administration of oestrogens. The corresponding variation in reactivity of the corpus is less pronounced, so that the intrauterine pressure gradient is largely a function of cervical response. This gradient is shown in relationship to the ovarian cycle in Fig. 3. Cervical dominance is marked at oestrus and corpus dominance at mid-cycle, as illustrated in Figs. 4 and 5.

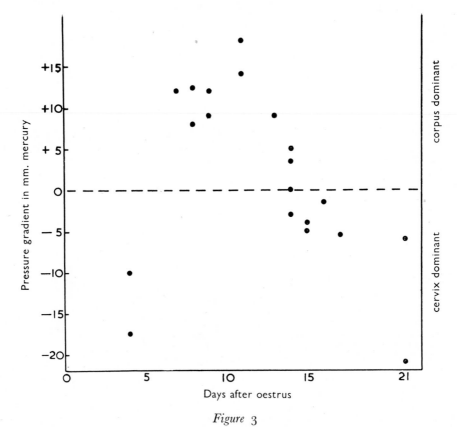

Figure 3

The pressure gradient from corpus to cervix after oxytocin, is plotted against stage of ovarian activity in the non-pregnant cow.

The concept of differential reactivity of corpus and cervix to oxytocin gives two contrasting relationships in the intact animal. At oestrus the responses combine to favour retention of uterine contents and propulsion of fluid from cervix to corpus, i.e. a mechanism appropriate to sperm ascent. In contrast to this, immediately before parturition the combination of responses favours expulsion of uterine contents, as appropriate to delivery of the young.

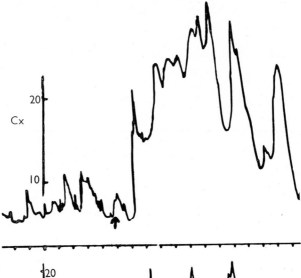

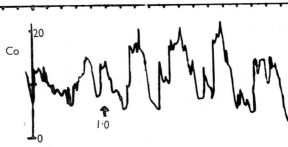

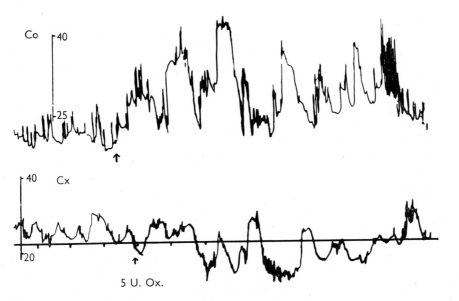

5 U. Ox.

Figure 5

Simultaneous kymograph records of corpus (Co) and cervical (Cx) responses to 5·0 U. oxytocin i.v. in a cow during the luteal phase of ovarian activity, showing corpus dominance.
Time intervals, 1 min. Pressure scale in mm. of mercury.

It is worth recalling Ferguson's (1941) interesting explanation of the co-ordinating mechanism for successive births in pluriparous species. This author has shown that in the parturient rabbit, mechanical stretching of the cervix results in uterine contractions attributed to the reflex release of oxytocin, whilst dilation of the vagina provokes a sympathetic nervous response. In the same species, it has also been shown (Bonnycastle & Ferguson, 1941) that *in vitro* the pattern of cervical and cornual response to oxytocin favours uterine emptying whereas that to adrenaline favours retention of uterine contents. Thus presentation of a foetus against the cervix will liberate oxytocin to accelerate delivery, whilst its passage into the vagina will liberate adrenaline and temporarily retard the advance of the next member of the litter. The implications of this are not confined to pluriparous species; in particular in man there is evidence that excessive sympathetic discharge during labour may interfere with the normal development of fundal dominance, resulting in cervical dystocia (Sauter, 1948).

Our results, in another species *in vivo* are in keeping with the views expressed by Ferguson.

REFERENCES

ABRAHAMS, V. V. & PICKFORD, M. (1954). Simultaneous observations on the rate of urine flow and spontaneous uterine movements in the dog and their relationship to posterior lobe activity. *J. Physiol. (Lond.)* **126,** 329–46.

ADLER, J., BELL, G. H. & KNOX, J. A. C. (1944). The behaviour of the cervix uteri *in vivo. J. Physiol. (Lond.)* **103,** 142–54.

ALLAN, H. & WILES, P. (1932). The role of the pituitary gland in pregnancy and parturition. *J. Physiol. (Lond.)* **75,** 23–8.

AMES, ROSE G., MOORE, D. H. & VAN DYKE, H. B. (1950). The excretion of posterior pituitary antidiuretic hormone in the urine and its detection in the blood. *Endocrinology* **46,** 215–27.

ANDERSSON, B. (1951). Observations on the neuro-hormonal regulation of milk ejection. *Acta physiol. scand.* **23,** 1–7.

BELL, G. H. & MORRIS, S. (1934). The oxytocic property of the blood of the cow. *J. Physiol. (Lond.)* **81,** 63–9.

BELL, G. H. & ROBSON, J. M. (1935). Oxytocic properties of blood extracts and their physiological significance. *J. Physiol. (Lond.)* **84,** 351–61.

BISSET, G. W. & WALKER, J. M. (1954). Assay of oxytocin in blood. *J. Physiol. (Lond.)* **126,** 588–95.

BLANDAU, R. J. (1945). On the factors involved in sperm transport through the cervix uteri of the albino rat. *Amer. J. Anat.* **77,** 253–72.

BONNYCASTLE, D. D. & FERGUSON, J. K. W. (1941). The action of Pitocin and adrenaline on different segments of the rabbit uterus. *J. Pharmacol.* **72,** 90–8.

CAMPBELL, B. & PETERSEN, W. E. (1953). Milk 'let down' and the orgasm in the human female. *Hum. Biol.* **25,** 165–8.

CANTAROW, J. H. (1954). Planned rapid labour. *Obstet. Gynec.* **4,** 213–6.

COCKRILL, J. R., MILLER, E. G. & KURZROK, R. (1934). Presence of oxytocic substances in urine during labour. *Proc. Soc. exp. biol. (N.Y.)* **31,** 572–3.

CROSS, B. A. (1951). Suckling antidiuresis in rabbits. *J. Physiol. (Lond.)* **114,** 447–53.

CROSS, B. A. (1955). The posterior pituitary gland in relation to reproduction and lactation. *Brit. med. Bull.* **11,** 151–5.

DALE, H. H. (1906). On some physiological actions of ergot. *J. Physiol. (Lond.)* **34,** 163–206.

DANDY, W. E. (1940). Section of the human hypophysial stalk. *J. Amer. med. Ass.* **114,** 312–4.

DANFORTH, D. N. (1954). The distribution and functional activity of the cervical musculature. *Amer. J. Obstet. Gynec.* **68,** 1261–71.

DEY, F. L., FISHER, C. & RANSON, S. W. (1941). Disturbances in pregnancy and labour in guinea-pigs with hypothalamic lesions. *Amer. J. Obstet. Gynec.* **42,** 459–66.

DICKER, S. E. & TYLER, CHRISTINE M. (1953). Vasopressor and oxytocic activities of the pituitary glands of rats, guinea-pigs and cats and of human foetuses. *J. Physiol. (Lond.)* **121,** 206–14.

VON EULER, U. S. (1937). On the specific vaso-dilating and plain muscle stimulating substances from accessory genital glands in man and certain animals (prostaglandin and vesiglandin). *J. Physiol. (Lond.)* **88,** 213–34.

EVANS, E. I. (1933). The transport of spermatozoa in the dog. *Amer. J. Physiol.* **105,** 287–93.

FERGUSON, J. K. W. (1941). A study of the motility of the intact uterus at term. *Surg. Gynec. Obstet.* **73,** 359–66.

VON FEKETE, K. (1930). Beiträge zur Physiologie der Gravidität. *Endokrinologie* **7,** 364–9.

FIROR, W. M. (1933). Hypophysectomy in pregnant rabbits. *Amer. J. Physiol.* **104,** 204–15.

FISHER, C., MAGOUN, H. W. & RANSON, S. W. (1938). Distocia in diabetes insipidus. The relation of pituitary oxytocin to parturition. *Amer. J. Obstet. Gynec.* **36,** 1–9.

FITZPATRICK, R. J. (1951). The activity and pharmacological reactivity of the cervix and body of the uterus in ruminants. *Proc. roy. Soc. Med.* **44,** 870–1.

FITZPATRICK, R. J. (1956). Unpublished observations.

FITZPATRICK, R. J. & HUGHES, JUNE M. (1956). Unpublished observations.

FLETCHER, J. G. (1953). A note on the *invivo* and *invitro* dose response curves for the rat uterus. *J. Pharm. Pharmacol.* **5,** 251–3.

FLOREY, H. & WALTON, A. (1932). Uterine fistula used to determine the mechanism of ascent of the spermatozoon in the female genital tract. *J. Physiol. (Lond.)* **74,** 5P.

GADDUM, J. H. & HAMEED, K. A. (1954). Drugs which antagonise 5-hydroxytryptamine. *Brit. J. Pharmacol.* **9,** 240–8.

GADDUM, J. H., PEART, W. S. & VOGT, MARTHE (1949). The estimation of adrenaline and allied substances in blood. *J. Physiol. (Lond.)* **108,** 467–81.

GARVEN, JEAN D. (1956). The estimation of 5-hydroxytryptamine in the presence of adrenaline. *Brit. J. Pharmacol.* **11,** 66–70.

GUNTHER, MAVIS (1948). The posterior pituitary and labour. *Brit. med. J.* i, 567.

HAMMOND, J. (1936). The physiology of milk and butterfat secretion. *Vet. Rec.* **48,** 519–35.

HARRIS, G. W. (1948). Further evidence regarding the endocrine status of the neurohypophysis. *J. Physiol. (Lond.)* **107,** 436–48.

HARRIS, G. W. (1955). *Neural Control of the Pituitary Body.* London: Edward Arnold.

HARRIS, G. W. & PICKLES, V. P. (1953). Reflex stimulation of the neurohypophysis (posterior pituitary gland) and the nature of posterior pituitary hormone(s). *Nature (Lond.)* **172,** 1049.

HATERIUS, H. O. & FERGUSON, J. K. W. (1938). Evidence for the hormonal nature of the oxytocic principle of the hypophysis. *Amer. J. Physiol.* **124,** 314–21.

HARTMAN, C. G. & BALL, JOSEPHINE (1930). On the almost instantaneous transport of spermatozoa through the cervix and uterus of the rat. *Proc. Soc. exp. Biol. (N.Y.)* **28,** 312–4.

HAWKER, R. W. (1955). Inactivation of antidiuretic hormone and oxytocin during pregnancy. *J. Endocr.* **13,** vP.

HAYS, R. L. & VANDEMARK, N. L. (1952). The effect of hormones on uterine motility and sperm transport in the perfused genital tract of the cow. *J. Dairy Sci.* **35,** 499–500.

HOLTON, PAMELA (1948). A modification of the method of Dale & Laidlaw for standardization of posterior pituitary extract. *Brit. J. Pharmacol.* **3,** 328–34.

HOLZBAUER, MARGARETHE & VOGT, MARTHE (1954). The concentration of adrenaline in the peripheral blood during insulin hypoglycaemia. *Brit. J. Pharmacol.* **9,** 249–52.

IVY, A. C., HARTMAN, C. G. & KOFF, A. (1931). The contractions of the monkey uterus at term. *Amer. J. Obstet. Gynec.* **22,** 388–99.

KALLIALA, H., KARVONEN, M. J. & LEPPÄNEN, V. (1952). Release of antidiuretic hormone during nursing in the dog. *Ann. med. exp. Biol. Fenn.* **30,** 96–107.

KARLSON, S. (1949). On the motility of the uterus during labour and the influence of the motility pattern on the duration of labour. *Acta obstet. gynec. scand.* **28,** 209–50.

KNAUS, H. (1934). *Periodic Fertility and Sterility in Woman.* Vienna: Wilhelm Maudrich.

KREHBIEL, R. H. & CARSTENS, S. G. P. (1939). Roentgen studies of the mechanism involved in sperm transport in the female rabbit. *Amer. J. Physiol.* **125,** 571–7.

LIVERMORE, A. H. & DU VIGNEAUD, V. (1949). Preparation of high potency oxytocic material by the use of counter current distribution. *J. biol. Chem.* **180,** 365–73.

MCPHAIL, M. K. (1935). Studies on the hypophysectomized ferret. The effect of hypophysectomy on pregnancy and lactation. *Proc. roy. Soc. B.* **117,** 34–5.

MARAÑON, G. (1947). Diabetes insipidus and uterine atony. *Brit. med. J.* ii, 769–71.

NEWTON, W. H. (1934). Reciprocal activity of the cornua and cervix uteri of the goat. *J. Physiol.* (*Lond.*) **81,** 277–82.

NEWTON, W. H. (1937). The insensitivity of the cervix uteri to oxytocin. *J. Physiol.* (*Lond.*) **89.** 309–15.

NIXON, W. C. W. & SMYTH, C. N. (1956). Physiological and clinical aspects of uterine action. *J. Obstet. Gynaec. Brit. Emp.* In press.

OLIVECRONA, H. (1954). Relation of the paraventricular nucleus to the pituitary gland. *Nature* (*Lond.*) **173,** 1001.

PAGE, E. W. (1946). The value of plasma pitocinase determinations in obstetrics. *Amer. J. Obstet. Gynec.* **52,** 1014–22.

PEETERS, G. & COUSSENS, R. (1950). The influence of the milking act on the diuresis of the lactating cow. *Arch. int. Pharmacodyn.* **84,** 209–20.

PENCHARZ, R. I. & LONG, J. A. (1933). Hypophysectomy in the pregnant rat. *Amer. J. Anat.* **53,** 117–39.

PERCHARZ, R. I. & LYONS, W. R. (1934). Hypophysectomy in the pregnant guinea-pig. *Proc. Soc. exp. Biol.* (*N.Y.*) **31,** 1131–32.

PIANA, G. & CURTO, G. M. (1950). Il compito della Postipofisi nella emissione del latte. *Atti Soc. Ital. Sci. Vet.* **4,** 1–4.

PICKLES, V. R. (1953). Blood-flow estimations as indices of mammary activity. *J. Obstet. Gynaec. Brit. Emp.* **60,** 301–11.

PIERCE, J. G., GORDON, S. & DU VIGNEAUD, V. (1952). Further distribution studies on the oxytocic hormone of the posterior lobe of the pituitary gland and the preparation of an active crystalline flavianate. *J. biol. Chem.* **199,** 929–40.

RATZAN, W. J. & SCHULMAN, A. (1955). Intravenous Pitocin in elective induction of labor. *Obstet. Gynec.* **6,** 493–98.

REYNOLDS, S. R. M. (1930). Studies on the Uterus. 1. A method of recording uterine activity in chronic experiments on unanaesthetized animals. *Amer. J. Physiol.* **92,** 420–9.

REYNOLDS, S. R. M. (1949). *Physiology of the uterus.* 2nd ed. New York: Paul Hoeber.

ROBSON, J. M. (1933). The reactivity and activity of the human uterus at various stages of pregnancy and at parturition. *J. Physiol.* (*Lond.*) **79,** 83–93.

ROBSON, J. M. (1947). *Recent advances in Sex and Reproductive Physiology.* 3rd ed. London: Churchill.

ROTHSCHILD, Lord (1953). The Movements of Spermatozoa. In *Ciba Symposium on Mammalian Germ Cells.* 124–33. London: Churchill.

ROWSON, L. E. (1955). The movement of radio-opaque material in the bovine uterine tract. *Brit. Vet. J.* **111,** 334–42.

RUSSELL, C. S. (1943). The response of isolated muscle strips from the upper and lower segments of the human full-time pregnant uterus to Pitressin and to Pitocin. *J. Obst. Gynaec. Brit. Emp.* **50,** 287–98.

SAUTER, H. (1948). Verwendung von Dihydroergotamin (D.H.E.4 5) in der Geburtshilfe. *Schweiz. med. Wschr.* **78,** 475–80.

SAWYER, W. H. (1954). Inactivation of oxytocin by homogenates of uteri and other tissues from normal and pregnant rats. *Proc. Soc. exp. Biol.* (*N.Y.*) **87,** 463–5.

SCHILD, H. O. (1951). Activity of the cervix of the human uterus and its response to drugs. *Proc. roy. Soc. Med.* **44,** 869–70.

SCHILD, H. O., FITZPATRICK, R. J. & NIXON, W. C. W. (1951). Activity of human cervix and corpus uteri. Their response to drugs in early pregnancy. *Lancet* **260,** 250–3.

SCHOFIELD, BRENDA M. (1949). The action of isopropylnoradrenaline on the cornu and cervix uteri. *J. Physiol.* (*Lond.*) **110,** 21P.

SCHOFIELD, BRENDA M. (1952). The innervation of the cervix and cornu uteri in the rabbit. *J. Physiol.* (*Lond.*) **117,** 317–28.

SCHUBEL, K. & GEHLEN, W. (1933). Eine neue zuverlässige Methode zur Standardisierung von Hypophysenninterlappenextrakten. *Arch. exp. Path. Pharmak.* **173**, 633–41.

SELYE, H., COLLIP, J. B. & THOMSON, O. L. (1933*a*). Effect of hypophysectomy upon pregnancy and lactation. *Proc. Soc. exp. Biol.* (*N.Y.*) **30**, 589–90.

SELYE, H., COLLIP, J. B. & THOMSON, O. L. (1933*b*). Effect of hypophysectomy upon pregnancy and lactation in mice. *Proc. Soc. exp. Biol.* (*N.Y.*) **31**, 82–3.

SMITH, P. E. (1946). Non-essentiality of hypophysis for maintenance of pregnancy in rhesus monkeys. *Anat. Rec.* **94**, 497.

STARKE, N. C. (1949). The rate of sperm travel in the genital tract of the ewe. *Onderstepoort J.* **22**, 415–525.

TGETGEL, B. (1926). Untersuchung über den Sekretionsdruck und über das Einschiessen der Milch im Euter des Rindes. *Schweiz. Arch. Tierheilk.* **68**, 335–48 and 369–87.

THEOBALD, G. W., GRAHAM, A., CAMPBELL, J., GANGE, P. D. & FRISCOLL, W. J. (1948). The use of post-pituitary extract in physiological amounts in obstetrics. *Brit. med. J.* ii, 123–7.

TYLER, CHRISTINE M. (1955). *The elaboration and utilization of posterior pituitary hormones.* Ph.D. Thesis, University of London.

USUELLI, F., PIANA, G. & CURTO, G. M. (1952). Sui momenti secretori e sulle modalità d'azione dell'ossitocina durante il parto. *Boll. Soc. ital. Biol. sper.* **28**, 1677–9.

VANDEMARK, N. L. & HAYS, R. L. (1951*a*). Stimulatory action of breeding on the release of oxytocin as measured by intramammary pressure. *J. Dairy Sci.* **34**, 496–7.

VANDEMARK, N. L. & HAYS, R. L. (1951*b*). The effect of oxytocin, adrenaline, breeding techniques and milking on uterine motility in the cow. *J. Animal Sci.* **10**, 1083.

VANDEMARK, N. L. & HAYS, R. L. (1952). Uterine motility responses to mating. *Amer. J. Physiol.* **170**, 518–21.

VANDEMARK, N. L. & HAYS, R. L. (1953). Effect of stimulation of the reproductive organs of the cow on the release of an oxytocin-like substance. *Endocrinology* **52**, 634–7.

VANDEMARK, N. L. & HAYS, R. L. (1954). Rapid sperm transport in the cow. *Fertility & Sterility* **5**, 131–6.

VANDEMARK, N. L. & MOELLER, A. N. (1951). Speed of spermatozoan transport in reproductive tract of oestrous cow. *Amer. J. Physiol.* **165**, 674–9.

DU VIGNEAUD, V., RESSLER, C., SWAN, J. M., ROBERTS, C. W., KATSOYANNIS, P. G. & GORDON, S. (1953). The synthesis of an octapeptide amide with the hormonal activity of oxytocin. *J. Amer. chem. Soc.* **75**, 4879–80.

VOGT, MARTHE (1953). Vasopressor, antidiuretic and oxytocic activities of extracts of the dog's hypothalamus. *Brit. J. Pharmacol.* **8**, 193–6.

WERLE, E., HEVELKE, A. & BUTHMANN, K. (1941). Zur Kenntnis des oxytocinabbauenden Prinzips des Blutes. *Biochem. Z.* **309**, 270–82.

WOODBURY, R. A., AHLQUIST, R. P., ABREU, B., TORPIN, R. & WATSON, W. G. (1946). The inactivation of Pitocin and Pitressin by human pregnancy blood. *J. Pharmacol.* **86**, 359–65.

WOODBURY, R. A., TORPIN, R., CHILD, G. P., WATSON, H. & JARBOE, M. (1947). Myometrial physiology and its relation to pelvic pain. *J. Amer. med. Assoc.* **134**, 1081–5.

Discussion

Chairman : Sir S. Zuckerman

Cross. I would like to make a point regarding the effect of adrenaline in antagonizing the action of oxytocin on the uterus and mammary gland which has been referred to in this and in the previous paper. There is no evidence that adrenaline blocks the central release of oxytocin although it certainly can block the peripheral effect of the hormone on the mammary gland and on the uterus. The central inhibition of oxytocin release that occurs during emotional disturbance of the milk-ejection reflex might be due to adrenaline but there is no proof; it could equally well be due to a purely nervous inhibition. Dr. Fitzpatrick's direct evidence of the secretion of oxytocin into the bloodstream following manual stimulation of the cervix is valuable since some of the previous evidence of American workers (VanDemark & Moeller, *Amer. J. Physiol.* **165,** 674, 1951) is not fully convincing. In the cow the latent period found by these workers was less than 10 sec. which seems to be too short to be explained in terms of a neurohormonal pathway, since even intravenously injected oxytocin has a latent period of about 15 sec. It is possible that the uterine contractions recorded by the American workers could have been entirely nervous in origin. Ferguson (*Surg. Gynec. Obstet*, **73,** 359, 1941) for instance in the rabbit was able to produce uterine contractions by dilation of the vagina even after the spinal cord had been sectioned to eliminate the possibility of reflex oxytocin secretion. I have recently confirmed this observation.

Fitzpatrick. I have found in the bovine too that adrenaline may have a dramatic antagonistic effect on oxytocin induced uterine contraction. Further, this is seen both *in vivo* and *in vitro*, which eliminates the possibility of the effect being an indirect one.

Dr. Cross made reference to the experiments of VanDemark and his co-workers. I have no information on the latent period between mating stimulus and myometrial response other than that obtained by examination of the published tracings, and these are not clear on this point.

Cross. I have heard directly from Dr. VanDemark confirming that responses were obtained in bovines within 10 sec. of cervical stimulation, both from the uterus and from the mammary gland. The milk-ejection reflex in the cow usually takes some 40 sec. There is no known nervous motor path whereby milk ejection may be initiated, but it is very difficult in this type of experiment to exclude the possibility of milk-ejection artefacts, associated with changes in the posture of the cow.

Dale. Are there any figures for the rate of ascent of sperm in the guinea-pig uterus?

Fitzpatrick. Only of those of Florey & Walton (*J. Physiol. (Lond.)* **74,** 5P, 1932) based on a fistula technique.

Dale. The point is that the innervation of the guinea-pig uterus as far as I know, is entirely inhibitory. Otherwise it might seem more likely that a nervous mechanism would explain this rapid ascent of the sperm; it would not be so easy to imagine that a hormone, in very small doses, would elicit such a co-ordinated, antiperistaltic wave, as would seem to be necessary.

Fitzpatrick. I know of no direct evidence of such a wave of 'antiperistalsis' but I do not see that it is necessarily impossible to consider an 'antiperistaltic' wave if one accepts a response at other times in the form of a 'peristaltic' wave.

Dale. It would perhaps be possible to suppose that if an antiperistaltic activity is normally present, then oxytocin might merely intensify it.

Fitzpatrick. There is some further evidence in agreement with my observations of a differential pressure gradient in the uterus. Millar (*Aust. Vet. J.* **28,** 127, 1952) has shown that a negative pressure develops in the uterus of the mare at the time of mating, in keeping with the concept of fluid being forced up the uterine tract and not downwards.

Some degree of inhibitory response of uterine muscle to sympathetic discharge and to adrenaline applies, in my opinion, to most species; Dr. Cross suggested that some of VanDemark's recordings of uterine contraction could be attributed to sympathetic nervous reflexes rather than oxytocin. The only known motor innervation of the bovine uterus is sympathetic, and the response of the intact bovine uterus to adrenaline, *at the time of oestrus*, I have found to be predominantly inhibitory and not contractile. Cupps & Asdell (*J. Animal Sci.* **3,** 351, 1944) working with *in vitro* techniques, also found that when under the influence of oestrogen, the uterine muscle of the bovine was inhibited by adrenaline.

Cross. Some of my records of uterine response to hypothalamic stimulation look remarkably like those published by VanDemark.

Fitzpatrick. In which species is this?

Cross. The rabbit.

Dale. The rabbit has a purely motor innervation through the sympathetic nerves.

Cross. In the rabbit the response is both motor and inhibitory.

Dale. But predominantly motor.

Cross. On stimulating the sympathetic centres of the hypothalamus one sees initial contraction followed by inhibition.

Dale. I was referring rather to direct stimulation of the sympathetic nerve, as having a purely motor effect.

Zuckerman. That must be the final path! The hypothalamus is a long way from this.

Dale. Stimulating the hypothalamus does not ultimately differentiate between a nervous effect and a hormonal effect.

Has Dr. Fitzpatrick made any observations using vasopressin? Does the response of the bovine uterus to the subsidiary oxytocic activity of vasopressin vary in parallel with that of the activity of oxytocin?

Fitzpatrick. There is an increase in reactivity of the bovine uterus to vasopressin over the last two weeks of pregnancy, which is not paralleled by a corresponding increase in reactivity to oxytocin. Conversely the sudden augmentation of response to oxytocin seen immediately prior to parturition is not seen with vasopressin. It is possible to estimate the relative potency of oxytocin and vasopressin in these experiments, and from mid-pregnancy until the thirty-eighth week (i.e. 2 weeks before term) oxytocin is between $7\frac{1}{2}$ and 10 times as potent as vasopressin. After the thirty-eighth week the ratio changes in favour of vasopressin, i.e. the ratio tends towards unity. Thirty-four to thirty-six hours before parturition there is an increase in reactivity to oxytocin which swamps that to vasopressin so that the ratio rises to 20 to 1 or more. After parturition reactivity to oxytocin is lost more rapidly than that to vasopressin and the ratio approaches unity again for a short while, before returning eventually to the usual value of about ten to one. I have shown recently (*J. Pharm. Pharmacol.* **8,** 403, 1956) that in the intact animal, parenteral magnesium chloride treatment increases reactivity of the bovine uterus to vasopressin but not to oxytocin, and it may be relevant that there is a rise in the magnesium concentration in serum in this species a short time before parturition (Moodie, Marr & Robertson, *J. comp. Path.* **65,** 20, 1955). It is possible, although at present pure speculation, that this physiological increase in magnesium concentration may be related to the early increase in vasopressin reactivity.

Croxatto. I want to comment on the oxytocinase activity of the blood, during pregnancy in human beings. We made observations some years ago which indicate that this activity increases progressively during the last month.

Noble. When Page (*Amer. J. Obst. Gynec.* **52,** 1014, 1946) first published his account of human serum in pregnancy inhibiting oxytocin, we repeated and confirmed his experiments. Dr. A. Eiger (unpublished observations) however, showed that although incubation with serum apparently destroys the activity of added Pitocin, the oxytocic activity returns if the mixture is left in the refrigerator overnight. Thus the supposed destruction of oxytocin is better referred to as a reversible inactivation. We think this probably indicates a pharmacological rather than a physiological process.

Release of vasopressin and oxytocin in response to drugs

by

J. M. WALKER

Department of Pharmacology, University of Oxford

It is known that the neurohypophysis can be stimulated by a number of drugs. Table I gives a list of some of the important ones. This list may not be comprehensive,

TABLE I

Substances which release vasopressin and oxytocin

	Vasopressin	Oxytocin
Ether (Ginsburg & Heller, 1953)	+	
Phenobarbitone (de Bodo & Prescott, 1945)	+	
Pentobarbitone (de Bodo & Prescott, 1945)	+	
Acetylcholine (Abrahams & Pickford, 1954)	+	+
Nicotine (Burn, Truelove & Burn, 1945)	+	
Morphine (de Bodo, 1944)	+	
Yohimbine (Fugo, 1944)	+	
Ferritin (Baez, Mazur & Shorr, 1952)	+	
ATP (Dexter, Stoner & Green, 1954)	+	

and it contains only the names of those for whose stimulant action there is reasonably good experimental support. At first sight the drugs in the list appear so diverse that it is difficult to draw any conclusion at all. They include some, but by no means all, of the anaesthetics; nicotine-like drugs; an analgesic; and various others. This diversity might imply that their stimulant actions were exerted in different ways, or even at different sites. Indeed, there is evidence that their modes of action are not all the same, for the stimulant action of acetylcholine is dependent on the state of the cholinesterase in the supraoptic nucleus while that of morphine is not (Pickford, 1953). However, there is one fact which is suggestive, namely, that nicotine and acetylcholine (by a nicotinic action), are effective. Now we know that the antidiuretic hormone and oxytocin are released, as it were reflexly, as a result of certain stimuli such as coitus and suckling. We know also from the work of Pickford and her colleagues (Pickford, 1947; Duke, Pickford & Watt, 1950) that small amounts of acetylcholine or of the anticholinesterase DFP, when injected into the region of the supraoptic nucleus, cause a transient antidiuresis. It seems possible therefore that the nucleus is analogous to a peripheral autonomic ganglion, in that it possesses a synapse at which acetylcholine is the transmitter and which is stimulated by nicotine. The second point of interest about the list is that very little appears to be known about the release of oxytocin. If we had information on this point, we should be able to calculate the ratio of oxytocin to vasopressin in the secretions of the gland in response to drugs, compare it with the ratio in the secretions produced by electrical and physiological stimulation, and thus perhaps gain some knowledge about the mode of release of the two hormones. It is these two points, the behaviour of the synapse and the release of hormones in response to drugs, that I want now to consider in detail.

METHODS

1. *Estimation of hormone content of the neurohypophysis*

It is possible to study the depletion of the neurohypophysis of its hormones, and this has been done with success in order to find out what happens when the supra-optico-hypophysial tract is cut, when hypertonic saline is given or water withheld, and under various other conditions (for references see Heller, 1955). But, as Dr. Ginsburg has emphasized, the method has the disadvantage that it does not distinguish *per se* between the rate of the release of the hormones and their rate of formation, for the amount of active substance in the gland at any moment must depend on these two variables. For instance, Ginsburg & Brown (1956) found that when rats were anaesthetized with pentobarbitone and a large amount of blood was withdrawn from the circulation, there was actually a significant increase of pressor and oxytocic activity in the neurohypophysis, although presumably in the meantime antidiuretic hormone had been released by the gland. This suggests that the formation of the hormones had been accelerated under these conditions.

2. *Effects of drugs in the whole animal*

With this method, the drug is administered to the animal, and the effect of the consequent output of neurohypophysial hormone is observed. It is the method that has been most frequently used, but is liable to give the most misleading results. A serious difficulty is that the compound which is being investigated may have effects of its own on the target organ (e.g. the kidney) which is being used to study the activity of the neurohypophysis; or it may mask in some way the action on that organ of the hormones that are being secreted. At Oxford, Dr. G. W. Bisset and I have worked chiefly with rats, and we have found that changes in the animals' blood pressure produced by some of the drugs we were testing had distorting effects on urine flow which complicated the antidiuretic action we were studying. Two examples of the importance of the blood pressure in this regard may be mentioned. First, if nicotine is injected into a group of rats at the beginning of a water diuresis, the chart of excretion of urine shows two peaks. The first peak, which occurs soon after the injection, is, we believe, caused by a rise of blood pressure, because a similar peak can be produced by a purely pressor agent like tyramine, and because it is abolished if the nicotine is preceded by hexamethonium, which prevents its pressor action. The second example is illustrated in Fig. 1, which shows the arterial blood pressure and urinary flow, simultaneously recorded, of a rat anaesthetized with ethanol. It can be seen how exactly the pressor or depressor actions of the substances injected were matched by changes in the rate of formation of urine.

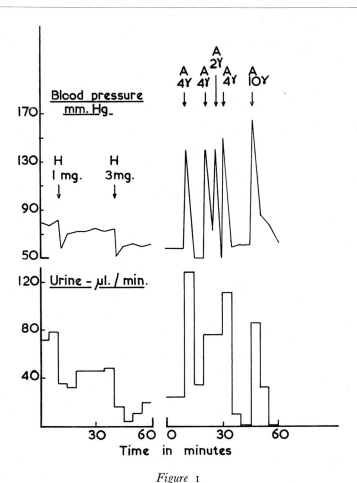

Figure 1

Rat anaesthetized with ethanol. Arterial blood-pressure and urine flow.
Arrows mark intravenous injections of
hexamethonium (*H*) and adrenaline (*A*).

3. *Estimation of vasopressin and oxytocin in body fluids*

For these reasons it is important, if possible, to extend results obtained by method 2 by assaying directly the hormone content of the body fluids. Urine is not satisfactory, since it has not been found possible to get rid of non-specific substances which contract the isolated uterus and therefore interfere with the assay of oxytocin. It seemed best therefore to do the assays on blood itself. The antidiuretic hormone is rapidly destroyed in its passage round the body and we have therefore done our assays on blood from the external jugular vein, which in the rat is the main path of venous drainage from the hypophysis. There is no lack of suitably sensitive methods for assaying antidiuretic hormone and the preparation we have used is that of Ames & van Dyke (1952). But in order to assay oxytocin we had to evolve a method by which blood was treated with acid ethanol and then concentrated by evaporation under reduced pressure, and which allowed us to test the resulting extract on the isolated uterus of the rat (Bisset & Walker, 1954). There are two points about the results obtained with this method. In the first place, in order to obtain sufficient material on which to carry out the assays, it was necessary to take quite large amounts of blood. Ginsburg & Heller (1953) have shown that withdrawal of blood may itself be a potent stimulus for production of antidiuretic hormone, and this fact complicates the interpretation of our findings. The second point is that there are present in the extracts oxytocic factors that are not of pituitary origin, for it has not always been possible to destroy all the oxytocic activity by sodium thioglycollate. One of these factors, which we think was potassium, is easily got rid of by dialysis. Another factor, however, is sometimes present. Since Armstrong, Keele, Jepson & Stewart (1954) showed that if blood was allowed to come into contact with a water-wettable surface such as glass, a pain-producing substance was formed which was also oxytocic, we tried the experiment of collecting blood in syringes and beakers made of polythene. We have found that under these conditions non-specific factors seldom appear. This method has been applied by Dr. Bisset to experiments on man, about which I hope he will tell us at the end of the paper.

RESULTS

We were led to do the experiments to which I shall refer by some earlier work on the excretion of chlorides. When commercial whole posterior lobe extract is injected subcutaneously into rats, there is not only an antidiuresis but also an increase in the total chloride excretion. When oxytocin is injected, there is a 'chloruresis' without an antidiuresis, and the major part of the chloruretic effect of whole lobe extract has therefore been ascribed by many workers to the oxytocic hormone. I am aware that there is some doubt about this, and that the whole picture is now altered by the very interesting results which Miss Pickford has described to us at this meeting. Moreover, it would obviously not be possible to interpret the increased chloride excretion after the administration of drugs without investigating the renal function of the treated animals. Nevertheless, we thought it would be of interest to see whether it was possible to correlate the size of the antidiuresis produced by a drug with the level of antidiuretic hormone in the jugular blood on the one hand, and the size of the chloruresis with the level of oxytocin on the other. Accordingly, nicotine was injected into groups of hydrated rats, water and chloride excretion was measured, and the effects were compared with those of commercial extract. It was found (Fig. 2) that nicotine, in a dose which was equal in antidiuretic power to a given dose of posterior lobe extract caused a rather greater chloruresis. It was possible therefore that after nicotine there would be both vasopressin and oxytocin present in the jugular blood, and on investigation this proved to be so. There was more oxytocin than vasopressin, and the mean ratio was 1·8 though the figures varied considerably from one animal to another (mean level of oxytocin 5·7 mU. per ml.; vasopressin 3·1 mU. per ml.; see Fig. 3). The levels of both oxytocin and vasopressin were significantly raised above those of the control animals.

If, as I suggested earlier, the supraoptic nucleus can be regarded as analogous to a peripheral autonomic ganglion, a blocking agent such as hexamethonium might be expected to block the stimulant action of nicotine. However, we have found (Bisset & Walker, 1953) that even in large doses which completely block both pressor and

CHLORIDE EXCRETION

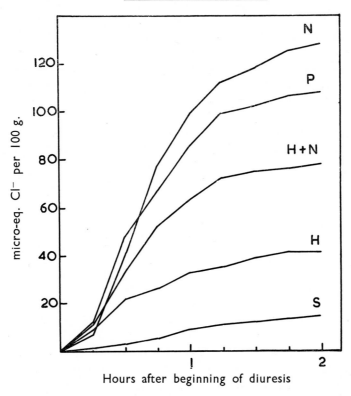

Figure 2

The effect of drugs on the chloride excretion in rats. N = nicotine, H = hexamethonium, P = pituitary (posterior lobe) extract. In the test groups, drugs were given in doses of equal antidiuretic potency. Control groups (S) received an injection of saline. (Bisset & Walker, 1956.)

convulsive effects of nicotine, hexamethonium does not block its antidiuretic action. Some other blocking agents do not do so either (Supek & Eisen, 1953). There is a slight but significant diminution of the chloruretic effect of nicotine when it is preceded by hexamethonium (see Fig. 2), but this diminution cannot be confidently ascribed to a central inhibitory action, for although the mean concentration of oxytocin in the blood after hexamethonium and nicotine is lower than that after nicotine alone, the difference is not significant at the 5 per cent. level (P = approximately 0·1).

In the course of this work, it was found that hexamethonium itself, given in the large dose of 5 mg. per 100 g., had an antidiuretic effect equal to that of nicotine, but that this was accompanied by only a very small chloruresis (Fig. 2). This antidiuretic effect can be shown not to be due to a delay in the absorption of water from the gut. It could be, of course, and very likely is at least partly due to a haemodynamic effect on the kidney. But when the jugular blood was assayed it was found

225

that the antidiuretic hormone content was significantly raised above that of the controls—raised in fact to about the value found in rats that had received nicotine—whereas the oxytocin was not altered. It is possible that hexamethonium stimulated the neurohypophysis indirectly by causing a profound fall of blood-pressure. Figure 3 summarizes these results.

When we were taking the blood from the jugular veins, it was convenient to have the rats anaesthetized, and in the experiments hitherto described the anaesthetic used was ethanol, which was given by mouth in a large volume of water, so that the rats were hydrated to a degree similar to that of the rats in the earlier experiments on chloride excretion. Ethanol was chosen for two reasons. First, though it interferes

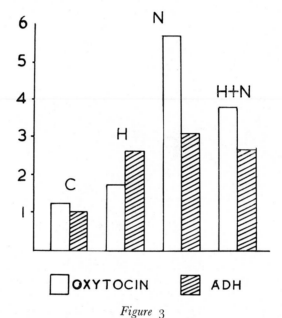

Figure 3

Concentrations of antidiuretic hormone and oxytocin in the jugular venous blood of rats under ethanol. Values in mU. per ml. blood. N = nicotine, H = hexamethonium, C = controls. (Bisset & Walker, 1956.)

with the output of antidiuretic hormone under physiological conditions, previous work had shown us that it did not abolish the antidiuretic effect of nicotine. Second, it was thought that ethanol would not itself cause release of antidiuretic hormone. In fact it can be seen (Fig. 3) that the level of hormones in the blood of these controls was about 1·0 mU. per ml. This accords with Dr. Ginsburg's finding that the fourth and fifth millilitre of blood withdrawn from an anaesthetized rat have quite high levels of antidiuretic hormone; since we withdrew from 4 to 6 ml., our mean value of 1·0 mU. per ml. does not seem unreasonable. In some more recent work, ether was used instead. It was found that when nicotine was injected into rats under ether, the oxytocin level of the jugular blood was not significantly different from that in the blood of animals under ethanol; but the mean level of antidiuretic hormone was

1·0 mU. per ml. in the former against 3·1 mU. per ml. in the latter. Thus in these experiments ether, which itself is known to cause release of antidiuretic hormone, apparently diminished the power of nicotine to do so, without interfering with the release of oxytocin.

CONCLUSIONS

From these results, certain conclusions are possible. In the first place, if hexamethonium reaches the supraoptic nucleus in what would be an effective concentration and yet does not block the action of nicotine, the synapse there must have pharmacological properties quite different from those of peripheral autonomic ganglia. Second, nicotine produces a secretion of both oxytocin and antidiuretic hormone in the rat, but in a ratio of the former to the latter much lower than is thought to be usual in other animals. Thus estimates of the ratio vary from about 5 in the rabbit (Harris, 1948) to about 20 in the dog (Abrahams & Pickford, 1954) whereas we have found a ratio of 1·0–1·8. There are a number of possible reasons for this discrepancy. The conditions of our experiments were different, in that our rats were anaesthetized whereas the animals used by most other workers were not. Again, we used nicotine, whereas others used other forms of stimulation. But let us suppose for a moment that the low ratio in the rat is characteristic of the species. Now it is not known what function oxytocin has in the male, or in the non-pregnant or non-lactating female animal; Dr. Pickford has discussed the possibility that it helps to control the excretion of sodium by the kidney. In most species, the amount of oxytocin which has to be given in order to affect sodium excretion seems to be very much larger than the amount of vasopressin which is antidiuretic, and it has therefore sometimes been assumed that this action of oxytocin is an incidental one of no physiological significance. But, as Dr. Pickford has pointed out, it is not correct to calculate doses on the arbitrary basis of the amounts of activity in commercial extracts. They should rather be calculated on a basis of the activities apparent when the animal's own neurohypophysis is in action. If this is a correct way of looking at the problem, it might be expected that an animal which secreted comparatively small amounts of oxytocin would possess a kidney which was sensitive to the electrolyte-controlling action of the hormone. It would thus be most interesting to know how the rat's kidney reacts to small amounts of purified oxytocin and vasopressin.

But knowledge of the actions of drugs on the neurohypophysis might have an even wider significance. Let us suppose that the hypothalamic nuclei are analogous not to a peripheral ganglion, as I suggested at the beginning, but to a nucleus which is also part of the autonomic system, namely, that of the third cranial nerve. This nucleus has sometimes been thought of as being under continuous inhibitory influences from higher levels in the central nervous system. When the influences are removed by sleep or anaesthesia, the nucleus becomes active and the pupil constricts. A similar set of conditions might apply to the supraoptic nucleus. Thus, in a conscious animal which was conserving water, impulses from osmoreceptors would keep the nucleus in a state of activity, and antidiuretic hormone would be continuously released. During a water diuresis, however, the nucleus would be inhibited by influences from elsewhere in the central nervous system, and in the absence of osmoreceptor activity would remain inactive. The analogous situation with respect to the

R

third nerve nucleus would be in the conscious animal in the light, with pupil constricted, on the one hand, and the conscious animal in the dark, with pupil dilated, on the other. Under anaesthesia inhibitory influences would be removed and the supraoptic nucleus would become active, causing antidiuretic hormone to be produced. In the present state of our knowledge perhaps this can hardly amount to more than a fanciful analogy. But it might point the way to explaining some of the earlier work by Bonsmann (1930) for instance, who showed in dogs that some hypnotics, such as phenobarbitone, prevent the normal response to water administration, while others, such as paraldehyde, do not. The effect of an anaesthetic on water metabolism would depend on whether or not it removed these inhibitory influences from the supraoptic nucleus. Moreover, a hypnotic could easily act at two sites at once; it could remove 'extrahypothalamic' inhibition and thus promote secretion of neurohypophysial hormones and at the same time it might, by acting directly on the nucleus, interfere with the stimulant action of a drug like nicotine. These two modes of action would explain why phenobarbitone, which itself releases antidiuretic hormone, nevertheless diminishes the antidiuretic action of nicotine (Supek & Eisen, 1953), and also why ether, as we have shown, though itself a releaser of antidiuretic hormone, reduces the amount of the hormone released by nicotine. Conceivably morphine might be in the special position of stimulating the nucleus direct; the available evidence suggests that its action in constricting the pupil is due to a stimulant effect at or near the third nerve nucleus (for discussion see McCrea, Eadie & Morgan, 1942) rather than to a removal of cortical inhibition, and Pickford (1953) has shown that morphine produces antidiuresis when injected direct into the supraoptic nucleus.

All this must remain mere speculation until further work is done, but it may be useful in suggesting the lines on which such work might profitably be undertaken. First, we need reliable information about the action of anaesthetics, based if possible on a direct determination of the level of hormones in the blood. Second, we should know what is the reaction of the hypothalamo-hypophysial system to newer substances such as reserpine and chlorpromazine, which are thought to act primarily on the hypothalamus. Third, we must find out more about the release by drugs of oxytocin, a subject about which we are still very ignorant.

Finally, there is one aspect of the problem which has not, so far as I know, yet received attention. In the rat, the neurohypophysial hormones are partly associated, like histamine and 5-hydroxytryptamine, with particles of mitochondrial size (Pardoe & Weatherall, 1955), and recently Dr. L. Martini and I have found that the same is true for the dog. It has been shown that histamine is released from its particles by histamine-releasers (Mongar & Schild, 1954) and that 5-hydroxytryptamine is released in the same way from its particles by reserpine (Giarman, 1956). It will be very interesting to see if vasopressin or oxytocin can be liberated from their particles by pharmacological agents, and if so whether these agents stimulate the neurohypophysis in the living animal.

REFERENCES

ABRAHAMS, V. C. & PICKFORD, M. (1954). Simultaneous observations on the rate of urine flow and spontaneous uterine movements in the dog, and their relationship to posterior lobe activity. *J. Physiol. (Lond.)* **126**, 329–46.

AMES, R. G. & VAN DYKE, H. B. (1952). Antidiuretic hormone in the serum or plasma of rats. *Endocrinology* **50**, 350–60.

ARMSTRONG, D., KEELE, C. A., JEPSON, J. B. & STEWART, J. W. (1954). Development of pain-producing substance in human plasma. *Nature (Lond.)* **174**, 791–2.

BAEZ, S., MAZUR, A. & SHORR, E. (1952). Role of the neurohypophysis in ferritin-induced antidiuresis. *Amer. J. Physiol.* **169**, 123–33.

BISSET, G. W. & WALKER, J. M. (1953). The effect of hexamethonium on the antidiuretic action of nicotine in the rat. *Abst. Commun. XIX Int. Physiol. Congr.*, 215.

BISSET, G. W. & WALKER, J. M. (1954). Assay of oxytocin in blood. *J. Physiol. (Lond.)*, **126**, 588–95.

BISSET, G. W. & WALKER, J. M. (1957). In preparation.

DE BODO, R. C. (1944). The antidiuretic action of morphine and its mechanism. *J. Pharmacol.* **82**, 74–85.

DE BODO, R. C. & PRESCOTT, K. F. (1945). The antidiuretic action of barbiturates (phenobarbital, amytal, pentobarbital) and the mechanism involved in this action. *J. Pharmacol.* **85**, 222–33.

BONSMANN, M. R. (1930). Schlafmittel und Diurese beim Hunde. *Arch. exp. Path. Pharmak.* **156**, 160–75.

BURN, J. H., TRUELOVE, L. H. & BURN, I. (1945). The antidiuretic action of nicotine and of smoking. *Brit. med. J.* i, 403–6.

DEXTER, D., STONER, H. B. & GREEN, H. N. (1954). The release of posterior pituitary antidiuretic hormone by adenosine triphosphate. *J. Endocr.* **11**, 142–59.

DUKE, H. N., PICKFORD, M. & WATT, J. A. (1950). The immediate and delayed effects of diisopropylfluorophosphate injected into the supraoptic nuclei of dogs. *J. Physiol. (Lond.)* **111**, 81–8.

FUGO, N. W. (1944). The antidiuretic action of yohimbine. *Endocrinology* **34**, 143–8.

GIARMAN, N. J. (1956). Quoted by Blaschko, H. In *Hypotensive Drugs*. London and New York: Pergamon Press.

GINSBURG, M. & HELLER, H. (1953). Antidiuretic activity in blood obtained from various parts of the cardiovascular system. *J. Endocr.* **9**, 274–82.

GINSBURG, M. & BROWN, L. M. (1956). *Brit. J. Pharmacol.* **11**, 236.

HARRIS, G. W. (1948). Further evidence regarding the endocrine status of the neurohypophysis. *J. Physiol. (Lond.)* **107**, 436–48.

HELLER, H. (1955). The active principles of the neurohypophysis. *J. Pharm. Pharmacol.* **7**, 225–47.

McCREA, F. D., EADIE, G. S. & MORGAN, J. E. (1942). The mechanism of morphine miosis. *J. Pharmacol.* **74**, 239–46.

MONGAR, J. L. & SCHILD, H. O. (1954). The effect of histamine releasers and anaphylaxis on intracellular particles of guinea-pig lung. *J. Physiol. (Lond.)* **126**, 44P–45P.

PARDOE, A. U. & WEATHERALL, M. (1955). The intracellular localization of oxytocic and vasopressor substances in the pituitary glands of rats. *J. Physiol. (Lond.)* **127**, 201–12.

PICKFORD, M. (1947). The action of acetylcholine in the supraoptic nucleus of the chloralosed dog. *J. Physiol. (Lond.)* **106**, 264–70.

PICKFORD, M. (1953). Substances affecting the release of the antidiuretic hormone from the posterior pituitary. *J. Endocr.* **9**, 3P.

SUPEK, Z. & EISEN, B. (1953). The action of nervous depressants on the antidiuretic and chloruretic effect of nicotine. *Arch. int. Pharmacodyn.* **93**, 75–82.

Discussion

Chairman: Sir S. Zuckerman

Bisset. I should like to report on some clinical extensions of this work which I carried out with Dr. J. Lee. Blood was withdrawn into a siliconed syringe by puncture of the internal jugular vein, in patients at operation, within 10 to 15 min. of the induction of anaesthesia with sodium thiopentone. Concentrated alcohol extracts were assayed for antidiuretic activity by intravenous injection in the Ames and van Dyke preparation and for oxytocic activity on the isolated rat uterus. The sensitivity of the assay rats for antidiuretic hormone ranged from 10 to 30 μU./ml. blood. In only 2 of 9 cases was antidiuretic activity detected, the concentrations were 12 and 20 μU./ml. blood. Satisfactory oxytocic assays were carried out in 8 cases; the concentrations of oxytocin varied from 1,200 to 2,300 μU./ml. blood with a mean of 1,600 μU./ml. The activity was abolished by sodium thioglycolate.

We hope to determine whether the level of oxytocin in the blood is raised during parturition and lactation, and conversely, whether certain types of uterine inertia and of dystocia, and painful engorgement of the breast during lactation, are associated with a deficient secretion of the oxytocic hormone.

Determination of both oxytocin and vasopressin in a single specimen of a body fluid may have further interesting applications. For example, assay of oxytocic and antidiuretic activity in the blood after damage to, or stimulation of, the supraoptic and paraventricular nuclei might indicate the relative importance of these two structures in the secretion of oxytocin and vasopressin.

We wish also to determine the ratio in which the hormones are released after stimuli such as injection of nicotine, since Dr. Pickford has shown that it is necessary to know this ratio before determining the effects of the hormones on such functions as renal sodium excretion.

Heller. I was very interested in Dr. Bisset's remarks. I can—to some extent—confirm his findings on the antidiuretic activity in human internal jugular blood. We (Heller & Schnieden, unpublished observations) drew blood by direct puncture of the vein in local anaesthesia but we have results in three subjects only. The antidiuretic activity in two subjects was less than 20 μU./ml. and in a third case less than 11 μU./ml. I am mentioning this not only because it agrees with Dr. Bisset's observations, but also because it stresses the fact that only very small amounts of antidiuretic activity can be expected in the blood of 'normal' adults. Results like these make the statements of various authors that several milliunits per millilitre may be found in the peripheral blood of normal human beings rather difficult to understand.

van Dyke. What volume of blood did you take from the external jugular vein in rats?

Walker. We took between four and six millilitres. We were conscious of the fact that the withdrawal of such a volume would influence the hormone level but there appeared to be no correlation between the volumes of blood taken and the concentrations we found. There might have been a correlation if we had had information about the blood pressure of the rats.

van Dyke. The significance of these relatively higher concentrations of oxytocin is difficult to appraise. I don't think that even the use of the thioglycollate test necessarily proves that the substance is oxytocin. All it shows is that the active substance has such a chemical constitution that its biological activity can be destroyed by reduction.

I wanted also to ask what significance you attach to the change in the ratio (V/O) of the hormones in the blood. You spoke of its being raised in some instances and not in others.

Walker. The answer to the first point is that without definite chemical identification we cannot be absolutely certain that the substance is oxytocin. We think it is, because it behaves in every way that we have tried, like the pituitary hormone. We have never found any in peripheral blood (though we have not done many experiments on this) and it appeared in jugular blood in amounts which did not seem to us to be unduly high considering the amounts of antidiuretic hormone Ginsburg & Heller found. Finally we looked for it in the jugular blood of hypophysectomized animals and although it was still present (possibly because our hypophysectomies were technically at fault) the amount was very greatly reduced. If these results were entirely due to chance, it seems to me unlikely that we should have such differences between one series and another.

Ginsburg. How do you know that you have not got any nicotine in your blood extract?

Walker. Because we dialysed it. In any case, nicotine does not elicit uterine contraction.

Gross. I want to ask Dr. Walker whether he has measured the sodium output under the influence of his various pituitary stimulating agents and if so whether it parallels chloride output?

Walker. We did not do that because we had no flamephotometer at hand at that time. I think that Dr. Pickford showed yesterday that chlorides move in the same way as sodium.

Zuckerman. Do you imagine that the same nerves which are involved in neurosecretion also transmit nervous impulses?

Walker. Yes, I have always thought so.

Dale. Do I understand that you have extracted whole blood? Is there any reason for that?

Walker. We had the impression from the literature that if we had centrifuged the red cells off we might have lost some of the activity. We found that extracting whole blood was quite satisfactory and so we stuck to it.

Dale. If you are extracting whole blood you are loading your extract with all sorts of substances, both from the red cells and from other formed elements. I wonder if there is any evidence that the hormone is stuck to the red corpuscle.

Fitzpatrick. Using an extraction procedure similar to that of Bisset and Walker I found that added Pitocin is not absorbed onto red blood cells. On the other hand during the time required for centrifugal separation of the plasma, there is a decrease in activity—suggesting that there is some direct inactivation.

How important is 5-hydroxytryptamine in these extractions? In taking whole blood one is also taking the platelets which Hardisty & Stacey (*J. Physiol. (Lond.)*, **130,** 711, 1955) found to contain most of the 5-hydroxytryptamine. We find that added 5-hydroxytryptamine comes through the extraction procedure in sufficient quantity to interfere with oxytocin assays on the rat uterus. It may be dangerous to use lysergic acid diethylamide in the final assay procedure to eliminate the effect of

5-hydroxytryptamine since lysergic acid diethylamide also inhibits uterine response to oxytocin.

Walker. In cases where we thought that we might have had an effect from 5-hydroxy-tryptamine in our extracts, we found that doses of lysergic acid diethylamide which were sufficient to abolish the effect of 5-hydroxytryptamine did not affect the responses to oxytocin.

Pickford. If you were to allow 5-hydroxytryptamine to continue in its contact with the uterus, you would soon differentiate between it and the oxytocin because the preliminary contraction is not maintained as it is with oxytocin.

Zaidi. We have used a modification of Dr. Walker's extraction procedure and I would like to ask him whether he ever found unspecific antidiuretic substances in his extracts: Professor Croxatto has mentioned that mere acidification will produce antidiuretic activity in blood.

Walker. No. We usually did the oxytocic assays first and in cases where we did suspect a non-specific oxytocic action there was no evidence of a non-specific antidiuretic effect.

Zaidi. To refer to your analogy between the neurohypophysial system and the third cranial nerve: we noticed that when rats go to sleep, the urine flow often falls, and I wonder whether this cannot also be explained by this analogy.

Walker. I do not want to go back to this analogy too much, but if you were to press me and ask for an answer, then it would be yes.

The adrenal-neurohypophysial interrelationship

ROBERT GAUNT, CHARLES W. LLOYD and J. J. CHART

Research Department, CIBA Pharmaceutical Products Inc., Summit, New Jersey
and the Department of Obstetrics and Medicine, State University of New York
Upstate Medical Center, Syracuse, New York

INTRODUCTION

THIS subject will lead into complexities of homeostatic mechanisms from which clear concepts have not yet emerged. We will begin, therefore, by outlining four groups of widely accepted facts which serve as the basis for the problem: (1) The antidiuretic hormone (vasopressin) is the main mammalian humoral agent acting to inhibit water excretion and prevent fluid loss through the kidney; under certain conditions it enhances sodium excretion. (2) The 17-hydroxy (hydrocortisone-like) hormones of the adrenal cortex, depending upon circumstances, may act either to enhance or inhibit water and sodium excretion. (3) The aldosterone-like adrenal hormones are the main humoral agents acting to inhibit sodium excretion and because of that fact must to some degree tend to cause water retention; they, too, however, *can* act as water diuretics. (4) The secretion of antidiuretic hormone is regulated in part by the osmotic pressure of the extracellular fluids and probably to some degree by extracellular fluid volume changes. The secretion of aldosterone is regulated likewise partly by electrolyte concentrations in body fluids and again perhaps by extracellular fluid volume. Unlike aldosterone, the secretion of the hydrocortisone-like steroids is under the control of corticotrophin.

These facts show that the adrenal cortex and neurohypophysis affect related phenomena and are regulated in part by similar influences. The problem is to define the nature of the interrelationship between them. The attempt to do so began in 1938 and has not yet succeeded fully.

In 1938 Silvette & Britton called attention to some of the essentially antagonistic actions of the neurohypophysis and adrenal cortex and emphasized their probable functional significance. In elaborating this concept (e.g., Corey & Britton, 1941) they dealt with gross phenomena and did not attempt to specify the mechanisms through which these overall antagonistic influences might operate.* Since that time numerous authors have dealt more or less comprehensively with the subject in attempts to correlate admittedly difficult and conflicting data into comprehensible working hypotheses (e.g., Lloyd, 1952; Heller, 1952; Pitts, 1952; Montastruc, 1954; Morel, 1955; Chester Jones, 1956). The attempts of the senior author and his associates to force knowledge from all sources as it existed in 1949 and 1950 into some

---

* It is now apparent that in some respects the corticoids may enhance rather than antagonize the actions of neurohypophysial hormones (See Sect. II).

degree of coherence were summarized in two publications (Gaunt, Birnie & Eversole, 1949; Gaunt, 1951). Their suggested cause-and-effect relations were admittedly tentative and tenuously bound. In some respects they have proved too fragile to withstand subsequent critical scrutiny. Let us look, then, briefly at some past work in the field and deal especially with more recent observations. The need for brevity will require evaluations more dogmatic than are justified either by the evidence at hand or the authors' self-confidence; unfortunately, only a fraction of the relevant literature can be cited. Since work in the lower vertebrates is being covered by Dr. Chester Jones in a subsequent paper of this symposium, we omit all references to this field. Also, since it is not relevant to our main theme, no further note will be made of the important new work of Ingle & Li (1955) implicating vasopressin as an essential agent in the repair of the deficient muscle work performance of adrenalectomized animals.

I. PROBLEMS CONCERNING THE NATURE OF THE ADRENAL-NEUROHYPOPHYSIAL RELATIONSHIP

The facts at hand permit the postulation of an almost infinite number of sites and means of interaction between the hormones of the two glands in question. Many of these possibilities have been explored to some degree with a resultant large literature that is notable for its lack of agreement. Some of the questions at issue follow.

A. Circulating levels of antidiuretic hormone in adrenal insufficiency

Several investigators have presented evidence indicating that increased quantities of some circulating antidiuretic substance (ADS) exist in adrenal insufficiency. The relation of this ADS to the antidiuretic hormone, however, is not clear, largely because of question concerning specificity of the assay methods used (Ames & van Dyke, 1952; van Dyke, Adamsons & Engel, 1955) and contradictory findings concerning facts involved. Nevertheless, questions concerning the identity of such substances should not be allowed to obscure the fact that the phenomena which have been observed are not illusory. Any satisfactory solution of the problem must account for the presence in adrenal insufficiency of an excess or easy release of some substance(s) which in certain tests resembles the neurohypophysial antidiuretic hormone (Birnie, Eversole, Boss, Osborn & Gaunt, 1950; Slessor, 1951; Lloyd, 1952; Leaf & Mamby, 1952; Mirsky, Stein & Paulish, 1954a, 1954b; Ginsburg, 1954; Montastruc, 1954).

B. Relation of filtration rate to renal actions of corticoids and antidiuretic hormone

It is generally agreed that the antidiuretic hormone influences water and electrolyte excretion without affecting the glomerular filtration rate (G.F.R.). It is also agreed that the sodium-retaining action of corticoids can be effected independently of the G.F.R. There has, however, been much confusion concerning the superimposed relation of the definite G.F.R.-increasing action of the corticoids to such phenomena (Boss, Birnie & Gaunt, 1950; Rosenbaum, Davis & Ferguson, 1951; Pitts, 1952; Davis & Howell, 1953; Stribling & Spurr, 1954; Skillern, Corcoran & Scherbel, 1956). The question is important because if some of the effects of corticoids, e.g., effects on water diuresis, are due indirectly to changes in the G.F.R. there would be no need to invoke altered function of the neurohypophysis in their explanation.

Otherwise a neurohypophysial participation might logically be suspected. The nature of the problem is such that definitive evidence is difficult or impossible to obtain, in view of the possibility that changes in G.F.R. too small to be measurable by available methods can affect electrolyte and water excretion (Selkurt, 1954). Nevertheless, impressive evidence suggests that there are effects on water excretion attributable to corticoids or their lack which are not explicable by changes in renal hemodynamics (Rosenbaum, *et al.*, 1951; Sala, Sereni & Ballabio, 1951; Stribling & Spur, 1954; Skillern, *et al.*, 1956; Dingman & Thorn, 1955; Dustan, Corcoran & Farrell, 1955; Ikkos, Luft & Olivecrona, 1955; Garrod, Davies & Cahill, 1955). This does not by itself implicate participation by the neurohypophysis, as several authors concerned have pointed out, but does open a door to such possibilities. An additional complicating factor in such studies is that experimental work on hypophysectomized animals and in human subjects with diabetes insipidus have a well-known limitation of lack of certainty that neurohypophysial function is completely abolished (cf. Sect. IV.*B*.3).

The concept that the decreased tubular reabsorption of water (increased free-water clearance) sometimes clearly associated with the administration of corticoids represents a direct tubular action has not fared well in recent studies (e.g., Skillern *et al.*, 1956). Alternatively, it has been proposed that the potassium deficiency induced by corticoids leads to an inability of the renal tubule to reabsorb water (Corcoran & Dustan, 1956).

C. *Effect of corticoids on the sensitivity to antidiuretic hormone and on thirst*

Some time ago it was suggested (Birnie, *et al.*, 1950; Lockett, 1952) that adrenal-ectomized animals are hypersensitive to exogenous vasopressin. The subsequent demonstration that adrenalectomy delays the rate of inactivation of vasopressin (Sect. III) seemed to provide a sound basis for such observations. Nevertheless, others have failed to find that such a hypersensitivity exists in man (Chalmers & Lewis, 1951; Dingman & Thorn, 1955). Whatever may be true in adrenal deficiency states, it is clear from numerous observations, beginning with those of Ragan, Ferrebee, Pfyfe, Atchley & Loeb, 1940 (Winter, 1952; Swingle, Fedor, Ben, Maxwell, Baker & Barlow, 1953; Dustan, *et al.*, 1955; Conn, 1955) that excess corticoids, including aldosterone, reduce the responsiveness to vasopressin (cf. Figs. 1 and 2) although the opposite has been reported in hypopituitarism (Stribling & Spurr, 1954). The mechanisms involved are not well established, but one factor seems to be indirect: the corticoids cause a polydipsia which seems to be an important element in the altered fluid exchanges in chronic experimental situations (above references; Gaunt, 1951; Skillern *et al.*, 1956; Ikkos, *et al.*, 1955).

D. *Relation of antidiuretic hormone and corticoids to electrolyte excretion*

In pharmacological experiments various types of interactions between various corticoids and vasopressin on sodium and potassium excretion are demonstrable; some examples are illustrated in Sect. II. It can be questioned whether such effects of vasopressin are direct or indirect (Leaf, Bartter, Santos & Wronz, 1953). Despite considerable effort, however, no well-documented story has yet emerged showing convincingly a physiological counterpart of these pharmacological observations

(Murphy, 1950; Black & Thompson, 1951; Chalmers, Lewis & Pawon, 1951; Holland & Stead, 1951; Lauson, 1951; Maxwell & Breed, 1951; Pitts, 1952; Davis, Howell & Hyatt, 1954; Cole, 1955). Although some recent work such as that of Anslow & Wesson (1955) and Chester Jones (1956) gives promise of clarification, there is still scant evidence of *deficiency* phenomena which would be anticipated if the neurohypophysial hormones had important effects on electrolyte metabolism.

II. CORTICOID-VASOPRESSIN INTERACTION:
PHARMACOLOGICAL CONSIDERATIONS

There have been many studies in which vasopressin and some adrenal cortical preparation were given simultaneously (e.g., Ragan, *et al.*, 1940; Corey & Britton, 1941; Sartorius & Roberts, 1949; Winter, 1952; Swingle, *et al.*, 1953; Morel, 1955). We have recently extended work of this sort to try to distinguish between the different actions of several corticoids at varying dosages on the response to Pitressin*. At the present time it is obviously not permissible to speak of adrenal influences

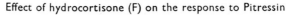

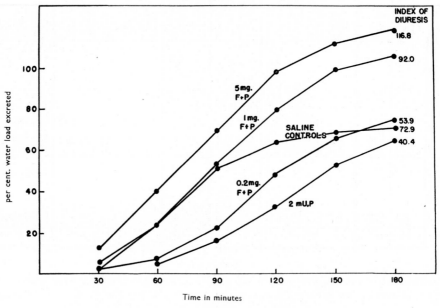

Figure 1

Showing the effect of graded doses of hydrocortisone on the antidiuretic effect of Pitressin. The 'Index of 'Diuresis' represents in cm.² the area under each curve.

* We utilized simple acute experimental procedures in normal male rats. Fasted animals were given a hydrating dose, 5 ml./100 g., of 0·2 per cent. sodium chloride solution by stomach tube together with a standard subcutaneous injection of 2 mU. Pitressin/100 g. The effect on the response to Pitressin of varying doses of the several steroids, given subcutaneously two hours before Pitressin, was then determined in terms of water, sodium and potassium excretion over a period of 180 min. In order that values for water excretion might be expressed as one figure, the area under cumulative curves of water excretion was plotted (see Krieger & Kilvington, 1940) and designated the index of diuresis. One centimetre on the ordinate represented excretion of 10 per cent. of the fluid load and one centimetre on the abscissa represented 10-min. time.

without specifying the particular type of adrenal hormone involved. The results illustrated in Figs. 1 and 2 are based upon the means of all animals receiving any particular treatment. Untreated and Pitressin-treated controls were run simultaneously with all treated groups and hence served as a check on possible erroneous conclusions due to day-to-day variations.

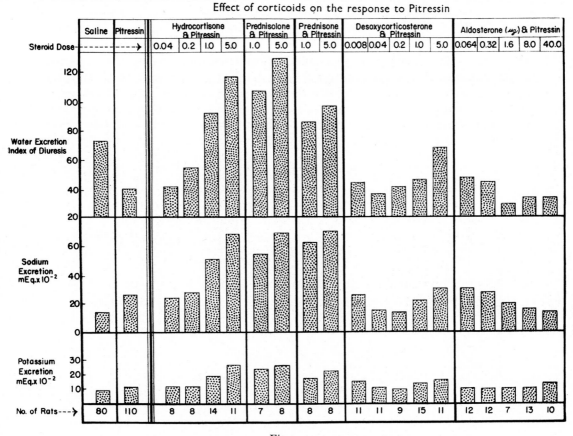

Effect of corticoids on the response to Pitressin

Figure 2

Showing the effects of various corticoids on the response to a standard dose (2 mU.) of Pitressin in experiments of 180 min. duration. The 'Index of Diuresis', representing the amount of water excreted, is illustrated in Fig. 1 and defined in the footnote on p. 236.

The results are complex and indicate that no simple rule governs the observed responses. Hydrocortisone in doses of 200 μg. or higher antagonized partially or completely the antidiuretic effect of Pitressin* and at the higher doses (1–5 mg.) it actually caused dehydration (Fig. 1). On the other hand, hydrocortisone augmented Pitressin-induced natriuresis and to a lesser degree kaliuresis. Prednisone and prednisolone had quantitatively different effects. For instance, prednisolone was the most active compound in stimulating water excretion, whereas prednisone enhanced

---

* We are at a loss to correlate these findings with those of Winter (1952) who found cortisone to enhance the antidiuretic effect of Pitressin, whereas desoxycorticosterone acetate antagonized it.

sodium excretion relatively more than water. (These actions of the Δ'-compounds are of interest because of their relative absence of effect on sodium and water metabolism under most conditions of clinical use).

Desoxycorticosterone in the presence of Pitressin had no effect on water excretion except to enhance it at high dosage—an action definitely weaker than that of the glucocorticoids. In contrast to the glucocorticoids, desoxycorticosterone in small doses reduced sodium excretion whereas large doses were without effect. This apparent anomaly might result from a rise of the G.F.R. produced by large doses of desoxycorticosterone.

Aldosterone was available only in microgram doses. In these amounts it had no effect on water excretion except for a suggestion of enhancement, which could not be established statistically, of the antidiuretic action of Pitressin at certain doses. Other work (Renzi, Renzi, Chart & Gaunt, 1956) leads to the presumption that aldosterone in larger dosage would have a hydrocortisone-like diuretic action greater than that of desoxycorticosterone. Aldosterone in amounts of 1·6 μg. or more inhibited the natriuretic action of Pitressin, qualitatively like the intermediate doses of desoxycorticosterone. When used in minimal effective dose ranges, aldosterone seemed to have about 25 times the antinatriuretic activity of desoxycorticosterone. This corresponds closely to the relative sodium-retaining activity of these two steroids in some other but not all kinds of test situations (Gaunt, Renzi & Chart, 1955).

It is clear from this study that one cannot simply speak of 'corticoid-vasopressin antagonism'. The effects of Pitressin may be either antagonized, enhanced or unaltered by a corticoid depending upon the steroid used, its dose, or the variable measured. Such pharmacological observations do not tell us with certainty what to expect when these hormones are secreted in physiological amounts under variable conditions. They do suggest, however, that no simple general rules apply and that segregation of influences involved under clinical conditions will be a discouragingly difficult problem.

III. RELATION OF ADRENAL TO INACTIVATION OF ANTIDIURETIC HORMONE

The work of Birnie (1953) and Ginsburg (1954) seems to establish unequivocally on the basis of both *in vivo* and *in vitro* experiments that adrenal hormones support the mechanisms, possibly enzymatic and/or nutritional (Lloyd, 1952), which are responsible for the rapid inactivation of vasopressin. After adrenalectomy the half-life of circulating exogenous vasopressin was doubled, a process partially blocked by cortisone but not by sodium chloride therapy.

Such observations, together with suggestive evidence of high blood-levels and accelerated release of antidiuretic hormone, make it probable that adrenal insufficiency results in a *hyper-vasopressinism*. One cannot be certain, however, because of lack of definite evidence in such cases that the neurohypophysis does not reduce its rate of secretion and thus compensate homeostatically for a reduced rate of hormone destruction.

IV. INTERACTION BETWEEN RELEASE MECHANISMS OF ADRENAL AND NEUROHYPOPHYSIAL HORMONES

Insofar as the adrenal and neurohypophysial hormones act antagonistically, it might be anticipated that a hypersecretion of one would incite a hypersecretion of the other. Within the range of physiological dosage, pharmacological evidence to support such an idea has not been forthcoming. On the other hand, reciprocal function might be attained by one hormone suppressing the secretion of the other. It is in this general field that the greatest progress has been made recently.

A. *Vasopressin-like substances and release of corticotrophin (ACTH)*

In the search for the neurohumour which presumably traverses the hypothalamico-hypophysial portal circulation to cause ACTH release, much attention has been directed to the possibility that vasopressin is the substance concerned. Exogenous vasopressin in large dosage (like large doses of many other things) can cause ACTH release (Nagareda & Gaunt, 1951; Kimura, 1954; McCann & Brobeck, 1954; Sobel, Levy, Marmorston, Schapiro & Rosenfeld, *et al.*, 1955; Martini & Morpurgo, 1955; Shibusawa, Saito, Fukuda, Kawai & Yoshimura, 1955; Sayers & Burks, 1955) although under certain conditions the opposite may occur (Itoh & Arimura, 1954). That it does so in what might be considered physiological amounts* has not been shown; this and other more critical evidence has led to doubt that vasopressin could be the neurohumour involved (Nagareda & Gaunt, 1951; Harris, Lloyd & Lobotsky, 1953; Munson & Briggs, 1955; Guillemin & Rosenberg, 1955). Much interest awaits attempts to extend the reports suggesting that the hypothalamic neurohumour in question is a substance present in posterior pituitary extracts but different from vasopressin or oxytocin (Guillemin & Hearn, 1955; Saffran, Schally & Benley, 1955; Porter & Rumsfeld, 1956; Swingle, Brannick, Barrett, LeBrie & Parlow, 1956; Guillemin, Hearn, Cheek & Housholder, 1956).

It is also possible that the antidiuretic hormone affects corticoid excretion by indirect routes, e.g., expansion of the extracellular fluid volume (Davis, *et al.*, 1954), or simple excess hydration (Nagareda & Gaunt, 1951). Beck, Dyrenfurth, Giroud & Venning, (1955) have shown an increased excretion of aldosterone only during the period *after withdrawal* of Pitressin therapy, a result suggesting the operation of indirect influences.

B. *Effect of corticoids on neurohypophysial activity*

Cavallero, Dova & Rossi (1954), working in Heller's laboratory, were the first to report that the hormones of the adrenal cortex affected the pituitary content of antidiuretic hormone. This content was reduced by adrenalectomy and restored to varying degrees by salt, desoxycorticosterone acetate and cortisone—the latter apparently being the most effective. These findings are apparently in some disagreement with those of Diamond (1952). They are not entirely consistent in detail but are consistent in principle with our observations noted below.

---

* 'Physiological amount' is an even more elusive term in this case than usual. Even if 'physiological' levels of vasopressin could be well estimated in the systemic circulation, that would not necessarily imply that the same concentration occurs in the hypothalamico-hypophysial portal vessels if vasopressin, arising from the hypothalamus, was actually acting as a neurohumour at such a site.

The authors' approach to the problem has been of two types: (*a*) the vasopressin-like content of extracts of the posterior pituitary and hypothalamus was assayed in various experimental situations (Lloyd and associates in the Syracuse laboratories); (*b*) an attempt was made to quantitate the amount of stainable neurosecretory material in the neurohypophysis under various conditions (Gaunt, Chart & Antonchak (1956) in the CIBA laboratories).

1. *The effect of adrenal and pituitary hormones on the content of antidiuretic substance in the pituitary and hypothalamus.* The content of antidiuretic substance of posterior pituitary and hypothalamus was estimated by determining the decrease in urine flow caused by the intravenous injection of homogenates of these tissues into rats anaesthetized with ethanol. All of the donor animals were sacrificed by decapitation under Nembutal anaesthesia. It had previously been shown that the content of hypothalamic and posterior pituitary antidiuretic substance was essentially unchanged by Nembutal. Both lobes of the hypophysis were routinely included in the material assayed because numerous experiments under different conditions failed to demonstrate antidiuretic activity in the anterior lobe. The results (Lloyd & Pierog, 1955; Lloyd & Oldford, 1955; and unpublished data) are shown in Table 1, classified in terms of the following groups.

Group I. Antidiuretic substance (ADS) is present in large amounts in the posterior lobes (200–400 mU. equivalents of vasopressin) and in lesser amounts in the hypothalami (10–20 mU. equivalents) of normal rats. Moderate dehydration produced a variable increase of hypothalamic but loss of pituitary antidiuretic activity. Hydration resulted in slightly lower levels of hypothalamic activity. Both procedures decreased pituitary ADS levels. Preliminary observations in two cases suggested that intracarotid injection of hypertonic saline solution caused a marked depletion of all antidiuretic hormone stores.

Group II. Immediately after hypophysectomy the hypothalamus and blood contained very little antidiuretic activity but after a month or two the hypothalamic and blood-levels increased significantly. The secretory activity of the hypothalamus retained a certain flexibility as demonstrated by the decrease of ADS following a moderate degree of dehydration and the accumulation of ADS upon hydration. These findings suggest that in the presence of an intact hypothalamico-neurohypophysial system efficient mechanisms of synthesis and release easily accommodate to moderate changes in antidiuretic hormone requirement, whereas in the hypophysectomized animal supply more readily reflects changes in demand.

The presence of the adenohypophysis in the absence of the neurohypophysis influences the hypothalamic ADS content. Low levels of blood ADS and very little hypothalamic ADS were found in rats with diabetes insipidus resulting from neurohypophysectomy after a postoperative interval sufficiently long to permit reorganization of the hypothalamus and release of ADS in totally hypophysectomized animals (Lloyd & Pierog, 1955). The explanation of the role of the anterior lobe can only be speculative at the moment. The lowering of hypothalamic ADS is not simply the result of the rapid water exchange which takes place in these animals because the levels of ADS are considerably lower than those in intact animals with a comparable rate of water turnover resulting from the use of a liquid diet.

TABLE I

The antidiuretic hormone-like content of the hypothalamus and posterior pituitary of rats
(From Lloyd, *et al.*, 1955, and unpublished.)

	Treatment	ADS content mU. Pitressin equiv. ±S.E.		No. of rats
		Hypothalamus	Post. pit.	
Group I Altered hydration in intact animals	Untreated controls	12·4±−3·9	302±74	14
	No water—48 hr.	25·0±10·7	100±72	8
	Intracarotid hypertonic saline*	6·6	100	2
	Liquid diet 48 hr.	9·7± 0·7	—	6
Group II Hypophysectomy (Hpx.) and neurohypophy-sectomy	Hpx. 3 to 8 days	2·0	—	6
	Hpx. 30 days	10·0	—	6
	Hpx. 30 days—no water for 48 hr.	5·0	—	6
	Hpx. 30 days—liquid diet for 48 hr.	24·0	—	6
	Neurohpx. 30 days—diabetes insipidus	2·0	—	6
Group III Stress and hydro-cortisone in intact animals	Formalin stress†	2·5± 0·1	61± 24	6
	Hydrocortisone‡	50·0±24·6	414±195	6
	Stress+hydrocortisone‡	2·6± 2·26	2113	6
Group IV Stress and hydro-cortisone in hypo-physectomized animals	Hpx.—30 days+stress	2·0	—	6
	Hpx.—30 days+hydro-cortisone‡	71·0±42·0	—	7
	Hpx.—30 days+hydro-cortisone‡ and stress	2·6± 0·73	—	6
Group V Adrenalectomy (Adx.)	Adx.—Salt - free diet 2 days	4·9± 1·8	172± 60	6
	Adx.—Salt - free diet 2 days+hydrocorti-sone§	6·3± 1·6	307± 69	6
	Adx.—Salt - free diet 5 days	4·9± 2·0	91± 32	6
	Adx.—Salt - free diet 5 days+hydrocorti-sone§	8·3± 1·5	193± 70	7

* 2 ml. of 2·5 per cent. NaCl.
† 0·2 ml. of 10 per cent. formalin subcutaneously 60–90 min. before test.
‡ 2·5 mg. twice per day for total of 5 doses.
§ 5·0 mg. twice per day for total of 5 or 10 doses.

Group III. In intact animals the administration of a stress in the form of sub-cutaneous formalin results in decreased hypothalamic and posterior lobe ADS. The administration of hydrocortisone caused a marked increase in ADS of both hypo-thalamus and posterior lobe of intact animals.

Priming with hydrocortisone before formalin was given caused intact animals to accumulate large amounts of ADS in the posterior lobe while the hypothalamus be-came depleted.

Group IV. In contrast, hydrocortisone caused an increase of hypothalamic ADS in hypophysectomized animals but did not protect against depletion as a result of stress.

These experiments could be interpreted as suggesting that a noxious substance such as formalin causes a movement of ADS out of the hypothalamus into the posterior lobe and thence into the blood-stream in the intact rat and perhaps directly into the blood-stream of the hypophysectomized animals. Adrenal steroids do not prevent the migration from the hypothalamus but do seem to block release from the posterior lobe.

Group V. Adrenalectomized rats maintained on 1 per cent. saline solution seemed to have relatively little change in ADS content of hypothalami or posterior lobes, but due to technical difficulties reliable quantitative figures are not yet available. It was only after depletion of salt and development of insufficiency that significant lowering of hypothalamic and posterior-lobe ADS occurred. If animals were maintained on a low salt diet, administration of very large amounts of hydrocortisone which would have caused accumulation of huge amounts of ADS in intact rats, caused only partial return toward normal values. The corollary experiments, comparing the effects of desoxycorticosterone and NaCl with those of the 17-OH steroids, are still in an early stage. Our preliminary impression is that maintenance of animals in good health by either saline or DCA tends to prevent depletion of hypothalamic and posterior-lobe ADS.

In all of these experiments one consistent finding was that hydrocortisone caused increases in the amounts of ADS in the posterior pituitary, relative to comparable controls, whatever may have been its effect on hypothalamic stores of this substance. Such observations are in general agreement with those cited below.

2. *Effects of adrenal hormones on neurosecretory material*.* In our hands no measurable effect on this material could be obtained with mild or short-term stimuli such as nicotine injections or short periods of dehydration. We could not prevent depletion by giving 150 or 750 mU. of Pitressin tannate although 2·5 U. gave suggestive results. Obviously the procedure as we used it is a less sensitive one than that of bioassaying total content of the tissue concerned. Severe dehydration,† however, caused marked

---

* These experiments were done in collaboration with our associate, Mr. Ben Antonchak, who was responsible for the histological work. We are greatly indebted to Professor E. Scharrer, Albert Einstein College of Medicine, for detailed advice and suggestions concerning techniques and procedures, and to Professor J. H. Leathem, Rutgers University, for technical help.

† Preliminary experimentation indicated that a simple dehydration procedure which would produce a distinct depletion of neurosecretory material in both intact and adrenalectomized animals, was as follows: mature, non-fasted, male rats were given 3 ml. of 5 per cent. NaCl solution per 100 g. body-weight by stomach tube at 9 a.m. and this dose was repeated at 12 noon on the day the experiments started. The animals were sacrificed at 24 hr., i.e., 9 a.m. of the second day. Depletion was negligible when animals were killed at 7 hr.

depletion of the neurosecretory material as others have found (cf. Scharrer & Scharrer, 1954) (Fig. 3).

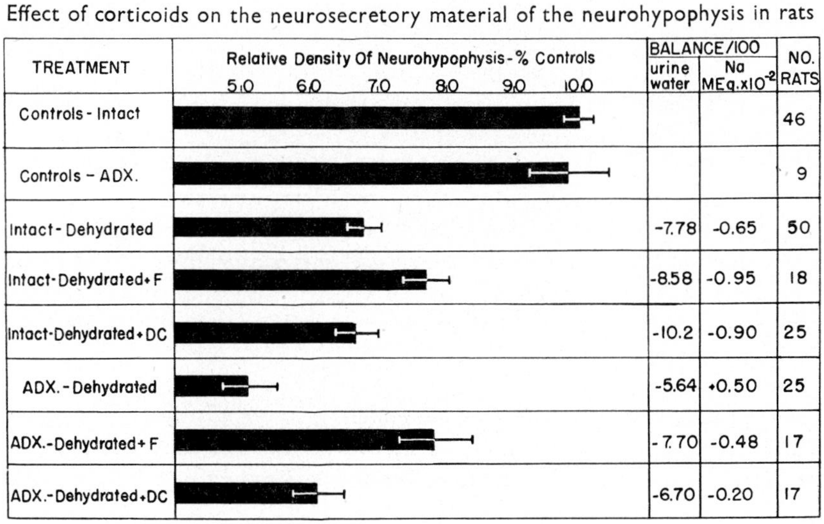

Effect of corticoids on the neurosecretory material of the neurohypophysis in rats

TREATMENT	Relative Density Of Neurohypophysis - % Controls			BALANCE/100		NO. RATS
	5.0 6.0 7.0 8.0 9.0 10.0			urine water	Na MEq.x10⁻²	
Controls - Intact						46
Controls – ADX.						9
Intact - Dehydrated				-7.78	-0.65	50
Intact-Dehydrated + F				-8.58	-0.95	18
Intact-Dehydrated + DC				-10.2	-0.90	25
ADX. - Dehydrated				-5.64	+0.50	25
ADX.-Dehydrated + F				-7.70	-0.48	17
ADX.-Dehydrated + DC				-6.70	-0.20	17

Figure 3

General explanations in text. The term 'Balance/100' represents the excretion of water and sodium greater or less than that administered during the 24-h. dehydration period. Units = ml. or mEq./100 g. body-weight.

There was slight, if any, depletion of neurosecretory material in animals which developed spontaneous severe adrenal insufficiency from 7 to 21 days after operation. This confirms the work of Sawyer & Roth (1953) and Rennels, Russell & Drager, (1955), but it does not agree with the findings of Eichner (1953). Neither did animals adrenalectomized for 18 hr. show any differences from normal controls. Adrenalectomized rats subjected to the 24-hr. dehydrating procedure, however, showed a consistently greater depletion than intact animals (Fig. 3). This was associated with an expected smaller urinary loss of water and sodium than in normal animals.

Hydrocortisone in total doses of 7·5 mg. (acting over a 40-hr. period) prevented depletion clearly in adrenalectomized rats and probably in intact ones ($P = <0·05$). Desoxycorticosterone (free alcohol) was without consistent effect in intact rats; after adrenalectomy it prevented depletion but less effectively than hydrocortisone. In

No food or water was allowed during the experiment. Animals were kept in metabolism cages and the amounts of urine excreted measured at intervals; the amounts of sodium and potassium excreted were determined for the 24-hr. period.

When steroid hormones were given the total dose was divided into three equal parts and injected as follows: at 4 p.m. on the day before the experiment (which was the time of adrenalectomy for operated animals) and with each of the two doses of hypertonic saline. The total dose acted over a 40-hr. period.

Posterior pituitaries were fixed in Zenker-Formol solution, cut at 5µ and stained with Gomori-Halmi-Dawson aldehyde-fuschin. The amounts of neurosecretory material were estimated by averaging the relative density of stainable material in 7 sections (450× magnification) from each gland. The readings, made on a Photovolt Densitometer and expressed in percentage terms, are the figures shown in Fig. 3.

similar experiments 2·5 mg. doses of desoxycorticosterone were without effect and the same amount of hydrocortisone showed only suggestive protection. It is difficult to reconcile these results with the report of Billenstien & Leveque (1955) that desoxycorticosterone facilitates discharge of neurosecretory material from regenerated neurohypophysial tissue of hypophysectomized rats. For some curious reason, however, some intact animals in our series showed unexpectedly great depletion when given desoxycorticosterone. This was not a consistent finding but was possibly related to Billenstien & Leveque's results.

These experiments, together with those cited in the previous section, show that adrenalectomy and steroid hormones affect both the neurohypophysial content of antidiuretic material and the visible substances associated with it. This presumably means either that the corticoids inhibit release of this material, facilitate its synthesis, or both. The choice of interpretation in such a case is one that has plagued students of the hormone-content of glands for many years. Some work pertinent to the question is cited below.

3. *Effect of adrenal hormones on release of antidiuretic hormone.* Ginsburg (1954) provided evidence that adrenalectomy in animals facilitates the release of antidiuretic hormone. In retrospect that interpretation probably best explains previous data of

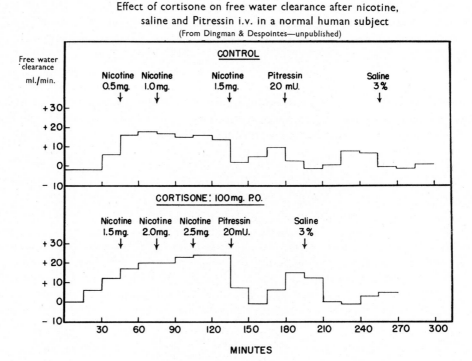

Figure 4

Showing an increased free-water clearance and decreased responsiveness to nicotine under the influence of cortisone (given 105 min. before the test) in a subject maintained under a constant water load of 20 ml./kg.

244

Birnie, *et al.* (1950) in which relatively high levels of circulating antidiuretic activity were associated with blood-withdrawal in adrenalectomized rats. Winter (1952) first stated that cortisone (in contrast to desoxycorticosterone acetate) might inhibit the release of antidiuretic hormone. Recently the work of Dingman (1954), Dingman & Thorn (1955) and Dingman & Despointes (1956) indicates that cortisone, hydrocortisone and their Δ'-analogues have this effect in man.

In studying patients with diabetes insipidus, they concluded that in certain cases hypothalamic centres could release antidiuretic hormone in response to small doses of nicotine when this did not occur in response to hypertonic saline. The antidiuretic response to nicotine was effectively blocked by cortisone given two hours prior to the nicotine. In normal subjects the nicotine-induced decrease in free water clearance was blocked by cortisone, hydrocortisone and prednisolone, whereas that to hypertonic saline and Pitressin was not (Fig. 4). The effects were independent of osmolar or electrolyte excretion. The polyuria induced in diabetes insipidus patients with cortisone was associated with an increased free water clearance. These results, together with those of Sect. IV.*B.*1, are most easily interpreted on the basis that the 17-hydroxycorticoids inhibit some part of the mechanism for the release of the antidiuretic hormone.

V. CONCLUSIONS

A review has been made of work concerned with various possible sites and mechanisms of interaction between the hormones of the neurohypophysis and adrenal cortex. Most of this work has failed to lead to clean-cut conclusions of a widely acceptable sort. To what extent, for instance, the abnormalities of water metabolism in adrenal insufficiency or adrenal hyperfunction are due to some aberrant function of the neurohypophysis is still not clear. Recent work, however, has established several apparently definite facts which, although yet to be fitted into a comprehensive physiological picture, nevertheless represent distinct contributions toward that end. This work, which had its origin in numerous laboratories, may be summarized as follows:

1. Different types of adrenal hormones have different effects on the responses to vasopressin. Vasopressin actions may be antagonized, augmented or unaffected by simultaneous steroid administration, depending upon the nature of the steroid, its dose and the variable measured. Therefore, generalizations in this regard about 'adrenal' influences as such are not appropriate.

2. The hydrocortisone-like adrenal steroids, under experimental conditions at least, either inhibit the release or facilitate the synthesis of antidiuretic hormone and its visible neurosecretory substrate. The former interpretation seems to be the preferred one, although a combination of the two is not excluded. A distinct difference exists, possibly qualitative in nature, between the effects of hydrocortisone and desoxycorticosterone in this respect.

3. The maintenance of the mechanism in various tissues which accounts for the rapid inactivation of antidiuretic hormone is functionally dependent on hydrocortisone-like adrenal steroids.

4. The postulated neurohumoral substance of hypothalamic origin which causes

release of corticotrophin (ACTH) is probably closely related chemically to the known neurohypophysial hormones.

Such findings suggest that the functional 'interrelationship' between the adrenal cortex and neurohypophysis is a many-faceted one. The corticoids apparently affect neurohypophysial activity *per se* but in addition affect the response to neurohypophysial hormones and such related matters as their rate of inactivation. A reciprocal aspect is that ACTH release, and hence certain aspects of adrenal function, is probably under the control of hypothalamic neurohumours closely related to the known neurohypophysial hormones. If all of this is the case, the relationship involved cannot be reduced to terms of simple definition and generalization analogous to those between the trophic hormones and their target glands.

REFERENCES

AMES, R. G. & VAN DYKE, H. B. (1952). Antidiuretic hormone in the serum or plasma of rats. *Endocrinology* **50**, 350–60.

ANSLOW, W. P., Jr. & WESSON, L. G., Jr. (1955). Some effects of pressor-antidiuretic and oxytocic fractions of posterior pituitary extract on sodium, chloride, potassium and ammonium excretion in the dog. *Amer. J. Physiol.* **182**, 561–6.

BECK, J. C., DYRENFURTH, I., GIROUD, C. & VENNING, E. H. (1955). Observations on the regulatory mechanisms of aldosterone secretion in man. *Arch. intern. Med.* **96**, 463–9.

BILLENSTIEN, D. C. & LEVEQUE, T. F. (1955). The reorganization of the neurohypophyseal stalk following hypophysectomy in the rat. *Endocrinology* **56**, 704–17.

BIRNIE, J. H., EVERSOLE, W. J., BOSS, W. R., OSBORN, C. M. & GAUNT, R. (1950). An antidiuretic substance in the blood of normal and adrenalectomized rats. *Endocrinology* **47**, 1–12.

BIRNIE, J. H. (1953). The inactivation of posterior pituitary antidiuretic hormone by liver extracts. *Endocrinology* **42**, 33–8.

BLACK, D. A. K. & THOMPSON, A. E. (1951). Day-to-day changes in sodium and water output with and without posterior pituitary extract. *Clin. Sci.* **10**, 511–20.

BOSS, W. R., BIRNIE, J. H. & GAUNT, R. (1950). Renal factors in the adrenal cortical control of water metabolism. *Endocrinology* **46**, 307–13.

CAVALLERO, C., DOVA, E. & ROSSI, L. (1954). Antidiuretic activity in the neurohypophysis of rats after adrenalectomy and replacement therapy. *J. Endocr.* **10**, 228–37.

CHALMERS, T. M. & LEWIS, A. A. G. (1951). The effect of adrenocorticotropic hormone on the diuretic response to water in panhypopituitarism. *Lancet* **ii**, 1158–60.

CHALMERS, T. M., LEWIS, A. A. G. & PAWAN, G. L. S. (1951). The effect of posterior pituitary extracts on the renal excretion of sodium and chloride in man. *J. Physiol. (Lond.)* **112**, 238–42.

HESTER JONES, I. (1956). The role of the adrenal cortex in the control of water and salt-electrolyte metabolism in vertebrates. *Mem. Soc. Endocrin.* **5**, 102–20. Ed. Chester Jones, I. & Eckstein, P. Cambridge: University Press.

OLE, D. F. (1955). The excretion of intravenously administered saline by the rat. *Acta endocr. (Kbh.)* **19**, 397–405.

CONN, J. W. (1955). Primary aldosteronism, a new clinical syndrome. *J. Lab. clin. Med.* **45**, 3–17.

CORCORAN, A. C. & DUSTAN, H. P. (1956). Central society for clinical research. *Lancet* i, 50.

COREY, E. L. & BRITTON, S. W. (1941). The antagonistic action of desoxycorticosterone and post-pituitary extract on chloride and water balance. *Amer. J. Physiol.* **133**, 511–19.

DAVIS, J. O. & HOWELL, D. S. (1953). Comparative effect of ACTH, cortisone and DCA on renal function, electrolyte excretion and water exchange in normal dogs. *Endocrinology* **52**, 245–55.

DAVIS, J. O., HOWELL, D. S. & HYATT, R. E. (1954). Effect of chronic Pitressin administration on electrolyte excretion in normal dogs and in dogs with experimental ascites. *Endocrinology* **55**, 409–16.

DIAMOND, M. C. (1952). Antidiuretic activity of rat hypothalamus and neurohypophysis. *Amer. J. Physiol.* **171,** 719.

DINGMAN, J. F. (1954). Selective failure of osmoreceptor function as a cause of diabetes insipidus. *Fed. Proc.* **13,** 36.

DINGMAN, J. F. & DESPOINTES, R. H. (1956). Hypothalamic action of adrenal steroids. *J. clin. Endocr. Metab.* **16,** 936-7.

DINGMAN, J. F. & THORN, G. W. (1955). Cortisone inhibition of ADH secretion from the neurohypophysis. *J. clin. Endocr. Metab.* **15,** 871-2.

DUSTAN, H. P., CORCORAN, A. C. & FARRELL, G. L. (1955). The renal water concentration defect in primary aldosteronism: differentiation from diabetes insipidus. *J. Lab. clin. Med.* **46,** 809-10.

VAN DYKE, H. B., ADAMSONS, K., Jr. & ENGEL, S. L. (1955). Aspects of the biochemistry and physiology of the neurohypophyseal hormones. *Recent Progr. Hormone Res.* **11,** 1-35.

EICHNER, D. (1953) Über den morphologischen Ausdruck funktioneller Beziehungen zwischen Nebennierenrinde und neurosekretorischem Zwischenhirnsystem der Ratte. *Z. Zellforch.* **38,** 488-508.

GARROD, O., DAVIES, S. A. & CAHILL, G., Jr. (1955). The action of cortisone and desoxycorticosterone acetate on glomerular filtration rate and sodium and water exchange in the adrenalectomized dog. *J. clin. Invest.* **34,** 761-76.

GAUNT, R. (1951). The adrenal cortex in salt and water metabolism. *Recent Progr. Hormone Res.* **6,** 247-68.

GAUNT, R., BIRNIE, J. H. & EVERSOLE, W. J. (1949). Adrenal cortex in water metabolism. *Physiol. Rev.* **29,** 281-310.

GAUNT, R., CHART, J. J. & ANTONCHAK, B. (1956). Effect of adrenal hormones on the neurosecretory material of the neurohypophysis. *J. clin. Endocr. Metab.* **16,** 915.

GAUNT, R., RENZI, A. A. & CHART, J. J. (1955). Aldosterone—a review. *J. clin. Endocr. Metab.* **15,** 621-46.

GINSBURG, M. (1954). The secretion of antidiuretic hormone in response to haemorrhage and the fate of vasopressin in adrenalectomized rats. *J. Endocr.* **11,** 165-76.

GUILLEMIN, R. & HEARN, W. R. (1955). ACTH release by *in vitro* pituitary. Effect of Pitressin and purified arginine-vasopressin. *Proc. Soc. exper. Biol.* (*N.Y.*) **89,** 365-6.

GUILLEMIN, R., HEARN, W. R., CHEEK, W. R. & HOUSHOLDER, D. E. (1956). Isolation from the hypothalamus of a substance which stimulates release of ACTH *in vitro*. *Fed. Proc.* **15,** 84.

GUILLEMIN, R. & ROSENBERG, B. (1955). Humoral hypothalamic control of anterior pituitary: a study with combined tissue cultures. *Endocrinology* **57,** 599-607.

HARRIS, J. F., LLOYD, C. W. & LOBOTSKY, J. (1953). Some studies of posterior pituitary and adrenal cortical interrelationships in patients with and without cirrhosis of the liver. *J. clin. Invest.* **32,** 885-98.

HELLER, H. (1952). The influence of the suprarenal cortex on mineral and water metabolism. In *The Suprarenal Cortex.* Ed. Yoffey, J. M. Proc. Colston Res. Soc. 5th Symposium. London: Butterworth.

HOLLAND, B. C. & STEAD, E. A. (1951). Effect of vasopressin (Pitressin^R)-induced water retention on sodium excretion. *Arch. intern. Med.* **88,** 571-80.

IKKOS, D., LUFT, R. & OLIVECRONA, H. (1955). Hypophysectomy in man: effect on water excretion during the first two postoperative months. *J. clin. Endocr. Metab.* **15,** 553-67.

INGLE, D. J. & LI, C. H. (1955). Effect of pituitary extracts upon the work performance of adrenalectomized-hypophysectomized rats: identification of vasopressin as a principle affecting work. *Endocrinology* **57,** 383-90.

ITOH, S. & ARIMURA, A. (1954). Effect of posterior pituitary hormone on the release of adrenocorticotrophic hormone. *Nature* (*Lond.*) **174,** 37.

KIMURA, M. (1954). Influence of antidiuretic hormone on adrenal cortical activity in rats. *Jap. J. Physiol.* **4,** 24-31.

KRIEGER, V. I. & KILVINGTON, T. B. (1940). Antidiuretic substance in urine in relation to normal and toxaemic pregnancy. *Med. J. Aust.* **1,** 575-85.

LAUSON, H. D. (1951). The problem of estimating the rate of secretion of antidiuretic hormone in man. *Amer. J. Med.* **11,** 135-56.

LEAF, A. & MAMBY, A. R. (1952). An antidiuretic mechanism not regulated by extracellular fluid tonicity. *J. clin. Invest.* **31,** 60-71.

LEAF, A., BARTTER, F. C., SANTOS, R. F. & WRONG, O. (1953). Evidence in man that urinary electrolyte loss induced by Pitressin is a function of water retention. *J. clin. Invest.* **32,** 868–78.

LLOYD, C. W. (1952). Some clinical aspects of adrenal cortical and fluid metabolism. *Recent Progr. Hormone Res.* **7,** 469–500.

LLOYD, C. W. & OLDFORD, P. (1955). Studies of the antidiuretic content of the hypothalamus of intact and hypophysectomized rats. *J. clin. Endocr. Metab.* **15,** 873.

LLOYD, C. W. & PIEROG, S. (1955). Studies of the antidiuretic activity of blood and hypothalamus of hypophysectomized rats. *Endocrinology* **56,** 718–26.

LOCKETT, M. F. (1952). Preliminary studies on the sensitivity of adrenalectomized dogs to the antidiuretic hormone of the posterior pituitary gland. *Ciba Foundation Colloquia on Endocrinology* **4,** 517–24. London: Churchill.

MARTINI, L. & MORPURGO, C. (1955). Neurohumoral control of the release of adrenocorticotrophic hormone. *Nature (Lond.)* **175,** 1127–8.

MAXWELL, M. H. & BREED, E. S. (1951). The effect of the intravenous administration of Pitressin on renal function in man. *J. Pharmacol.* **103,** 190–5.

McCANN, S. M. & BROBECK, J. R. (1954). Evidence for a role of the supraoptico-hypophyseal system in regulation of adrenocorticotrophin secretion. *Proc. Soc. exper. Biol. (N.Y.)* **87,** 318–24.

MIRSKY, I. A., STEIN, M. & PAULISCH, G. (1954a). The antidiuretic activity of the plasma of adrenalectomized, hypophysectomized and adrenalectomized-hypophysectomized rats. *Endocrinology* **54,** 691–7.

MIRSKY, I. A., STEIN, M. & PAULISCH, G. (1954b). The secretion of an antidiuretic substance into the circulation of adrenalectomized and hypophysectomized rats exposed to noxious stimuli. *Endocrinology* **55,** 28–39.

MONTASTRUC, P. (1954). *Régulation hormonale du métabolisme de l'eau.* Toulouse: Laboratoire de Physiologie de la Faculté de Médecine de Toulouse.

MOREL, F. (1955). Quelques aspects de la régulation endocrinienne de l'équilibre hydrominéral enregistrés chez le rat à l'aide du radio-sodium Na^{24}. *Suppl. Bull. biol. France Belg.* **39,** 1–110.

MUNSON, P. L. & BRIGGS, F. N. (1955). The mechanism of stimulation of ACTH secretion. *Recent Progr. Hormone Res.* **11,** 83–117.

MURPHY, R. J. F. (1950). Studies on the mechanisms of saline diuresis. *J. clin. Invest.* **29,** 836.

NAGAREDA, C. S. & GAUNT, R. (1951). Functional relationship between the adrenal cortex and posterior pituitary. *Endocrinology* **48,** 560–7.

PITTS, R. F. (1952). Effects of adrenal cortical hormones on renal function. *Third Conference on Adrenal Cortex,* Josiah Macy, Jr. Foundation, New York. Caldwell, N. J.: Progress Associates.

PORTER, J. C. & RUMSFELD, H. W., Jr. (1956). Effect of lyophilized plasma and plasma fractions from hypophyseal-portal vessel blood on adrenal ascorbic acid. *Endocrinology* **58,** 359–64.

RAGAN, C., FERREBEE, J. W., PFYFE, P., ATCHLEY, D. W. & LOEB, R. F. (1940). A syndrome of polydipsia and polyuria induced in normal animals by desoxycorticosterone acetate. *Amer. J. Physiol.* **131,** 73–8.

RENNELS, E. G., RUSSELL, G. V. & DRAGER, G. A. (1955). A comparison of pituitary content of oxytocic hormone and the amount of Gomori-positive neurosecretion under normal and experimental conditions. *Anat. Rec.* **121,** 355.

RENZI, A. A., RENZI, M., CHART, J. J. & GAUNT, R. (1956). The effects of aldosterone and other steroids on water intoxication and renal function. *Acta endocr. (Kbh.)* **21,** 47–56.

ROSENBAUM, J. D., DAVIS, R. K. & FERGUSON, B. C. (1951). The influence of cortisone on water diuresis in man. *J. clin. Invest.* **30,** 668.

SAFFRAN, M., SCHALLY, A. V. & BENFEY, B. G. (1955). Stimulation of the release of corticotropin from the adenohypophysis by a neurohypophysial factor. *Endocrinology* **57,** 439–44.

SALA, G., SERENI, F. & BALLABIO, C. B. (1951). Effect of cortisone on water metabolism. *Lancet* **ii,** 1090.

SARTORIUS, O. W. & ROBERTS, K. (1949). The effects of Pitressin and desoxycorticosterone in low dosage on the excretion of sodium, potassium and water by the normal dog. *Endocrinology* **45,** 273–83.

SAWYER, W. H. & ROTH, W. D. (1933). Neurohypophyseal function in dehydrated and adrenalectomized rats as indicated by hormone assay and neurosecretory activity. *Fed. Proc.* **12,** 125.

SAYERS, G. & BURKS, R. (1955). Pitressin and blood ACTH in adrenalectomized rats. *J. clin. Endocr. Metab.* **15,** 840–1.

SCHARRER, E. & SCHARRER, B. (1954). Hormones produced by neurosecretory cells. *Recent Progr. Hormone Res.* **10,** 183–232.

SELKURT, E. E. (1954). Sodium excretion by the mammalian kidney. *Physiol. Rev.* **34,** 287–333.

SHIBUSAWA, K., SAITO, S., FUKUDA, M., KAWAI, T. & YOSHIMURA, F. (1955). On the role of the hypothalamic-neurohypophyseal neurosecretion in the liberation of the adenohypophyseal hormones. *Endocr. Japon.* **2,** 47–56.

SILVETTE, H. & BRITTON, S. W. (1938). Renal function in opossum and mechanism of cortico-adrenal and postpituitary action. *Amer. J. Physiol.* **123,** 630–69.

SKILLERN, P. G., CORCORAN, A. C. & SCHERBEL, A. L. (1956). Renal mechanisms in coincident Addison's disease and diabetes insipidus: effects of vasopressin and hydrocortisone. *J. clin. Endocr. Metab.* **16,** 171–82.

SLESSOR, A. (1951). Studies concerning the mechanism of water retention in Addison's disease and in hypopituitarism. *J. clin. Endocr.* **2,** 700–23.

SOBEL, H., LEVY, R. S., MARMORSTON, J., SCHAPIRO, S. & ROSENFELD, S. (1955). Increased excretion of urinary corticoids by guinea pigs following administration of Pitressin. *Proc. Soc. exper. Biol. (N.Y.)* **89,** 10–3.

STRIBLING, S. H. & SPURR, C. L. (1954). Polydipsia as a mechanism for the production of cortisone 'diuresis'. *J. Lab. clin. Med.* **44,** 936–7.

SWINGLE, W. W., BRANNICK, L. J., BARRETT, W., LEBRIE, S. J. & PAVLOW, A. F. (1956). A histamine-like component of commercial Pitressin. *Proc. Soc. exper. Biol. (N.Y.)* **91,** 223–6. (Footnote, p. 225.)

SWINGLE, W. W., FEDOR, E. J., BEN, M., MAXWELL, R., BAKER, C. & BARLOW, G. (1953). Induction of diabetes insipidus in adrenalectomized dogs with cortisone. *Proc. Soc. exper. Biol. (N.Y.)* **82,** 571–3.

WINTER, C. A. (1952). Comparison of the effect of cortisone acetate and of desoxycorticosterone acetate upon water balance. *Ciba Foundation Colloquia on Endocrinology* **4,** 499–514. London: Churchill.

Discussion

Chairman: H. B. van Dyke

Chalmers. I would like to ask a question concerning Dr. Lloyd's findings, and that is whether the antidiuretic material was depleted in the adrenalectomized animals treated with DCA?

Lloyd. We adrenalectomized animals leaving them for a week on 1 per cent. salt and then did measurements of the antidiuretic hormone content of the hypothalamus and posterior lobe and could not show any real decrease. We then decided that in order to get more definite changes we had to expose the animals to more severe conditions. We put the animals on a salt-free diet and found that we did get a reasonable depletion of the hormone content and with hydrocortisone we got a repletion. We now have got about seven animals in each group, that is to say animals which have been on desoxycorticosterone trimethylacetate plus salt and animals maintained on salt alone. These animals were maintained for as long as three weeks; there was moderate depletion but not nearly as great a depletion as in the animals which are allowed to become insufficient. We have now a few experiments with animals given DCA, and in contrast to cortisone we found very little increase in the antidiuretic activity in the hypothalamus or posterior lobe.

van Dyke. Do you feel that you have secured a significant lowering of the antidiuretic titres in the hypothalamus?

Lloyd. For fifteen observations the standard error is less than ± 20 per cent.

Bargmann. Did you get depletion after total adrenalectomy? Eichner (*Z. Zellforsch.* **37**, 406, 1953) obtained remarkable depletion of the neural lobe eighteen hours after adrenalectomy and I remember that Malandra and Corbetta (*Z. Zellforsch.* **39**, 318, 1953) also observed some depletion.

Gaunt. We are aware that some but not all others had found depletion after simple adrenalectomy. We did not. The difference might depend upon the handling or strain of animals. Certainly the adrenalectomized animal is susceptible to depletion after a stimulus such as dehydration.

Heller. I wonder if these observations do not fall into place when one considers the results of Ginsburg (*J. Endocr.* **11**, 165, 1954) who showed that haemorrhage is a more potent stimulus for hormone release from the neurohypophysis in adrenalectomized rats than in normal animals. Dehydration seems also to be a more potent stimulus after adrenalectomy.

Rossi. Dr. Gaunt stated that a stress by injection of formalin induced a marked depletion of antidiuretic hormone from the neurohypophysis. I should like to point out that in experiments which we have done in Prof. Heller's department (Cavallero, Dova & Rossi, *J. Endocr.* **10**, 228, 1954) we observed a similar depletion of the hormone through the stress of sham-adrenalectomy but this depletion disappeared within three to five days after the operation. Concerning Dr. Lloyd's report about the incomplete recovery of the antidiuretic hormone content in the neurohypophysis of adrenalectomized rats treated with compound F and sodium chloride, I would like to recall that we failed to find in the neurohypophysis of adrenalectomized rats after 5–7 days treatment with cortisone and salt any significant decrease in antidiuretic hormone as compared with normal control.

Garrod. I would like to ask Dr. Gaunt a question regarding the experiment in which hydrocortisone was limiting the antidiuresis from Pitressin. Has he got any evidence to suggest whether this is a direct antagonism at the renal tubular level or merely secondary to a rise in G.F.R.?

Gaunt. In our experiments direct renal effects of the steroids could theoretically have explained the results. We did not do the measurements to find out. However, in some experiment not considered here today, we got similar effect of steroids under conditions in which we could not detect (with our techniques) changes in G.F.R.

Reiss. Dr. Gaunt has raised the question as to whether the antagonism he has found between hydrocortisone and the antidiuretic hormone has any physiological significance. I would rather suggest that it has. We can show it in psychiatric cases, particularly in depressive patients who excrete very little urine. We have seen some who excrete only 220 ml. urine per day. If the depression improves, the rate of urine excretion goes up by about one thousand per cent. In such cases we have measured the rate of hydrocortisone excretion and found that when they excrete very little urine, there is only very little hydrocortisone in the urine, and when they recover there is an enormous increase in 17-ketosteroid output.

Heller. Returning to the question of the hormone content of the neural lobe in adrenalectomized rats: Dr. Gaunt mentioned that some workers found an increase and others a decrease. If I remember rightly Sawyer (Sawyer & Roth, *Fed. Proc.* **12,** 125, 1953) for example, measured the oxytocic content. That was at a time when we were not aware that the hormones may be secreted separately and I think that his results may have to be regarded in that light.

Sawyer. That is absolutely right. Another point is that our laboratory diet appears to have been relatively high in sodium content and when these adrenalectomized rats were maintained on this diet and tap water, they survived for about two weeks. They do lose a lot of weight and the plasma sodium levels are extremely low. The hormone content of the neural lobe, granted they were oxytocic assays, increased.

In the earlier part you were talking about the enhancement of natriuresis with compound F. Is this an effect of compound F itself, or an enhancement of the action of Pitressin?.

Gaunt. Compound F will have the effect when given alone but it is greater when given with Pitressin.

de Wardener. I wonder if the adrenal is concerned with the finding that in dehydration the concentration of the urine is greater than after giving Pitressin. This discrepancy becomes more marked with increasing hydration until in the case of obsessional polydipsia the patient may no longer be able to concentrate above the osmolarity of plasma however much Pitressin is given.

Gaunt. I do not know anything about such chronic states—if one hydrates with distilled water acutely, an adrenal ascorbic acid depletion occurs. Similar volumes of normal saline will not have any effect on this measure of adrenal activity.

Ginsburg. I am not happy about antidiuretic assays on gland extracts which may contain variable amounts of oxytocin, particularly if these assays were done on rats. It has been shown that the oxytocic principle can have a diuretic effect in rats and if the oxytocin content is changing in some unknown way, it may effect the antidiuretic assay. The other point I wish to make concerns Dr. Gaunt's use of the word 'inactivation' when referring to my work on the fate of Pitressin in adrenalectomized animals. I would rather say 'clearance'. All that I could show was that after injection of a large dose of vasopressin the activity disappeared from the blood rather more slowly than in normal animals. I do not know anything about what happened to the vasopressin when it was taken up by the inactivating tissues. As to the physiological significance of this observation, I was very careful about its interpretation because it seemed to be possible that it may be due to a vascular effect: if for example the renal vessels were very much more sensitive to the vasoconstrictor action of Pitressin in the adrenalectomized animal that could account for the failure of the kidneys to take up the material.

van Dyke. Does oxytocin have a diuretic effect after intravenous injection?

Ginsburg. I do not know. It has after subcutaneous injection but I do not think it has been tried after intravenous injection in rats.

Comparative aspects of adrenocortical-neurohypophysial relationships

by

I. CHESTER JONES

Department of Zoology, University of Liverpool

EVOLUTION of the vertebrates has been accompanied by elaboration of mechanisms which tend to preserve homeostasis. One essential attribute of the successful vertebrate, or of the Craniata at least, is the capacity to regulate water and ionic exchange. The Myxinoidea apart, which maintain in their plasma concentrations of inorganic ions equivalent to those of the surrounding sea-water (Robertson, 1954), members of the different vertebrate classes enjoy a constancy of internal medium, thereby withstanding the vicissitudes of environments varying from total immersion in fresh water to the dehydration of the desert. From consideration of experimental work on a few species of mammals, principally of the Eutheria, two glands of internal secretion, namely the adrenal cortex and the neurohypophysis (and associated hypothalamic centres) have been assigned a major role in that equipage of the vertebrate body which maintains internal steadiness in the face of external change. How far we are justified in extending the argument from mammals to include all vertebrates is not sure and there is little work in the field to help us (Chester Jones 1956*a*, *b*). Some of this work I shall discuss later. I should like in the first place, however, to consider some of the facts in the rat, an animal on which much of our knowledge is based. This part may be regarded as an appendix to Dr. Gaunt's excellent paper in which he and his colleagues have clearly shown the present position of the problem of adrenocortical-neurohypophysial relationships in mammals and have adduced helpful new data.

MAMMALIAN STUDIES

I have used rats from which the posterior lobe of the pituitary was removed. Neurohypophysectomy was done by the parapharyngeal approach and the posterior lobe removed without manifest disturbance of the anterior lobe of the pituitary. All such operated animals developed a marked polyuria, the water intake varying between 5 to 9 times that of the normal animal. This 'temporary' phase of diabetes insipidus lasted for up to three weeks when there was a decline. The water intake of many animals fell to that of normal rats. In the minority the decline was not so great, steadying at a water intake of 4 to 5 times the intake of normal animals and maintaining this level for up to three post-operative months, beyond which I have not kept them. Such animals are regarded as having 'permanent' diabetes insipidus. Examination of sections of the pituitary and hypothalamus of the rat with permanent diabetes insipidus reveals an anterior lobe of normal appearance and degeneration of the hypothalamic supraoptic and paraventricular nuclei.

Apart from the polyuria (the specific gravity of the urine being $1 \cdot 007 \pm 0 \cdot 003$, compared with the normal figure of $1 \cdot 051 \pm 0 \cdot 004$) the rats with diabetes insipidus show no obvious physiological abnormalities. Thus, the growth rate is unaltered: for example one group of 34 male rats weighed $151 \cdot 3 \pm 2 \cdot 7$ g. at operation and $213 \cdot 4 \pm 4 \cdot 4$ g., 48 days later, while the control group of 22 rats weighed $192 \pm 4 \cdot 4$ g. and $257 \cdot 1 \pm 5 \cdot 2$ g. over the same period. In female rats with diabetes insipidus the oestrous cycle is of normal duration. For example, one group of 7 females with 'permanent' diabetes insipidus investigated for a month had a mean body-weight of $202 \cdot 95 \pm 2 \cdot 4$ g., a food intake per 24 hr. of $16 \cdot 13 \pm 0 \cdot 18$ g., a water intake per 24-hr. period of $91 \cdot 92 \pm 1 \cdot 09$ ml. and a mean duration of oestrous cycle of $5 \cdot 2$ days. Six female controls over the same period gave, body-weight $229 \cdot 50 \pm 2 \cdot 24$ g., food intake $14 \cdot 82 \pm 0 \cdot 31$ g., water intake $21 \cdot 06 \pm 0 \cdot 75$ ml., and oestrous cycle of 5 days' duration. It seems reasonable to suppose that any physiological difference found to exist between normal rats and rats with diabetes insipidus would depend primarily on the increase in fluid exchange of the latter.

TABLE I

The adrenal weights of male and female rats with diabetes insipidus
compared with those of control animals
(Means $\pm$ standard error.)

	n	body-weight g.	adrenal weight mg./100 g. body-weight
(a) Neurohypophysectomized for one to two weeks			
Males with diabetes insipidus	19	$210 \cdot 52 \pm 5 \cdot 14$	$25 \cdot 23 \pm 1 \cdot 02$
Control males	39	$224 \cdot 59 \pm 2 \cdot 19$	$15 \cdot 61 \pm 0 \cdot 78$
Females with diabetes insipidus	10	$184 \cdot 50 \pm 3 \cdot 97$	$48 \cdot 81 \pm 2 \cdot 14$
Control females	19	$193 \cdot 42 \pm 5 \cdot 20$	$32 \cdot 07 \pm 1 \cdot 29$
(b) Neurohypophysectomized for two to three months			
Males with diabetes insipidus	28	$233 \cdot 75 \pm 6 \cdot 96$	$16 \cdot 29 \pm 0 \cdot 76$
Control males	20	$257 \cdot 20 \pm 5 \cdot 48$	$12 \cdot 15 \pm 0 \cdot 39$
Females with diabetes insipidus	6	$207 \cdot 83 \pm 12 \cdot 45$	$37 \cdot 73 \pm 1 \cdot 97$
Control females	12	$198 \cdot 25 \pm 5 \cdot 08$	$31 \cdot 10 \pm 1 \cdot 27$

One difference is that the adrenal weights of male and female rats with either 'temporary' or 'permanent' diabetes insipidus are greater than those of the glands from control animals; this is statistically significant $(P > 0 \cdot 001)$ (Table I). Histological sections of these enlarged adrenals (Plate I, nos. 1–6) show that the zona glomerulosa is narrow or absent. The zona fasciculata runs right up to the outer connective tissue capsule or, in other cases, a narrow zone of compact cells, probably

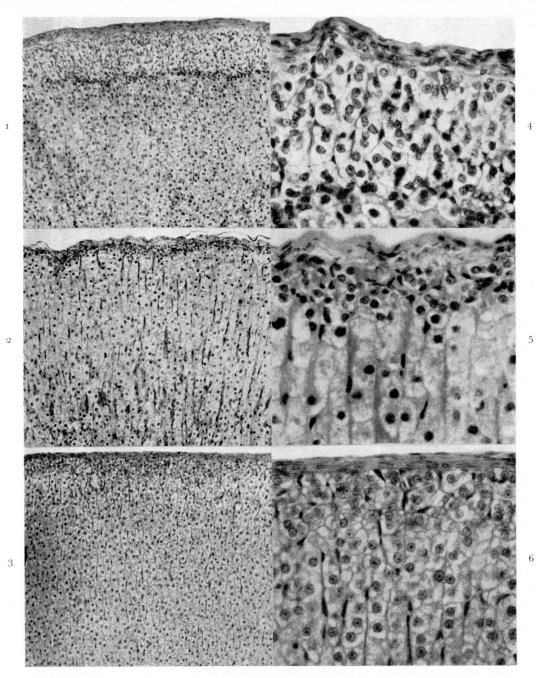

Plate 1

Photographs of part of the adrenal cortices of female rats in different experimental conditions (Bouin; H. & E.).

1. Normal. The outer connective tissue capsule, the zona glomerulosa, the zona intermedia and the outer zona fasciculata can be seen (×150).

2. Diabetes insipidus. A narrow zona glomerulosa intervenes between the capsule and the hypertrophied zona fasciculata (×150).

3. Normal, injected with 5 I.U. ACTH (long-acting, Armour) per day for 3 days. A narrow zona glomerulosa intervenes between the capsule and the hypertrophied zona fasciculata (×150).

4. Part of (1). The normal zona glomerulosa (×440).

5. Part of (2). The narrow zona glomerulosa lying between the capsule and the zona fasciculata (×440).

6. Part of (3). The narrow zona glomerulosa obtained after ACTH injection (×440).

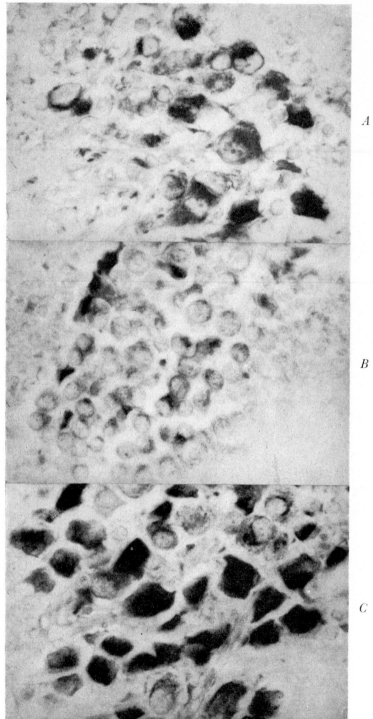

A

B

C

representing the zona glomerulosa and sometimes the zona intermedia, intervenes (Plate I, nos. 2 and 5: Chester Jones & Wright, 1954; Chester Jones, 1956*b*). The same effect can be obtained by injecting ACTH into normal rats (Plate I, nos. 3 and 6). It seems that rising titres of ACTH in the intact animal are accompanied by enlargement of the zona fasciculata and by diminution of the zona glomerulosa. This has been seen by other workers (Selye & Stone, 1950; Baker, 1952; Tonutti, Bahner & Muschke, 1954; Krohn, 1955). On the basis of weight change and histology the adrenal cortex of the rat with diabetes insipidus may be regarded as hyperactive. Baisset, Douste-Blazy, Planel & Montastruc (1954) come to a similar conclusion for dogs with experimental diabetes insipidus.

The consequences of adrenalectomy of the rat are well known and these must be due in large measure to the absence of corticosteroids. In addition, it has been suggested that the secretion of the posterior lobe of the pituitary and associated hypothalamic centres, now uninfluenced by cortical hormones, contributes to the enhanced renal reabsorption of water and to the increased sodium loss so characteristic of the adrenalectomized eutherian mammal (Gaunt, 1951). On this hypothesis it was to be expected that differences might be found between, on the one hand, adrenalectomized control animals which have antidiuretic hormone but no adrenocortical hormones and, on the other, adrenalectomized rats with 'permanent' diabetes insipidus which have no, or minimal, antidiuretic hormone and no adrenocortical hormones. Such proved to be the case (Table II). Control animals and rats

TABLE II

Changes in the sodium and potassium concentration of plasma and muscle following adrenalectomy of female rats with and without diabetes insipidus

(Means ± standard error.)

Group	*n*	Body-weight g.	Plasma mEq./l. Na	Plasma mEq./l. K	Muscle mEq./kg. wet wt. Na	Muscle mEq./kg. wet wt. K	Muscle per cent. water
Controls	12	190·63 ±4·94	148·36 ±4·22	4·96 ±0·22	23·39 ±0·31	100·26 ±0·99	75·43 ±0·33
Diabetes insipidus for 2 to 3 months	9	176·85 ±2·61	146·40 ±1·81	4·93 ±0·19	25·95 ±1·48	99·26 ±1·63	75·78 ±0·29
Controls, adrenalectomized for 8 days	12	189·88 ±5·90	131·85 ±2·70	7·84 ±0·13	18·33 ±1·49	110·08 ±1·92	76·60 ±0·39
Diabetes insipidus, adrenalectomized for 8 days	10	196·50 ±5·50	146·16 ±3·10	6·03 ±0·18	19·68 ±0·60	105·18 ±1·82	76·00 ±0·67

with diabetes insipidus had similar values for sodium and potassium content of plasma and muscle. Control adrenalectomized animals showed a fall in sodium content and an increase in potassium content of plasma and muscle, generally found in the adrenalectomized eutherian. Adrenalectomy of rats with diabetes insipidus was not followed, however, by a fall in plasma sodium content, the figure being of the same order as that found in control animals; the amount of plasma and muscle potassium was increased above normal values though in neither was the increase as great as that occurring in the adrenalectomized controls. The sodium content of the muscle of adrenalectomized rats with diabetes insipidus did not decline to the same extent as in adrenalectomized controls but the figure is clearly less than that for normals. The water content of muscle increased after adrenalectomy, a little more in the adrenalectomized controls than in the adrenalectomized rats with diabetes insipidus, but this difference is not statistically significant. This finding of normal sodium values for the blood of adrenalectomized rats with diabetes insipidus confirms those of Winter and his co-workers (Winter, Gross & Ingram, 1938; Ingram & Winter, 1938; Winter, Ingram, Gross & Sattler, 1941) for the cat adrenalectomized after the establishment of diabetes insipidus. It seems that the rat, in the absence of both adrenocortical and antidiuretic hormones, is able to conserve sodium, to some extent, even in the face of a continued excretion of an appreciable amount of water: the intake of the adrenalectomized rat with diabetes insipidus being about twice that of the normal animal per 24 hr. (see below). It may be that the enzyme systems in the tubular epithelium concerned with the active transport of sodium can function without these two types of hormone which modify but do not initiate their activity. Injection of posterior lobe hormones into adrenalectomized rats with diabetes insipidus brought about a decline in plasma sodium content but, in the doses used, also produced terminal symptoms which are in any case associated with sodium loss. Experiments to demonstrate whether oxytocin or vasopressin or both will lower the normal levels of plasma sodium in adrenalectomized rats with diabetes insipidus when still in good health are in progress.

Further evidence for differences in capacity for sodium conservation between adrenalectomized controls and adrenalectomized rats with diabetes insipidus is given by 24-hr. metabolic studies. The rat with 'permanent' diabetes insipidus eats about the same amount or a little more per 24 hr. than the normal animal and drinks four to five times as much (Fig. 1). After adrenalectomy of both kinds of animal the food intake declines sharply and then mounts slowly (Fig. 2) and falls precipitously before death. The water intake of the diabetes insipidus animal drops to about half after adrenalectomy (Fig. 1). Adrenalectomy of control animals is followed by either unchanged water intake or a slightly increased one. Both control and diabetes insipidus animals are in sodium and potassium balance. Adrenalectomized controls have a negative sodium and a positive potassium balance. In the adrenalectomized rat with diabetes insipidus there is some sodium loss up to 48 hr. after operation, this then becomes small; retention of potassium is not so marked as in the adrenalectomized controls. Figure 2, in which the ratio of sodium to potassium excreted is plotted against time, illustrates this trend.

The substitution of saline for tap-water to drink keeps both the adrenalectomized and the adrenalectomized rat with diabetes insipidus in apparently good health. Rats

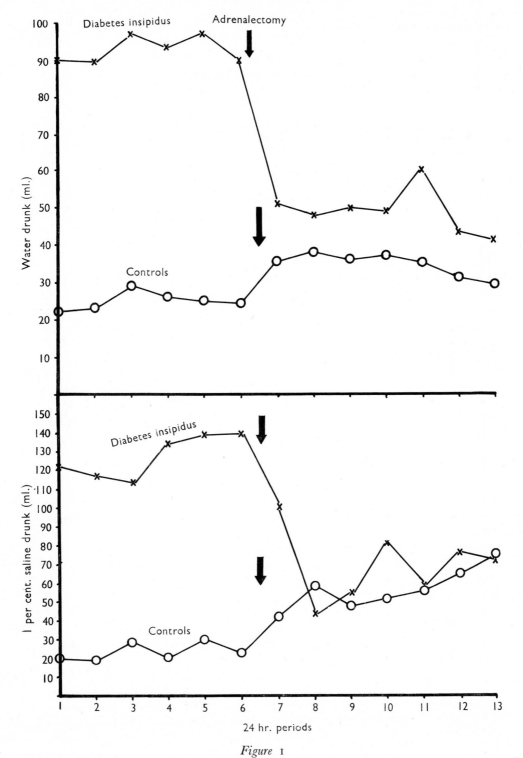

Figure 1

The amount of water and of saline drunk by normal rats and those with diabetes insipidus before and after adrenalectomy plotted against time.

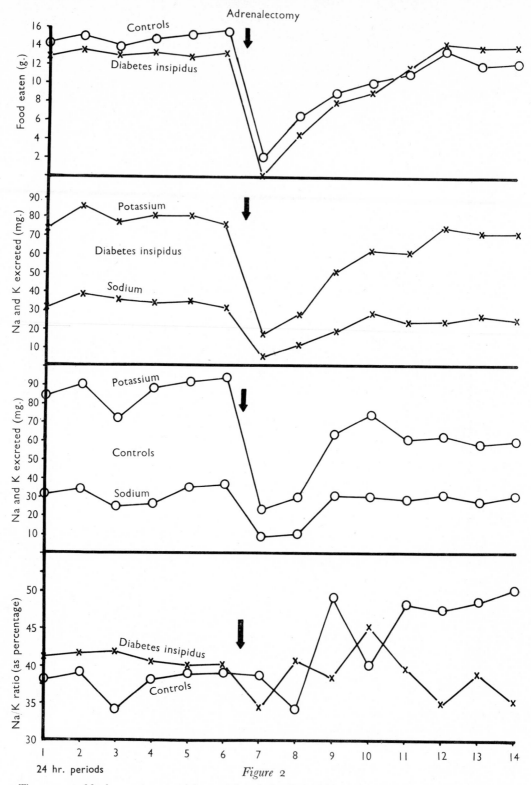

Figure 2

The amount of food eaten (commercial rat cake) and of sodium and potassium excreted by normal rats and those with diabetes insipidus, before and after adrenalectomy plotted against time; the bottom graph gives the ratio of Na to K excreted under these conditions.

with diabetes insipidus drink large quantities of saline before operation and although the intake drops immediately after operation, it then increases (Fig. 1) and can reach high figures. Most control animals drink about the same amount of saline as they do of tap-water but after adrenalectomy such animals match the adrenalectomized rats with diabetes insipidus in saline intake. Constant ingestion of saline keeps the distribution of electrolytes in the body at or near normal levels, presumably by osmotic means, and in the tubule may facilitate potassium excretion. It is probable that secretion of antidiuretic hormone in adrenalectomized controls has little relevance in the reactions to saline ingestion. In both types of animal the paramount factor is the absence of adrenocortical hormones, the rise in glomerular filtration rate, the large amount of sodium transported by the renal tubule and the tendency to dehydration.

The reactions of an animal to daily intake of food and water offered freely and those to an administered load differ widely. Loading rats by stomach tube with different solutions is a method whereby some aspects of hormonal competence can be assessed against a background of renal dynamics, not themselves easy of resolution. I used the method of giving either water or hypertonic saline or hypertonic potassium chloride to various categories of rats. Details including doses are given by Boss, Birnie & Gaunt, (1950), and Chester Jones & Spalding (1954). In all three types, there was a priming dose of water followed one hour later by either water, or saline or potassium chloride. These loads were given to the following categories of animals: (i) controls, that is animals with antidiuretic hormone and adrenocortical hormones; (ii) rats with 'permanent' diabetes insipidus, with no antidiuretic hormone (or minimal quantities) but with adrenocortical hormones (iii) adrenalectomized controls, that is animals with antidiuretic hormone but no adrenocortical hormones; (iv) adrenalectomized rats with diabetes insipidus, with no antidiuretic hormone or adrenocortical hormones. The results are given in Table III. It should be noted that adrenalectomized animals of both kinds have a slower rate of absorption from the gut (so that in the first hour normal animals have absorbed 50 per cent. of the water load, while adrenalectomized animals have absorbed 22·8 per cent.), a lower blood-pressure and a slower glomerular filtration rate than unadrenalectomized animals (Table III). This means that the actual rate of presentation of filtrate to the nephron is less than in normal animals. The following points may be made from examination of Table III:

I. *The consequences of loading with water*

(1) Normal rats and rats with diabetes insipidus excrete water at similar rates and have much the same G.F.R.

(2) Both adrenalectomized controls and adrenalectomized rats with diabetes insipidus have equal difficulty in excreting water; this despite the absence of detectable antidiuretic substances in the blood of the latter when the method of Birnie, Eversole, Boss, Osborn & Gaunt (1950) was used, although the blood of adrenalectomized animals does show antidiuretic activity after this method (Birnie *et al.* 1950; Ames & van Dyke, 1952; Ginsburg, 1954).

(3) Adrenalectomized animals excrete little urine but this is high in sodium content. Under these conditions any capacity possessed by adrenalectomized rats with diabetes insipidus to conserve sodium beyond that of adrenalectomized controls is not

TABLE III

The output of urine, sodium and potassium and the glomerular filtration rate (G.F.R.) of normal male and female rats, rats with 'permanent' diabetes insipidus, rats adrenalectomized for 4 days and rats with 'permanent' diabetes insipidus adrenalectomized for 4 days after loads (calculated at 3 ml./100 cm.^{2} surface area) by stomach tube of (i) distilled water; or (ii) hypertonic saline (5 mg./ml.); or (iii) hypertonic potassium chloride (5 mg./ml.). The blood pressure (taken in urethane anaesthesia) is also given for the four categories of animals

(Means ± standard error.)

	n	Urine ml./100 g. min.	Na micro-eq./100 g./ min.	K	G.F.R. ml./100 g./ min.	Blood-pressure mm. Hg.
Water-loading						
Controls	29	0·036 ±·0014	0·053 ±·0045	0·145 ±·019	0·600 ±·059	108·9 ±2·7
Diabetes insipidus	10	0·034 ±·0025	0·049 ±·0037	0·127 ±·009	0·581 ±·114	96·0 ±2·7
Adrenalectomized	30	0·0037 ±·0005	0·320 ±·053	0·101 ±·012	0·103 ±·016	52·5 ±1·5
Diabetes insipidus and adrenalec-tomized	12	0·0026 ±·0004	0·314 ±·077	0·097 ±·009	0·112 ±·026	55·9 ±1·3
Hypertonic saline-loading						
Controls	19	0·023 ±·0016	2·81 ±·27	0·362 ±·029	1·289 ±·181	
Diabetes insipidus	12	0·046 ±·0029	5·94 ±·17	0·399 ±·0069	1·407 ±·16	
Adrenalectomized	12	0·016 ±·006	1·87 ±·137	0·134 ±·012	0·143 ±·024	
Diabetes insipidus and adrenalec-tomized	9	0·014 ±·004	1·36 ±·26	0·126 ±·028	0·112 ±·023	
Hypertonic potassium chloride-loading						
Controls	30	0·031 ±·002	1·17 ±·09	2·96 ±·03	2·75 ±·49	
Diabetes insipidus	9	0·042 ±·004	1·32 ±·14	2·70 ±·12	3·14 ±·46	

revealed. Presumably (i) water ingestion does not tend to stimulate secretion of antidiuretic hormone in adrenalectomized controls; (ii) the kidneys react differently when the animal is coping with administered loads and when it responds to eating and drinking *ad libitum*.

II. *The consequences of loading with hypertonic saline*

(1) The administration of hypertonic saline clearly differentiates between control animals and those with diabetes insipidus (see Hare, Hare & Philips, 1943; Hickey & Hare, 1944). The urine output of normal animals is reduced compared with that obtained after the administration of an equivalent volume of water. The basis of this is the release of antidiuretic hormone under the influence of the increased 'effective' osmotic pressure of the blood (Verney, 1947). The rats with diabetes insipidus show a diuresis not only of water but also of sodium. The output of potassium is about the same in normal and in diabetes insipidus rats; it is increased beyond that obtained after water loads because of the increased G.F.R. brought about by hypertonic saline administration.

(2) Adrenalectomized rats given hypertonic saline do not show this significant increase of G.F.R. but the output of urine is increased above that given after water loads. Bristol & Drill (1952) have shown that the response of adrenalectomized rats to saline loads depends on the strength of solution and the time after operation it is administered, and one factor involved must be the capacity of the saline to alter glomerular filtration rate. Though both types of adrenalectomized animals have the same order of G.F.R. and excrete similar amounts of potassium (Table III), the output of sodium in adrenalectomized animals with diabetes insipidus is significantly smaller than that in adrenalectomized controls. It may be that under these conditions the absence of antidiuretic hormone allows of greater sodium reabsorption while antidiuretic hormone, uninfluenced by corticosteroids, actually enhances sodium excretion. Nevertheless the adrenalectomized rat with diabetes insipidus without antidiuretic hormone or adrenocortical hormones cannot respond to hypertonic saline by a water and sodium diuresis in the same way as the rat with diabetes insipidus and intact adrenals.

III. *The consequences of hypertonic potassium chloride loading*

(1) Hypertonic potassium chloride produces a good urine flow in both normal and diabetes insipidus rats; the former do not show such a prompt diuresis in hour 1 as do the latter. The glomerular filtration rates in both cases are considerably increased above those figures given after water and saline loading. The excretion of potassium is at a high rate in both types of animal. Of particular interest is the vast amount of sodium excreted though sodium was not administered. The amount is about 20 times that given after water loading though the G.F.R. with potassium chloride loading was increased only $4\frac{1}{2}$ times. Presumably potassium and sodium compete for hydrogen ion in a cation-exchange mechanism (Berliner, 1952). With the flooding of the renal tubule by potassium and its presumably copious re-secretion, there is reduced hydrogen ion secretion and this is mirrored in the alkalinity of the urine

after potassium ingestion. With less hydrogen ion available the normal reabsorption of sodium is lessened and more appears in the urine. This may operate without positive hormonal action. On the other hand rats with relative adrenal insufficiency after adrenal enucleation and regeneration (Chester Jones & Spalding, 1954; Chester Jones, 1956a) excrete water (0.027 ±0·0012 ml./100 g./min.) and potassium (2·65 ±0·087 micro-eq./100 g./min.) at about normal rates but sodium at a diminished rate (0·543 ±0·073 micro-eq./100 g./min.) (compare values in Table III). This may illustrate the need of adequate corticosteroid secretion both for reabsorption and for excretion of sodium, a paradox of the actions of adrenocortical hormones.

When we talk about adrenocortical hormones what hormones do we mean? The rat secretes corticosterone and aldosterone; other animals the latter and varying proportions of Kendall's compounds B and F among other steroids (Hechter & Pincus, 1954). I have recently started some experiments in which, rather than give a load by stomach tube, I have infused rats intravenously at a constant rate after external jugular vein cannulation (Ginsburg & Heller, 1953). My experiments are in the preliminary stages and so far I have only infused rats with hypertonic saline, chosen because it gives such an obvious difference between normal and diabetes insipidus rats. Thus during hour 1 of the infusion of 1·2 per cent. saline at 0·1 ml./min. rats with diabetes insipidus do not put out a great deal more urine than normal animals (Fig. 3). In hour 2 and subsequently, however, while normal rats reach a steady state, the output of urine in diabetes insipidus rats is rather more than the volume of saline infused, and indeed the diabetes insipidus rat loses about 2 per cent. of its bodyweight over a 4- or 5-hour infusion period. At the same time the output of sodium and potassium in normal and diabetes insipidus rats is about the same, rats with diabetes insipidus not showing a sodium diuresis as they did when hypertonic saline was given by stomach tube. Aldosterone, in a 3-microgramme dose, given slowly intravenously at the end of hour 1 (Fig. 3) depressed the urine output of animals with diabetes insipidus. This increased renal reabsorption of water seems to be correlated with the increased reabsorption of sodium which is also manifested. Aldosterone, then, does not seem to have any direct effect on the rate of water excretion in the doses used (Simpson & Tait, 1955). Similarly intravenous injection of aldosterone at hour 3 into adrenalectomized rats continuously infused with hypertonic saline does not alter the amount of urine excreted compared with normal rats under these conditions. On these grounds, it would be supposed that the hyperactive adrenal of the rat with diabetes insipidus is not secreting increased amounts of aldosterone but of corticosterone. It might be argued that corticosterone in rats, and 17-hydroxycorticosterone in some other animals, has a positive diuretic effect, contributing at the tubular level to the excretion of water by, as one conceivable mechanism, altering the permeability to water of the epithelium (as discussed by Dr. Wirz in this symposium). There is evidence that cortisol and cortone will cause a diuresis in adrenalectomized animals and in the Addisonian and that this effect is beyond that due to increased glomerular filtration rate. But cortisol can itself cause sodium retention and under certain conditions such an action may be accompanied by increased water reabsorption. Paradoxes arise because corticosteroids can only act within the limits of the renal dynamics at the time; their actions are in part determined by the composition of the filtrate in the renal tubule.

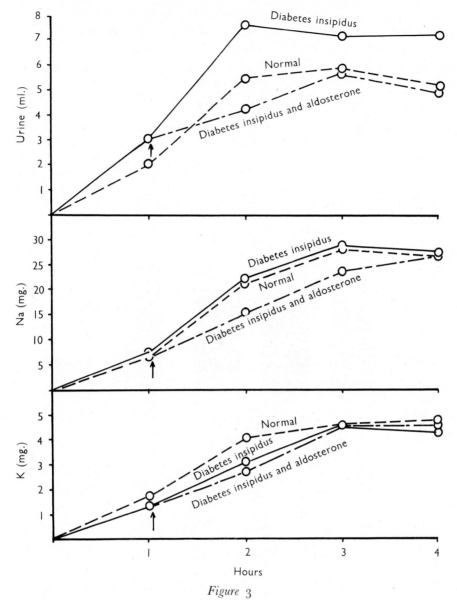

Figure 3

The urine, sodium and potassium output of normal rats and rats with diabetes insipidus infused intravenously with hypertonic saline (1·27 per cent.) at the rate of 0·1 ml. per min. for 4 hours. Aldosterone
(3 μg.) was infused slowly at the end of hour 1 into rats with diabetes insipidus: the marked water
diuresis of rats with diabetes insipidus following hypertonic saline was suppressed by aldosterone,
consequent on the accompanying sodium retention.

Other difficulties arise from the complex nature of the mechanisms apparently
controlling ACTH release. Workers who use changes in urine output as indicative
of antidiuretic hormone action alone are ignoring the factors introduced by corticosteroid secretion which may indeed be enhanced by the very test procedures used.

Thus, the manipulation necessary to give fluids by stomach tube causes a depletion of adrenal ascorbic acid content (Nowell, unpublished). The degree of this depletion is about the same with insertion of the stomach tube without giving a solution as with loading with hypertonic saline or with Ringer's solution isotonic to the body fluids. This means that results obtained by loading by stomach tube are affected by the handling of the animal and this must alter the results—in an unknown way. Especially so as we do not know what depletion of adrenal ascorbic acid content means in terms of the hormones secreted by the adrenal cortex. With the apparent multiplicity of types of corticotrophin and of the kinds of corticosteroids, not all being equally dependent on release by ACTH, this problem may be regarded as a little confused. But as aldosterone is at least in part if not wholly independent of ACTH secretion

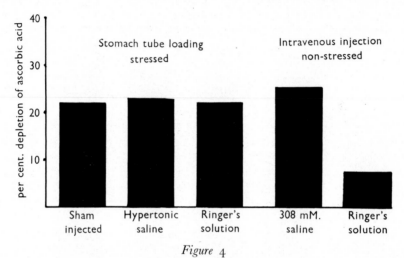

Figure 4

The depletion of adrenal ascorbic acid (estimated by Roe & Kuether's (1943) method) following use of the stomach tube and of intravenous injection. While the manipulation itself associated with the insertion of the stomach tube caused marked depletion, it was possible to give 6 ml. Ringer's solution slowly intravenously with only a small (7 per cent.) fall in adrenal ascorbic acid. On the other hand 6 ml. of hypertonic (twice isotonic) saline effected a marked depletion. The infusion of hypertonic saline presumably called forth anti-diuretic hormone secretion and this may be a factor accounting for the difference in response in terms of adrenal ascorbic acid change between this solution and the isotonic one. (From Nowell, unpublished.)

it would be reasonable to suppose that, in the rat, fall in adrenal ascorbic acid content is associated with increased corticosterone production. We have found, however, that it is possible to administer solutions to rats without causing stress by the very process of injection (Nowell & Chester Jones, unpublished). Rats with the external jugular vein cannulated can be given solutions through the cannula without awareness of the procedure by the rat in terms of variation in adrenal ascorbic acid content. Using this experimental approach, it was found that hypertonic saline (twice isotonic) delivered intravenously caused a marked fall in adrenal ascorbic acid content while the same volume of isotonic Ringer solution caused only a small drop (Fig. 4). This may mean that (i)—the addition of hypertonic saline to the blood caused the secretion of antidiuretic hormone which in turn is an effector in the release of ACTH. This then would be the *'obligatory' release of ACTH*. That is conditions which release antidiuretic hormone (or a substance accompanying it?) must of necessity, irrespective of the renal needs of the animal, release ACTH to activate the adrenal or that (ii)—hypertonic saline injection results in the need for the animal to excrete sodium. The renal mechanisms involved require corticosteroids and the corticotrophin-adrenocortical hormone mechanism is activated. This would imply increased secretion of corticosterone rather than any change in aldosterone secretion which may be diminished.

It is an interesting development of recent researches that the hypothalamic factor which is responsible for secretion of ACTH has been equated with the antidiuretic hormone or to a similar factor contained within commercial vasopressin (Pitressin) (see Martini & Morpurgo, 1955; Gaunt *et al.* above). If we consider the reaction of the rat with diabetes insipidus to stress we are examining an animal with no (or little) antidiuretic hormone. While control animals placed in the cold at 30°F. for 1 hour show a marked fall in adrenal ascorbic acid content, rats with diabetes insipidus show only a small drop of adrenal ascorbic acid content under these conditions (Fig. 5). Furthermore, injection of vasopressin in a dose of 0·3 U. half an hour before exposure to cold allows the adrenal ascorbic acid content to fall markedly, approaching though not equalling control figures (Fig. 5). Sham-injection does not have this effect nor does

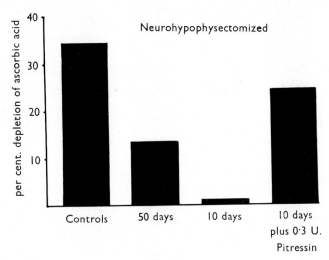

Figure 5

The change in adrenal ascorbic acid content of rats when exposed to 30°F. for 1 hour. Normal animals showed a 34·2 per cent. depletion of adrenal ascorbic acid. Rats with diabetes insipidus for 10 days showed little depletion and those with diabetes insipidus for 50 days rather more, but still only 14 per cent depletion. The injection of 300 mU. Pitressin half an hour before exposure to cold of rats neurohypophysectomized for 10 days was followed by a 24 per cent. depletion of adrenal ascorbic acid content. (From Nowell, unpublished.)

it occur in hypophysectomized animals; it seems therefore that something in Pitressin elicits ACTH release. The fact that the diabetes insipidus rat does not react to cold stress as does the normal animal may be due to (i) the lack of antidiuretic hormone (or an associated substance) so that the effector for the release of ACTH is absent or (ii) since the diabetes insipidus rat has a hyperactive adrenal in any case, the animal can cope with cold stress without further demand for corticosteroids and hence for the release of more ACTH. Experiments are in progress aimed to elucidate these points.

OTHER VERTEBRATES

When we turn to the consideration of other classes of vertebrates there are at least five groups of questions to which we must seek the answers:

(i) What adrenocortical steroids are produced in the different classes of vertebrates?

(ii) What tissues do the adrenocortical hormones affect: do they all influence the kidney epithelium, whether it be meso- or metanephros? Are they chiefly preoccupied with water and salt-electrolyte metabolism and does their scope include the gill epithelium of the fish and the skin of the amphibian and the selective permeability of the membrane of tissue cells?

(iii) Do the adrenocortical hormones interrelate with the actions of the neuro-hypophysial principles which seem to be concerned, at least in part, with water metabolism in those vertebrates in which a physiological role has been assigned to them?

(iv) Does an adenohypophysial corticotrophin regulate the secretions of the adrenal cortex in all vertebrates; if so, does the ACTH control all or only part of the adrenal cortex and its secretions?

(v) What are the mechanisms whereby ACTH is released and do the posterior lobe of the pituitary and the hypothalamus play a part in the control of anterior lobe functions?

The answers to these questions are not known. Nor can all the possibilities be discussed here. Some account of them has been given elsewhere (Chester Jones, 1956a, b). I should like, however, to discuss some results Fowler has obtained using the frog, *Rana temporaria* (Fowler & Chester Jones, 1955; Fowler, 1956). Because our knowedge is so limited we are predisposed to think of amphibian physiology in terms of the mammalian. As we survey both classes, the similarities of water and salt-electrolyte metabolism are striking. Both the neurohypophysial and the adrenocortical hormones seem to be capable of changing the extent of epithelial absorption of water and of sodium whether it be in the skin or in the kidney and whether the effects be primary or secondary ones. The problem is, on the one hand, one of the varying tissue permeability to water, occasioned perhaps by changing 'pore' size, and on the other the varying rate of sodium transport dependent on some enzyme system. While the action of neurohypophysial hormones in amphibians has been investigated many times (see Sawyer, 1956 and in this Symposium), the role of the adrenal cortex in amphibian water and salt-electrolyte metabolism has been little followed. Though the adrenal ectomized winter* frog (Chester Jones, 1956a) has no outward signs of ill-health,

---

* *Rana temporaria* is of the winter type from September to December inclusive, eating avidly at first and then sparsely. Frogs of the summer type cover the pre-spawning and spawning periods of January to March inclusive, the post-spawning period of April and the true summer frog of May to August inclusive, when the frogs eat, lay down fat, and their gonads regenerate. Broadly speaking the winter frog is metabolically inactive, the summer frog metabolically active.

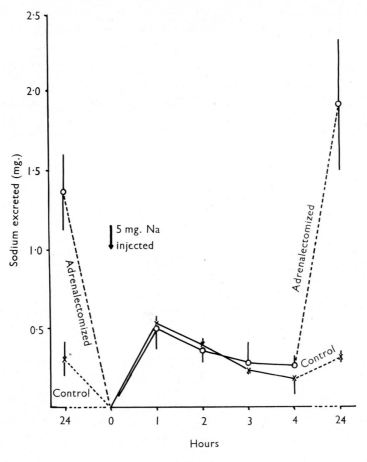

Figure 6

The loss of sodium in 24 hr. from normal and from adrenalectomized winter frogs (9 of each) when kept in distilled water. At zero 5 mg. Na (as frog Ringer's solution) was injected into the dorsal lymph-sac and the sodium excretion over the first 4-hr. period and then over 24 hr. is given. During the latter the excretion of sodium from the adrenalectomized frogs is the more marked (points shown with standard deviation). (From Fowler, 1956.)

it loses sodium at a faster rate than control animals when placed in distilled water for 24 hr. (Fig. 6). When 5 mg. Na (as frog Ringer's solution) was injected into the dorsal lymph-sac there was little difference over the first 4 hr. in the rate of sodium excretion between adrenalectomized and control animals. Over 24 hr., however, the sodium loss was much greater from the adrenalectomized animals and, indeed, the secretion rate of the controls did not vary greatly from that occurring before the injection of the sodium load (Fig. 6). Thus sodium loss, following adrenal removal, is characteristic both of the amphibian and the mammals. Saline replacement therapy too is successful in both cases. For it is possible to maintain adrenalectomized summer* frogs, which normally die 24 to 48 hr. after operation, in an active state by immersion in saline. Frog Ringer's solution is moderately and 0·73 per cent. saline (Aldred,

1940) is very effective in this respect. The latter solution allows the sodium and potassium muscle content of adrenalectomized animals to be within the normal range (Table IV).

TABLE IV

The maintenance of adrenalectomized summer frogs with saline solutions
(Means $\pm$standard error.) Fowler, 1956.

Summer frogs	n	Body-weight		Muscle				
		Exptl. period		Per-centage water	mEq./kg. Wet weight		mEq./kg. Dry weight	
		Start	End		K	Na	K	Na
Controls (kept in tap-water)	9		24·90 ±1·79	78·76 ±·58	81·73 ±1·41	23·47 ±1·41	425·33 ±4·33	121·88 ±2·38
Controls (kept in frog Ringer's soln.)	9	21·11 ±2·36	19·24 ±·92	83·25 ±·37	86·67 ±2·48	24·29 ±1·68	526·00 ±10·10	148·00 ±3·87
Adrenalectomized 24–48 hr. (tap-water)	8	27·87 ±1·87	30·87 ±2·15	86·5 ±1·49	62·50 ±2·00	9·30 ±·34	462·98 ±8·41	68·21 ±3·46
Adrenalectomized 5 days (Ringer's soln.)	8	25·87 ±1·48	29·40 ±1·70	80·53 ±·79	75·71 ±1·45	12·17 ±·68	441·44 ±4·33	96·88 ±3·03
Adrenalectomized 5 days (0·73 per cent. saline)	9	20·60 ±1·48	19·99 ±1·64	78·28 ±·21	92·21 ±1·26	26·34 ±·64	425·00 ±2·02	121·00 ±·88

A further point is revealed by these experiments, namely that there is an increase in body-weight consequent on adrenalectomy, due apparently to increased uptake of water through the skin. There is no weight increase when isotonic saline bathes the skin, the passive movement of water not occurring in the absence of osmotic difference between the internal and external media. Adrenalectomy, then, can be followed, in the active summer frog at least, by water uptake characteristic of the Brunn effect obtained by the injection of neurohypophysial extracts into intact frogs (Brunn, 1921; Heller, 1956; Sawyer, 1956). Sham-operations, not only of adrenalectomy but also of hypophysectomy, sometimes also produce oedema and this may well be due to adrenocortical exhaustion rather than the result of cutting the skin which in any case does not apply to pituitary removal (Table V). It may be supposed that the adrenocortical steroids alter the permeability of frog skin to water and conjoin in this effect with the posterior lobe secretions.

The loss of sodium from the muscle of both adrenalectomized winter and summer frogs also occurs when the anterior lobe of the pituitary (adenohypophysectomy) is removed (Table V). The extent of the changes in sodium and potassium are misleading when expressed in terms of wet weight of muscle because of the increase in muscle water content. In terms of muscle dry weight it can be seen that muscle potassium

268

TABLE V

The effects of adrenalectomy, of adenohypophysectomy and of hypophysectomy on the body-weight and on the water, sodium and potassium content of muscle of frogs

(Means ±standard error.) Fowler, 1956.

Frogs	n	Body-weight		Muscle				
		Exptl. period		Per-centage water	mEq./kg. Wet weight		mEq./kg. Dry weight	
		Start	End		K	Na	K	Na
Winter Controls	12		23·70 ±2·02	77·95 ±·41	80·54 ±1·55	25·00 ±·54	366·11 ±2·80	113·95 ±4·10
Adrenalectomized 14 days	8	25·51 ±1·79	24·65 ±1·52	79·49 ±2·04	73·91 ±2·18	14·50 ±2·00	363·11 ±10·60	71·08 ±3·44
Adenohypophysectomized 14 days	12	27·92 ±2·37	27·63 ±2·35	80·54 ±1·55	76·41 ±·82	17·20 ±·95	394·44 ±9·69	88·66 ±7·41
Summer Controls	9		24·90 ±1·79	80·65 ±·31	83·66 ±1·75	25·81 ±1·36	435·55 ±5·37	133·22 ±2·10
Adrenalectomized 24–48 hr.	8	27·87 ±1·87	30·87 ±2·15	86·50 ±1·49	62·50 ±2·00	9·30 ±·34	462·98 ±8·41	68·21 ±3·46
Sham-adrenalectomized showing oedema	5	26·15 ±1·38	28·45 ±2·00	86·96 ±1·11	54·60 ±1·33	7·96 ±1·70	406·12 ±7·24	64·32 ±5·10
Adenohypophysectomized 24–48 hr.	9	24·59 ±1·45	29·25 ±1·96	86·50 ±1·10	59·90 ±2·00	12·34 ±3·1	446·77 ±12·54	91·36 ±7·03
Hypophysectomized 24–48 hr.	10	22·02 ±2·27	25·47 ±1·37	88·10 ±·61	48·00 ±2·60	16·20 ±1·40	414·33 ±14·33	136·33 ±4·00

content does not change with the loss of sodium in adrenalectomized and adeno-hypophysectomized animals. It was interesting to find that when both lobes of the pituitary were removed (hypophysectomy) loss of sodium (per kg. dry weight of muscle) was not apparent though other symptoms of adrenal insufficiency occurred. Though more work is required on this point, the situation is reminiscent of the ad-renalectomized rat with diabetes insipidus which showed some capacity for sodium conservation beyond that of the adrenalectomized control. We may suppose that the loss of sodium in the frog is manifested because the normal tubular reabsorption of sodium which must accompany the production of a hypotonic urine cannot go on in the absence of adrenocortical hormones. The posterior lobe hormones probably influence not only glomerular filtration rate but also tubular reabsorption of water. It is conceivable that this latter similarity to the position in mammals may also be joined by the action of neurohypophysial hormones on sodium excretion in both classes, though even in mammals their influence on salt-electrolyte metabolism has not been shown to be of normal physiological occurrence. Change in sodium outflux through the skin is an additional complicating factor in amphibia.

Though we discuss frog adrenocortical hormones, what these are is not known. There are a few clues to their general identity. Mammalian ACTH injected into hypophysectomized frogs will maintain the sodium content of muscle at about normal values (Table VI) and we may suppose that steroids akin to those of the eutherian

TABLE VI

The effects of the injection of mammalian ACTH and of deoxycortone acetate on the water, sodium and potassium content of the muscle of normal and adenohypophysectomized summer frogs (Fowler, 1956) and on that of the snake (Natrix natrix) (Wright, unpublished.)

	n	Body-weight		Muscle				
		Exptl. period		Per-centage water	mEq./kg. Wet weight		mEq./kg. Dry weight	
		Start	End		K	Na	K	Na
Summer frogs Controls, sham-injected	9	23·37 ±1·02	22·29 ±1·33	78·76 ±·65	77·79 ±·41	25·32 ±1·24	366·33 ±3·24	118·88 ±2·05
ACTH (1 I.U./day for 10 days)	7	20·30 ±·98	19·53 ±1·04	79·87 ±·77	67·90 ±1·04	30·40 ±1·08	339·00 ±4·71	151·00 ±3·10
DCA (2·0 mg./day for 10 days)	12	20·14 ±·77	19·20 ±·68	79·81 ±·46	76·37 ±2·23	24·76 ±1·00	378·55 ±4·86	122·45 ±1·56
Adenohypophysectomized 24–48 hr.	9	24·59 ±1·45	29·25 ±1·96	86·50 ±1·10	59·90 ±2·00	12·34 ±3·10	446·77 ±12·54	91·36 ±7·03
Adenohypophysectom-ized and ACTH (2 I.U./day for 5 days)	5	17·10 ±1·14	15·10 ±1·45	82·00 ±·55	74·60 ±1·37	28·95 ±1·39	414·66 ±4·18	160·44 ±2·60
Snakes Controls, sham-injected	9	71·70 ±4·40	70·60 ±4·40	79·50 ±·44	86·30 ±3·00	51·40 ±4·70	420·00 ±14·50	230·00 ±21·00
DCA (0·5 mg./day for 11 days)	8	64·52 ±4·51	62·01 ±3·20	78·24 ±·64	83·92 ±1·41	48·81 ±1·22	385·43 ±6·40	224·12 ±5·51

adrenal were produced to effect this. Moreover, we have made a tentative identification of Kendall's compound *B* in adrenal blood of birds and snakes (Phillips, unpublished). The amphibian adrenal may secrete this compound too, but a steroid similar to aldosterone would also be expected. We have not had as yet adequate samples of adrenal blood to identify aldosterone in the lower vertebrates. It is interesting to find, however, that both frogs and snakes do not respond to the injection of deoxycortone acetate by change in the water, sodium and potassium content of muscle (for the duration and in the doses given) though the histological picture of the adrenal cortex is one of degeneration (Table VI). Clearly further data on the nature of adrenal secretion in the lower vertebrates are required.

Surveying what we know about adrenocortical function in vertebrates—and this is very little—the hypothesis may be advanced that these hormones act by altering the permeability of some epithelia and cell membranes generally to water and by changing the rate of the active transport of sodium in certain tissues. Neurohypophysial secretions may join with adrenocortical hormones certainly in the first and doubtfully in the last possibility. It may be supposed then that various parts of the vertebrate nephron are rendered less permeable to water in the presence of adrenocortical hormones and more permeable in their absence. The actual passive movement of water may be conceived as depending on the epithelial permeability plus the filtrate concentrations in the tubule at the same time; these latter in turn depending, among other things, on the rate of the active transport of sodium. The gill epithelium of the bony fish and the skin of the frog may both be influenced by these hormones, the passage of water through them being a passive process but the rate being conditioned by varying permeability under hormonal control. But though it can be shown that the amphibian responds to posterior lobe principles, the fish has so far resolutely refused to display water and salt-electrolyte changes with injection of these secretions. Indeed, the only demonstration of the activity of the posterior lobe in fish is that of Wilhelmi, Pickford & Sawyer (1955) who showed that fish and mammalian neurohypophysial preparations induced the spawning reflex response in *Fundulus*, the killifish. Should this be confirmed as a general mechanism in all bony fish, and so far we have failed to confirm it in trout, it might change our concepts of seeking the evolutionary change of posterior lobe function from that of water metabolic control to that of regulation of some aspects of reproduction.

Here the action of the neurosecretions would be central rather than on peripheral tissue. It would follow that the hypothalamic control of the anterior lobe of the pituitary by some substance of the nature of the neurohypophysial neurosecretions is the major mechanism appearing early in the evolution of the vertebrates. The water balance effect and the antidiuretic hormone could be considered, on this account, later evolutionary manifestations of the main central apparatus. Since, however, one prime need of the vertebrate was and is osmoregulation, it may be supposed that the adrenocortical secretions are active in this process throughout the vertebrates. Adrenocortical secretions require corticotrophin control and this anterior lobe hormone may in turn be regulated by the hypothalamic neurosecretion. So whether we consider the neurohypophysis to have activity primarily in the field of reproduction and secondarily in water and salt-electrolyte metabolism or the reverse of this, we arrive back at the hypothalamus and its possible role in the regulation of various hormonal activities and it is here that further research will be rewarding, not only in mammals but in the lower vertebrates.

ACKNOWLEDGEMENTS

The investigation of rats with diabetes insipidus was helped by a grant from the Medical Research Council; investigation of frogs and snakes was aided by a grant from the Nuffield Foundation for work in the field of Comparative Endocrinology. Dr. M. A. Fowler, now at the Department of Biology, Guy's Hospital Medical School, did the work on frogs while holding a Medical Research Council studentship, and Dr. A. Wright, now at the Department of Physiology and Histology, Liverpool University, that on snakes (only briefly mentioned here) while in receipt of, in the first place, a Nuffield and, later, an Agricultural Research Council Grant. Dr. N. W. Nowell was working in this laboratory while on leave of absence from the Department of Zoology, University of Hull. I wish to thank Mrs. M. H. Lawson for technical assistance.

REFERENCES

ALDRED, P. (1940). A note on the osmotic pressure of the blood of various animals. *J. exp. Biol.* **17,** 223–6.

AMES, R. G. & VAN DYKE, H. B. (1952). Antidiuretic hormone in the serum or plasma of rats. *Endocrinology* **50,** 350–60.

BAISSET, A., DOUSTE-BLAZY, L., PLANEL, H. & MONTASTRUC, P. (1954). Cortex surrénal et diabète insipide expérimental. *C.R. Soc. Biol. (Paris)* **148,** 1867–70.

BAKER, B. L. (1952). A comparison of the histological changes induced by experimental hyperadrenocorticalism and inanition. *Recent Progr. Hormone Res.* **7,** 331–73.

BERLINER, R. W. (1952). Renal secretion of potassium and hydrogen ions. *Fed. Proc.* **11,** 695–700.

BIRNIE, J. H., EVERSOLE, W. J., BOSS, W. R., OSBORN, C. M. & GAUNT, R. (1950). Antidiuretic substance in the blood of normal and adrenalectomized rats. *Endocrinology* **47,** 1–12.

BOSS, W. R., BIRNIE, J. H. & GAUNT, R. (1950). Renal factors in the adrenal cortical control of water metabolism. *Endocrinology* **46,** 307–13.

BRISTOL, W. R. & DRILL, V. A. (1952). Saline hydration and diuresis after adrenalectomy. *Endocrinology* **50,** 677–83.

BRUNN, F. (1921). Beitrag zur Kenntniss der Wirkung von Hypophysenextrakten auf den Wasserhaushalt des Froches. *Z. ges. exp. Med.* **25,** 170–87.

CHESTER JONES, I. (1956a). The role of the adrenal in the control of water and salt electrolyte metabolism in vertebrates. *Mem. Soc. Endocr.* **5,** 102–20.

CHESTER JONES, I. (1956b). *The Adrenal Cortex.* Cambridge: University Press.

CHESTER JONES, I. & SPALDING, M. H. (1954). Some aspects of zonation and function of the adrenal cortex. II. The rat adrenal after enucleation. *J. Endocr.* **10,** 251–61.

CHESTER JONES, I. & WRIGHT, A. (1954). Some aspects of zonation and function of the adrenal cortex. IV. The histology of the adrenal in rats with diabetes insipidus. *J. Endocr.* **10,** 266–72.

FOWLER, M. A. (1956). *Some endocrine interrelationships in the Amphibia.* Thesis for Degree of Ph.D., University of Liverpool.

FOWLER, M. A. & CHESTER JONES, I. (1955). The adrenal cortex in the frog *Rana temporaria* and its relation to water and salt electrolyte metabolism. *J. Endocr.* **13,** 6P.

GAUNT, R. (1951). The adrenal cortex in salt and water metabolism. *Recent Progr. Hormone Res.* **6,** 247–68.

GINSBURG, M. (1954). The secretion of antidiuretic hormone in response to haemorrhage and the fate of vasopressin in adrenalectomized rats. *J. Endocr.* **11,** 165–76.

GINSBURG, M. & HELLER, H. (1953). The antidiuretic assay of vasopressin by intravenous injection into unanaesthetized rats. *J. Endocr.* **9,** 267–73.

HARE, R. S., HARE, K. & PHILIPS, D. M. (1943). Renal excretion of chloride by the normal and by the diabetes insipidus dog. *Amer. J. Physiol.* **140,** 334–48.

HECHTER, O. & PINCUS, G. (1954). Genesis of adrenocortical secretion. *Physiol. Rev.* **34,** 459.

HELLER, H. (1956). The hormonal control of water and salt electrolyte metabolism with special reference to the higher vertebrates. *Mem. Soc. Endocr.* **5,** 25–36.

HICKEY, R. & HARE, K. (1944). The renal excretion of chloride and water in diabetes insipidus. *J. clin. Invest.* **23,** 768–75.

INGRAM, W. R. & WINTER, C. A. (1938). The effects of adrenalectomy upon the water exchange of cats with diabetes insipidus. *Amer. J. Physiol.* **122,** 143–9.

KROHN, P. L. (1955). The effect of ACTH and cortisone on the survival of skin homografts and on the adrenal glands in monkeys (*Macaca mulatta*). *J. Endocr.* **12,** 220–26.

MARTINI, L. & MORPURGO, C. (1955). Neurohumoral control of the release of adrenocorticotrophic hormone. *Nature (Lond.)* **175,** 1127–8.

ROBERTSON, J. D. (1954). The chemical composition of the blood of some aquatic chordates, including members of the Tunicata, Cyclostomata and Osteichthyes. *J. exp. Biol.* **31,** 424.

ROE, J. H. & KUETHER, C. A. (1943). The determination of ascorbic acid in whole blood and urine through the 2, 4-dinitrophenylhydrazine derivative of dehydroascorbic acid. *J. biol. Chem.* **147,** 399–407.

SAWYER, W. H. (1956). The hormonal control of water and salt electrolyte metabolism with special reference to the Amphibia. *Mem. Soc. Endocr.* **5,** 44–55.

SELYE, H. & STONE, H. (1950). *On the experimental morphology of the adrenal cortex.* Springfield, Ill.: Thomas.

SIMPSON, S. A. & TAIT, J. F. (1955). The possible role of electrocortin in normal human metabolism. *Ciba Found. Coll. Endocr.* **8,** 204–24.

TONUTTI, E., BAHNER, F. and MUSCHKE, E. (1954). Die Veränderungen der Nebennierenrinde der Maus nach Hypophysektomie und nach ACTH-Behandlung, quantitativ betrachtet am Verhalten der Zellkernvolumina. *Endokrinologie* **31,** 266–84.

VERNEY, E. B. (1947). The antidiuretic hormone and the factors which determine its release. *Proc. roy. Soc.* B **135,** 25–106.

WILHELMI, A. E., PICKFORD, G. E. and SAWYER, W. H. (1955). Initiation of the spawning reflex response in Fundulus by the administration of fish and mammalian neurohypophysial preparations and synthetic oxytocin. *Endocrinology* **57,** 243–52.

WINTER, C. A., GROSS, E. G. & INGRAM, W. R. (1938). Serum sodium, potassium and chloride after suprarenalectomy in cats with diabetes insipidus. *J. exp. Med.* **67,** 251–8.

WINTER, C. A., INGRAM, W. R., GROSS, E. G. & SATTLER, D. G. (1941). Sodium and chloride balance in cats as affected by diabetes insipidus, adrenal insufficiency, and Pitressin injections. *Endocrinology* **28,** 535–44.

Discussion

Chairman: H. B. van Dyke

L. Arvy. I would like to report some work done at the Sorbonne in collaboration with Dr. Gabe, on two species of marine teleost before and after the fishes had been placed in saline solutions of various concentrations.

If one take *Callionymus lyra* or *Ammodytes lanceolatus* from normal sea-water and examines paraffin sections of the hypophysis after staining with Gomori's chrome-haematoxylin-phloxin or by the aldehyde-fuchsin technique of Gabe, one sees significant quantities of neurosecretory substance. In the same species after a very short time (as little as thirty minutes) in concentrated sea-water, very pronounced depletion of the neurosecretory substance can be observed; if the fishes are returned to normal sea-water for one hour, the hypophysis recovers its normal content of neurosecretory material. If *Callionymus lyra* or *Ammodytes lanceolatus* are put in dilute sea-water their hypophyses contain more neurosecretory product than usual.

Plate II shows the pars parvo-cellularis of the nucleus preopticus of *Ammodytes lanceolatus*. When the fishes are kept in normal sea-water, the neurosecretory cells are full of secretion and the axons are also rich in this material which forms classical Herring bodies. In fishes which had been subjected to concentrated sea-water for one hour, the neurosecretory cells lost most of their neurosecretory product. In fishes which had then been returned to normal sea-water for one hour, the neurosecretory cells were again full of secretory material and had big lobulated, convoluted and multinucleolated nuclei: in short, they showed many cytological signs of great secretory activity. Similar changes in the amounts of neurosecretory material were found in the pars magno-cellularis and in the neurohypophysis.

If the hypothalamo-hypophysial tract of fishes subjected to concentrated sea-water is stained by Mann's method, marked hyperaemia can be seen; blood vessels are enlarged and filled with red cells. It seems that the hyperaemia is correlated with the rapid migration of neurosecretory material from the nucleus preopticus to the neuro-hypophysis and from there to the blood.

In conclusion, concentrated sea-water provokes a rapid decrease in concentration of neurosecretory material in the neurosecretory cells of the nucleus preopticus and in the hypophysis; the return to normal sea-water is followed by restoration of the normal appearance. Dilute sea-water provokes an increase in the concentration of neurosecretory material in the nucleus preopticus and the hypophysis. In each case the blood supply to the hypothalamo-hypophysial tract is greatly modified.

Stutinsky. It is a well-known fact that in rats experimental diabetes insipidus due to the removal of the posterior pituitary is more severe if the animals drink hypertonic salt solutions. The question arises—what happens in the adrenals of these rats? We have found that there are no marked changes in the zona glomerulosa but the modifications seen in the fasciculata are very important. Many cells contain colloid-like droplets of varying sizes, some as large as and even larger than a nucleus. The whole fasciculata shows many of these cells and colloid droplets which can also be seen in cells of the reticularis. The droplets can be stained with Azan or Masson's stain. They do not stain with Baker's acid haematin or Sudan Black but they stain remarkably well with the periodic acid-Schiff technique. I would suggest tentatively, that in normal rats drinking hypertonic saline, the secretions of the normal neural lobe protect the zona fasciculata against these morphological modifications.

Gross. Dr. Loustalot in our laboratories has seen this material in rats' adrenals quite often, and not only in animals treated with high doses of methylandrostenediol. When Selye produced hypertension with methylandrostenediol, he found these droplets regularly in the adrenals and claimed that they were specific for an increased production of mineralocorticoids but you may also find the same material in normal animals, especially in senile or poisoned ones. Rats of more than two years of age have been investigated by Dr. Loustalot, and these droplets have been seen quite regularly, but not on such a scale as in animals treated with high doses of DCA and salt. We think that these droplets are a sign of non-specific degenerative changes in the adrenals.

Stutinsky. I agree that this is not a specific effect.

Gross. I would like to ask Dr. Chester Jones whether in his experiments with adrenalectomized rats, the rats were really insufficient or did he do the experiments only one or two days after adrenalectomy? If I understood him correctly, he also found no